MICROPROCESSOR PROGRAMMING

and

SOFTWARE DEVELOPMENT

Prentice-Hall International
Series in Computer Science

C. A. R. Hoare, Series Editor

MICROPROCESSOR PROGRAMMING and SOFTWARE DEVELOPMENT

F. G. DUNCAN

University of Bristol, England

Prentice/Hall International

ENGLEWOOD CLIFFS, NEW JERSEY   LONDON   NEW DELHI
SINGAPORE   SYDNEY   TOKYO   TORONTO   WELLINGTON

To T. A. M. and to S. W. D.

Library of Congress Cataloging in Publication Data

Duncan, Fraser G., 1932–
  Microprocessor programming and software
  development.

  Bibliography: p.
  Includes index.
  1. Microprocessors–Programming. I. Title.
QA76.6.D84   001.6'42   78-27429
ISBN 0-13-581405-7

British Library Cataloguing in Publication Data

Duncan, Fraser George
  Microprocessor programming and software
  development.
  1. Microprocessors–Programming
  I. Title
  001.6'42   QA76.6
  ISBN 0-13-581405-7

© 1979 by PRENTICE-HALL INTERNATIONAL INC., LONDON

ISBN 0-13-581405-7

PRENTICE-HALL INTERNATIONAL, INC., LONDON
PRENTICE-HALL OF AUSTRALIA PTY. LTD., SYDNEY
PRENTICE-HALL OF CANADA, LTD., TORONTO
PRENTICE-HALL OF INDIA PRIVATE LIMITED, NEW DELHI
PRENTICE-HALL OF JAPAN, INC., TOKYO
PRENTICE-HALL OF SOUTHEAST ASIA PTE., LTD., SINGAPORE
PRENTICE-HALL, INC., ENGLEWOOD CLIFFS, NEW JERSEY
WHITEHALL BOOKS LIMITED, WELLINGTON, NEW ZEALAND

Type set in Monotype Times Roman and Univers
by HBM Typesetting Ltd., Chorley, Lancs.
Printed and Bound in Great Britain
by A. Wheaton & Co. Ltd., Exeter

79 80 81 82 83 5 4 3 2 1

Contents

PREFACE   xi

FRONTISPIECE   xv

1   Microprocessors and microprocessor systems   1

1.1   BASIC IDEAS   1

1.2   INTERNAL ORGANIZATION OF A MICROPROCESSOR   9
    1.2.1   Power supplies   9
    1.2.2   Clock   9
    1.2.3   Timing and control unit   9
    1.2.4   Instruction register and decoder   11
    1.2.5   Arithmetic-logic unit (ALU)   11
    1.2.6   Condition flags   12
    1.2.7   Accumulators   12
    1.2.8   Program counter   12
    1.2.9   Stack pointer   12
    1.2.10 Other addressing registers   13

1.3   THE STORE   13
    1.3.1   Main store and secondary store   13
    1.3.2   Semiconductor storage   13
        1.3.2.1   ROM ('read only memory')   14
        1.3.2.2   PROM ('programmable read only memory')   14
        1.3.2.3   RAM ('random access memory')   15
    1.3.3   Address buffering and decoding   16

1.4   PERIPHERAL DEVICES   18
    1.4.1   Interfaces   18

2   Instructions   19

2.1 BASIC IDEAS   19
2.2 REPRESENTATION OF INSTRUCTIONS   20
2.3 GENERAL NOTATIONS   23
    2.3.1   The bytes of an instruction   23
    2.3.2   Registers   23
    2.3.3   Assignment (copying or transfer of information)   23
    2.3.4   Interchange   24
    2.3.5   Values   24
    2.3.6   Addresses and storage locations   25
    2.3.7   Condition flags   28
2.4 ARITHMETIC AND LOGICAL OPERATIONS   28
    2.4.1   Meanings of a byte   28
    2.4.2   Signed and unsigned values   29
    2.4.3   Addition   30
        2.4.3.1   Addition (single-length)   30
        2.4.3.2   Addition (double-length)   32
        2.4.3.3   Addition (multiple-length)   33
        2.4.3.4   Addition of numbers of unequal length   34
    2.4.4   Inversion and negation   34
    2.4.5   Subtraction   35
        2.4.5.1   Subtraction (single-length)   35
        2.4.5.2   Subtraction (double-length)   36
        2.4.5.3   Subtraction (multiple-length)   37
        2.4.5.4   Subtraction of numbers of unequal length   37
    2.4.6   Logical (Boolean) operations   37
    2.4.7   'Test' and 'compare' operations   38
    2.4.8   'Shift' and 'rotate' operations   41
        1   Arithmetic shift up   41
        2   Arithmetic shift down   41
        3   'Logical' shift right   42
        4   Cyclic shift (rotation) left   42
        5   Cyclic shift (rotation) right   42
        6   Nine-bit cyclic shift left   42
        7   Nine-bit cyclic shift right   43
        8   Nibble shift left (Z80 only)   43
        9   Nibble shift right (Z80 only)   43
        Availability   44
    2.4.9   Other arithmetic and logical operations   44
        2.4.9.1   Increment and decrement   44
        2.4.9.2   Decimal adjustment   45
2.5 STACK OPERATIONS   46
2.6 JUMPS   48
2.7 SUBROUTINES   48

2.8 INPUT–OUTPUT 50
    (i) 'Bit by bit' 51
    (ii) 'Serial to parallel' 52
    (iii) A 'wait' interface 52

2.9 INTERRUPTION 53

2.10 OTHER INSTRUCTIONS (Z80 ONLY) 57
    Auxiliary registers 57
    Operations involving individual bits 57
    A counting jump 57
    Step and block instructions 58
        (i) Copy 58
        (ii) Search 58
        (iii) Input 59
        (iv) Output 59
    Interruption 60
    Notations 60

3 Instruction sets 61

3.1 EXPLANATION 61

3.2 MOTOROLA 6800 64
    Microprocessor 6800 64
        6800 Instruction set – main table 65
        6800 Substitution tables 66
        6800 Notes 67
        6800 Karnaugh map 68
        6800 Instructions in numerical order of operation code 70

3.3 INTEL 8080 AND 8085 71
    Microprocessor 8080 71
        8080 Instruction set – main table 72
        8080 Substitution tables 73
        8080 Notes 73
        8080 Karnaugh map 74
        8080 Instructions in numerical order of operation code 76
    Microprocessor 8085 77

3.4 ZILOG Z80 80
    Microprocessor Z80 80
        Z80 Instruction set – main table 78
        Z80 Substitution tables 81
        Z80 Notes 82
        Z80 Karnaugh map 84
        Z80 Instructions in numerical order of operation code 94

3.5 DICTIONARY OF INSTRUCTIONS 95

4   Programming: arithmetical operations   111

4.1   MINIMUM USABLE SYSTEM AND SOFTWARE   111
4.2   ASCII CODE   112
4.3   READING DECIMAL DIGITS   114
          Example 1   114
          Exercises   117
4.4   DECIMAL INTEGERS–INPUT AND OUTPUT   118
          Exercises   123
4.5   BINARY ARITHMETIC-INTEGERS   124
      4.5.1   Change of length of a number   124
      4.5.2   Comparisons   125
      4.5.3   Single-length multiplication   126
      4.5.4   Multiple-length multiplication   128
      4.5.5   Single-length division   130
              4.5.5.1   Multiple-length quotient of single-length numbers   132
      4.5.6   Division of multiple-length integers   133
4.6   BINARY ARITHMETIC OF NON-INTEGRAL QUANTITIES   134
      4.6.1   'Fixed-point' representation of non-integral quantities   134
      4.6.2   Multiplication   134
      4.6.3   Addition and subtraction   135
      4.6.4   Division   136
4.7   'FLOATING-POINT' BINARY NUMBERS   137
      4.7.1   Representation and conventions   138
              Variations   139
      4.7.2   Normalization   139
      4.7.3   Auxiliary routines   141
              4.7.3.1   Shifting triple-length numbers   141
              4.7.3.2   Adding triple-length numbers   141
              4.7.3.3   Subtracting triple-length numbers   141
              4.7.3.4   Multiplying triple-length numbers   141
              4.7.3.5   Dividing triple-length numbers   142
      4.7.4   The floating-point subroutines – general   142
      4.7.5   Floating-point input and output   144
              4.7.5.1   Floating-point output   144
              4.7.5.2   Floating-point input   145
      4.7.6   Simple programming with floating-point subroutines   146
              Example   146
              Exercises   148
      4.7.7   Condition flags and floating-point numbers   148
4.8   BINARY-CODED-DECIMAL ARITHMETIC   149
      4.8.1   Addition of unsigned integers   150
              4.8.1.1   Single-length   150
              4.8.1.2   Double-length   150
              4.8.1.3   Multiple-length   150
      4.8.2   Signed BCD integers   151

4.8.3 BCD multiplication 153
4.8.4 BCD fractions 155

5 Programming: non-numerical operations 156

5.1 NON-NUMERICAL QUANTITIES 156
5.2 COPYING 'BLOCKS' OF INFORMATION 156
5.3 SEARCHING A LIST 159
5.4 SORTING 162
      (i) Length of a list 169
      (ii) Elements of other kinds 169
5.5 'PACKED' INFORMATION – QUANTITIES LESS THAN ONE BYTE IN LENGTH 169
5.6 RECORDS AND FILES 171
5.7 SPECIAL PERIPHERAL DEVICES 172

6 Programming at higher levels 175

6.1 BASIC TOOLS FOR PROGRAMMING AT MACHINE-CODE LEVEL 175
    6.1.1 Monitor 176
        D – 'display' 177
        G – 'go' 177
        I – 'input' 177
        M – 'copy' 177
        R – 'resume program' 178
        S – 'substitute' 178
        X – 'examine register' 178
    6.1.2 Assembler 179
    6.1.3 Disassembler 181
    6.1.4 Programming and reading PROMs 181
6.2 SUBROUTINES 181
    6.2.1 Input 182
    6.2.2 Output 183
    6.2.3 Fixed-point arithmetic 184
    6.2.4 Floating-point arithmetic 188
6.3 MOVING UP FROM THE LEVEL OF MACHINE CODE 189
6.4 MOVING DOWN TO THE LEVEL OF MACHINE CODE 195

7 Software: organization, language, structure 197

7.1 MICROPROCESSORS IN CONTEXT 197
        Exercises 198
7.2 SOME CONSIDERATIONS IN THE PLANNING AND DESIGN OF SOFTWARE 199
7.3 NOTATIONS AND LANGUAGE 201
7.4 STRUCTURE AND STYLE 207

8   First software for a small 8080 system   210

8.1   HISTORY   210
8.2   THE MONITOR PROM (0000-03FF)   211
    8.2.1   The monitor program – main part   212
    8.2.2   Special subroutines   213
    8.2.3   The monitor program – branches   213
        I   ('input') at 00E3   214
        S   ('substitute') at 0106   214
        D   ('display' or 'dump') at 0133   214
        M ('mimic' or 'copy') at 0180   214
        R   ('resume') at 00CA   215
        G   ('go') at 0DC4   215
        X   ('examine registers') at 0215   215
    8.2.4   Other subroutines   216
    8.2.5   Programs for the PROM programmer (0360-03EB)   217
8.3   THE ASSEMBLER (0400-07E2, 0800-0BDF, 0C00-0D6E, 0D85-0DC9)   217
    OC20 onwards: processing on instruction   219
    Subroutines for the assembler   220
        'ASCII-Hex (assembler)'-entry 0B00   220
        'Operator'-entry 0B20   220
            'Construct J'-entry 0B60   220
            'Single-length register or J'-entry 0B1B   220
            'condition'-entry 0BC0   220
            'Form JK'-entry 0A00   220
            'Construct JK'-entry 0B80   221
8.4   THE DISASSEMBLER (2800-2B7F)   221
8.5   SUBROUTINES FOR INTEGRAL AND FIXED-POINT ARITHMETIC   222
8.6   FLOATING-POINT SUBROUTINES   223
8.7   ERRORS AND SHORTCOMINGS   224
8.8   ANNOTATED TEXT OF SOFTWARE   224
8.9   HEXADECIMAL TEXT OF SOFTWARE   307

INDEX   313

Preface

Microprocessor programming and software development is intended to provide new users of microprocessors with an introduction to programming and to the basic design of software. More precisely, it is meant as a teaching text and reference document for those newcomers to microprocessors and to programming who wish to understand fully both the programs they will write and the programs they will use.

The book originated in its author's own attempts to come to terms with a number of different microprocessors. It has subsequently derived a great deal from extensive discussions with students and colleagues facing the same task, and from the experience of many courses and seminars involving audiences of a wide variety of background and interest.

This book is offered in the first place as a text for students specializing in computer science in universities, polytechnics and similar institutions. It assumes no previous knowledge of programming, and its references to matters of logic design imply no more advanced experience of that subject than is normally acquired by such students in their first or second year. In the University of Bristol the material was first introduced to third-year students; by the time microprocessors have been established as a teaching medium throughout the undergraduate syllabus it will be a first-year text.

Mature students of many different backgrounds have worked through the material of the book, some by attending evening or vacation courses, others by unaided private study. Their very valuable criticisms and suggestions have been taken into account. It is hoped, therefore, that the book will be of use to other prospective users of microprocessors who, already competent in their own fields, require an introduction to programming that will give them a sound basis for their own future work and the foundation of a critical understanding of the work of others. Such a reader will find the book self-contained as regards its principal subject matter; but if he finds difficulty in reading the first chapter he will no doubt consult an elementary text on logic design. Having done so he will be in a better position to understand the structure of a microprocessor system and to meet the task of using a microprocessor in a context of his own specification.

The approach taken by the book is practical, and, while much of the material is more generally applicable, all detailed discussion is based on four widely used processors, the Motorola 6800, Intel 8080 and 8085, and Zilog Z80.[1] A self-contained software package for the 8080 is given as an integral part of the work, and provides material for illustration throughout.

Chapter 1 gives a brief outline sketch of the 'hardware' aspects of microprocessors and microprocessor systems from a programmer's point of view.

In Chapter 2 the machine instructions and their effects are described and discussed in detail. A common notation for the instruction sets is developed in a manner intended to enable the reader to pass easily from one machine to another. This notation differs radically from the sets of so-called 'mnemonics' constituting the 'assembly languages' designed by the manufacturers; its advantages, however, are considerable, and particularly to the user who does not wish to be restricted to one machine. The application of certain types of instructions, such as those for addition and subtraction, is discussed at length; the reader who feels that this discussion is more than his anticipated needs demand should omit it from his first reading and treat it as reference material for possible later use.

Chapter 3 is given over to tabulations in common form of the instruction sets of the four microprocessors, 6800, 8080, 8085 and Z80, together with an alphabetical 'dictionary' of the written forms, introduced in Chapter 2, of the instructions of the combined set. This superficially forbidding mass of reference material will repay study; at a later stage it will be found that a copy of one or other of the tables will be a convenient and usually sufficient reference during program-writing.

Programming is introduced in Chapter 4 through a series of graded examples. The first of these provide a basis for the simple input, output and processing of characters and numbers; later ones correspond to subroutines of a software package, which are given later in full.

Chapter 5 consists of a set of more or less disjoint sections on topics whose only common feature is that they are not primarily concerned with the processing of numerical quantities. In some, such as that on sorting, a fairly detailed treatment of at least one practical example has been possible; but in others, such as that on files and records, anything more than a brief description of the topic would have required considerably more space than was available.

In Chapter 6 a set of basic software aids to programming is described, and users' instructions for such a set—that given in the software package—are detailed. The chapter ends with discussion of possibilities for enhancing the programmer's power of expression through further software.

Chapter 7 is devoted to a necessarily subjective account of the historical context of microprocessor software, brief references to available packages, and an inconclusive discussion of possibilities for the future. A reader who, in addition to working through the programming exercises of this book, has also used one or other of the available high-level language compilers should be in a position to involve himself in this

---

[1]The extent to which the material applies to another processor will depend, of course, on how different it is from these four. While, no doubt, some of it applies to processors of word-lengths other than 8 bits, it is unlikely that very much of it can usefully be applied to 'bit-slice' devices.

discussion and perhaps carry it forward to the point of contributing his own ideas to the design and implementation of new languages or other, better, means of expression.

Chapter 8 contains the complete text, with detailed commentary, of the software package which has already served as a source of illustrations of programming techniques, instructions for the use of which were given in Chapter 6. This package, occupying 6K bytes of PROM, consists of a monitor, a PROM-programming program, an assembler and disassembler, and a set of arithmetic (including 32-bit floating point) subroutines. The assembler requires at least 1K, and, preferably, 2K, bytes of RAM for working space. However, as described in Chapter 8, parts of the package can be used with much less PROM and RAM. This software has been in use for some time, and it will, it is hoped, be useful to the reader. It is, of course, imperfect, and unlikely to satisfy the critical user for long. The reader who has discovered for himself its usefulness, its limitations and its shortcomings, and who has studied it carefully and observed its structure, its scars, flaws and blemishes, should be well on the way to designing and implementing good software and other programs of his own.

Programming is a practical skill which can be acquired only by practice on actual machines. Clearly, a reader who has an 8080 or 8085 or Z80 system on which the software of Chapter 8 will run will derive much more from this book than will another who has only some other machine. But the latter will be infinitely better off than a third reader who has no access to any machine. All three readers would benefit by getting together to learn to program both of their machines. It is well known that a bilingual programmer is far better able to adapt to new machines and languages than a programmer who can express himself in only one way. A beginner in the fortunate position of being able to buy his own equipment will learn far more from two different small systems than from one larger one.

There is very little, if anything, in this book about cross-assemblers, cross-compilers, debugging aids with elaborate diagnostics or development systems. Such things are distractions to the beginner and symptoms of muddle and despair when used by an experienced programmer. That of course is a provocative over-simplification. The truth is that the system on which a program is to run is the right system on which to develop that program; that, while mistakes are inevitable, muddle and needless complication are not; and that simple, well-designed and easily understood tools, in programming as well as in any other constructional activity, are much to be preferred to elaborate, complicated and unpredictable mechanisms.

The inevitable mistakes in this book, and any avoidable muddle and complication, are the fault of the author, and all expressed opinions are his alone. At the same time, credit for whatever is worthwhile in it belongs ultimately to the many colleagues, teachers, students and friends who, wittingly and unwittingly, have made it possible and who, because of their number, have to be acknowledged collectively. With specific regard to the book, however, thanks are due to Professor M. H. Rogers, Head of the Department of Mathematics, University of Bristol, for initially suggesting and continually supporting the work with microprocessors,[2] and for repeated reminders that the work ought to be documented; to Professor C. A. R. Hoare of

---

[2]Here, and elsewhere, an ambiguity is to be understood in at least two senses.

Oxford University, for much encouragement and constructive criticism; to Messrs H. Hirschberg, R. Decent and their colleagues at Prentice-Hall International for necessary stimulation and practical expertise; to the reviewers for pointing out that a book is meant to be read by readers; to Professor D. Zissos, Professor J. Mühlbacher, and Messrs K. R. Brooks, D. Harvey, G. Pritt, and M. G. Wilkins for their many varied and valued contributions; to Mesdames R. Martin, A. Plumley, A. Warren-Cox and Miss R. Wilkins for their typing; to those microprocessor companies whose products have brought pleasure back into programming; and last, but by no means least, to my wife and (on the whole) our three children, who have suffered much over the past year and yet have continued to provide agreeable conditions for working with microprocessors and even more agreeable means of escape from them.

POSTSCRIPT (*June 1979*)

While this book has been in production, the software of Chapter 8 has been transcribed for an 8085 system with PROM (4×2716) in 0000-1FFF and RAM in 2000 onwards. Some of the improvements suggested in 8.7 have been effected. The assembler with slightly better facilities is in one 2K PROM (1800-1FFF); the monitor with new lineprinter commands, the PROM programmer programs, and disassembler are in another (0000-07FF); the arithmetic and input–output subroutines are in a third (0800-0FFF); while the fourth (1000-17FF) has cassette and higher-level software under development. Users of this system should note the following transpositions:

8080	8085		8080	8085
0360, 03C0	0371, 03C9		0D6F-0D7F	086F-087F
07E6-07FF	0886-089F		0DCA-0FFF	08CA-0AFF
0BE0-0BFF	08A0-08BF		2400-27FF	0C00-0FFF
0CF1-0CF7	08C1-08C7		2B80-2BFF	0B80-0BFF

This postscript provides a welcome opportunity to express thanks to Messrs A. Whittle, P. Woodward, and R. Day for their persistent care with the text and illustrations.

F.G.D.

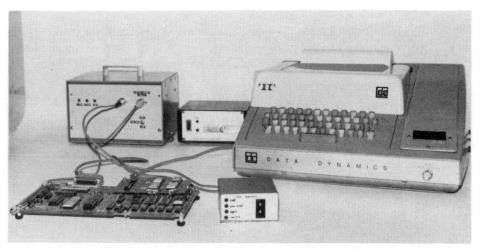

The 8080 system described on pages 210 and 211. The PROM programmer is
in the foreground; the power supply unit is on the left.

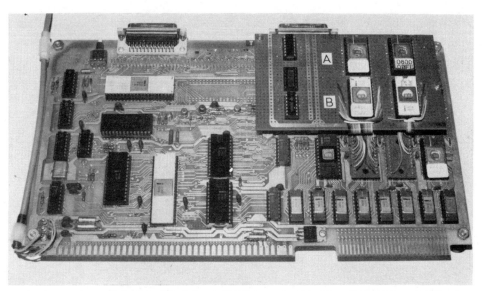

A closer view of the modified Intel SDK board with 6K of PROM and 2K of
RAM.

1

Microprocessors and microprocessor systems

1.1 BASIC IDEAS

Physically, a *microprocessor* is a very large-scale integrated circuit containing the equivalent of several thousands of discrete components on a silicon chip about 4 mm square encapsulated within a dual-in-line package with (typically) 40 pins. Logically, it is a clocked sequential circuit, that is a circuit which will change its internal state, and hence its output signals, in phase with clock pulses. The clock pulses are usually, though not in every case, generated externally. Each change of internal state is determined by the processor's current internal state together with the set of input signals. So far this description applies equally to, say, a JK flip-flop; the difference is in the matter of complexity, for there are very many possible combinations of input signals, very many possible internal states, and very many possible combinations of output signals.

The *operation* of the microprocessor can be seen, however, in fairly simple terms. Essentially it amounts to the repetition of a cycle of internal states. This cycle, the *instruction cycle*, always comprises the following stages.

(i)   A set of input signals (an *instruction*) is *read* (*latched*) into an internal register (the *instruction register*) of the processor.

(ii) The processor passes through a sequence of states determined by the bits composing the instruction, and possibly involving the reading of further input signals (*data*) or the generation of output signals (*results*). This is the *execution* of the instruction.

(iii) Finally, a set of output signals is generated (the *next instruction address*), which is used by external circuitry (normally the *store* or *memory*[1]) to determine the next instruction to be presented to the processor.

[1]'Memory: Part of a computer system used to store data. . . . Store: British word for "memory" ': Donald E. Knuth, *The Art of Computer Programming*. Volume 1: *Fundamental Algorithms*. Reading, Massachusetts: Addison-Wesley, 1968.
'*memory* (of a COMPUTER), see STORE. . . .
store. The most expensive part of a COMPUTER, where the information (both PROGRAM and data) is kept. The neutral term *store* is to be preferred to *memory* to avoid the danger of anthropomorphizing computers. . . . ': the late Christopher Strachey in *The Fontana Dictionary of Modern Thought*. London: Fontana Books, 1977.

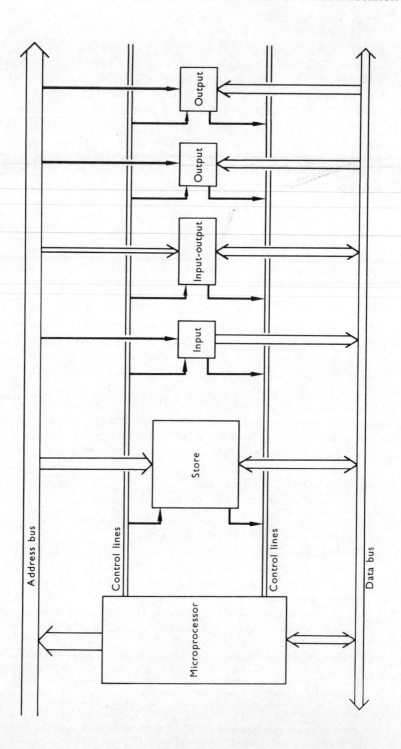

Figure 1.1. A typical microprocessor system.

The sequence of instructions required to cause the processor to accomplish some specific task is a *program*. The instructions of the program being executed are held in a *store* (conceptually a large array of bistable elements). As each instruction is required by the processor its *address* (the set of bits defining its location within the store) is generated by the processor and presented to the store. A copy of the instruction is then input to the processor; the contents of the store remain undisturbed. Now an address can be regarded as a binary number, and normally the *next instruction* is that whose address *follows* that of the current instruction in the numerical sense of having the next greater value. However, a given instruction may require to be followed in execution by an instruction which does not occupy the next address in store. The possibility of such *jump* instructions means that certain sequences of instructions may be executed many times while others may not be executed at all during some execution of the program, depending on the *data* with which the program is working. (The number of instructions stored is no clue to the number of instructions executed or to the time which a program will take to run.)

The microprocessor and store together form the basic *microprocessor system*. In general there will also be other system components, called *peripheral devices*. Typically there will be at least one *input device*, by means of which numbers or other quantities (for example, instructions or instrument readings) can be taken into the store or processor, and at least one *output device*, by means of which numbers (sets of bits) can be taken from the store or processor to the outside world (for example, to be printed, or to control the operation of a machine). A typical microprocessor system is illustrated in Figure 1.1.

The components are connected by sets of wires:

(i)   the *data bus*, which may at any given time be carrying
    (a)   an instruction from the store to the processor;
    (b)   a number from the store or an input device to the processor;
    (c)   a number (result) from the processor to the store or an output device;
    (d)   a number between one part of store and another, between store and a peripheral device, or between two peripheral devices;

(ii)   the *address bus*, which may at any given time be carrying
    (a)   the address of the next instruction required to be executed by the processor;
    (b)   the address of a number in store required for computation by the processor;
    (c)   the address into which a number computed by the processor is to be written;
    (d)   the address (or *device number*) of an input device from which the processor is to receive a number;
    (e)   the address (or device number) of an output device which is to receive a number from the processor;
    (f)   an address concerned in a transfer as in (i) (d) above;

(iii)   *control lines*, carrying timing and control signals which ensure the synchronization and coordination of the computer, in order to ensure the correct operation of transfers of information as listed under (i).

Some microprocessors require variations of this basic scheme. The integrated circuit may be so organized that the address bus and data bus have to share a common

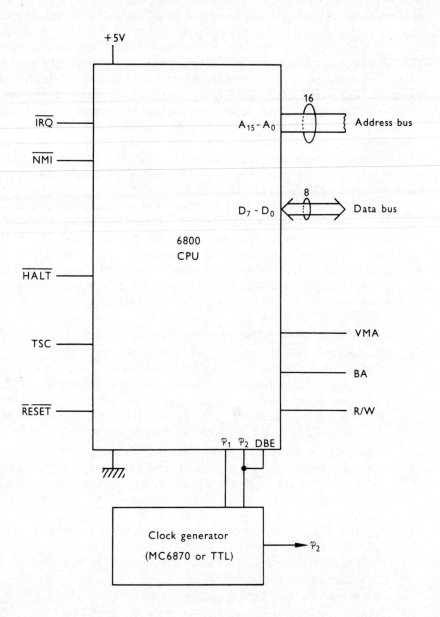

Figure 1.2.   Bus and control connections to 6800.

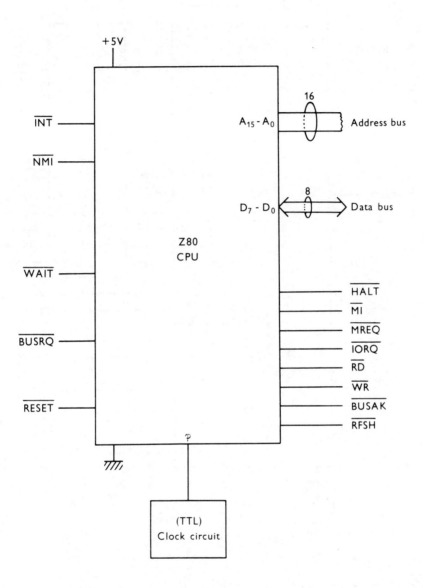

Figure 1.3. Bus and control connections to Z80.

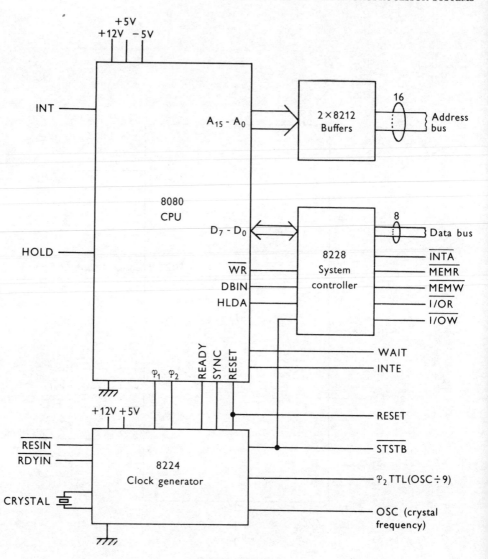

Figure 1.4. Bus and control connections to 8080.

set of pins (8085); or the data pins may be used additionally for further purposes such as communicating control information to be latched externally to the processor (8080).

Figures 1.2 to 1.5 show, in a simplified form, the bus and control line connections to the 6800, Z80, 8080 and 8085 respectively. The drawings for the 8080 and 8085 show additional components for latching and buffering the bus signals so that normal storage devices can be attached to the buses. (Certain special devices are available

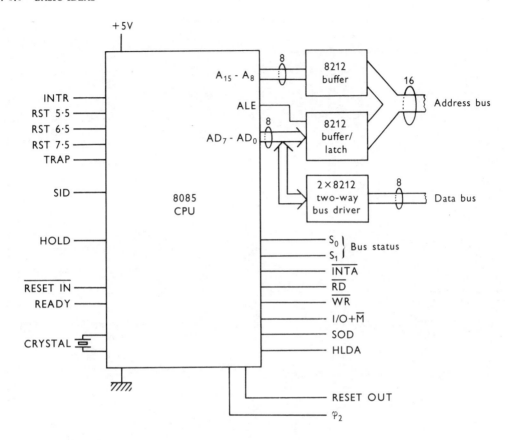

Figure 1.5. Bus and control connections to 8085.

which can be used without these additional components.) The 6800 and Z80 also require bus buffers if any reasonable amount of storage is to be used—see Section 1.3.3.

Table 1.1 gives a very rough functional classification and description of the control signals. This information is intended only to help the programmer to understand how these microprocessors communicate with store and peripherals. Precise technical descriptions are to be found in the appropriate manuals,[2] and comparative descriptions in textbooks such as Hilburn and Julich.[3]

[2]MCS-80 User's Manual (with introduction to MCS-85). Santa Clara, California: Intel Corporation, October 1977.

8085 Microcomputer Systems User's Manual—Preliminary. Santa Clara, California: Intel Corporation, November 1976.

M6800 Microcomputer System Design Data. Phoenix, Arizona: Motorola Semiconductor Products Inc., March 1977.

Z80-CPU, Z80A-CPU Technical Manual. Cupertino, California: Zilog, Inc., 1977.

[3]John L. Hilburn and Paul M. Julich, *Microcomputers/Microprocessors: Hardware, Software, and Applications*. Englewood Cliffs, New Jersey: Prentice-Hall, 1976.

	6800	8080†	8085	Z80	
Control inputs					
Reset	$\overline{\text{RESET}}$	RESIN	RESETIN	$\overline{\text{RESET}}$	Asynchronous reset signal (Ch. 3)
Ready		$\overline{\text{RDYIN}}$	READY	$\overline{\text{WAIT}}$	Machine to waiting state
Bus control	TSC	HOLD	HOLD	$\overline{\text{BUSRQ}}$	Buses to be detached from c.p.u.
	$\overline{\text{HALT}}$				Machine to stop, buses detached
	DBE				Data bus to be detached from c.p.u.
Interruption requests	$\overline{\text{IRQ}}$	INT	INTR RST5.5 RST6.5 RST7.5	$\overline{\text{INT}}$	Ordinary request Intermediate requests (Section 2.9 and Ch. 3)
	$\overline{\text{NMI}}$		TRAP	$\overline{\text{NMI}}$	High priority request
Special			SID		'Serial input data' (Ch. 3)
Buses					
Address	A_{15}–A_0	A_{15}–A_0	A_{15}–A_8	A_{15}–A_0	Address terminals
Address/data			AD_7–AD_0		Multiplexed address/data terminals
			ALE		Strobe for address
Data	D_7–D_0	D_7–D_0		D_7–D_0	Data terminals
Control outputs					
Data transfer control	{R/W VMA}	{$\overline{\text{MEMR}}$ $\overline{\text{MEMW}}$ $\overline{\text{I/OR}}$ $\overline{\text{I/OW}}$}	{$\overline{\text{RD}}$ $\overline{\text{WR}}$ $\overline{\text{I/O}+\text{M}}$}	{$\overline{\text{RD}}$ $\overline{\text{WR}}$ $\overline{\text{MREQ}}$ $\overline{\text{IORQ}}$}	Combinations of these output signals enable and time information transfers along the data bus to and from the specified location or device
Interruption timing		$\overline{\text{INTA}}$	$\overline{\text{INTA}}$	$\overline{\text{MI}}$	Timing of reading of interrupting instruction from data bus (Section 2.9)
C.p.u. state		WAIT INTE	SOD	$\overline{\text{HALT}}$	Information on state of c.p.u. (for INTE, SOD see Ch. 3)
Bus state	BA		HLDA S_1 S_0	BUSAK	Information on state of data bus (whether available, or direction and nature of current transfer)
Special				$\overline{\text{RFSH}}$	'Refresh' timing pulse for dynamic RAM (Section 2.10)
Synchronized outputs		RESET	RESETOUT		For use by interfaces (Section 1.4.1)

8080† = 8080 + 8224 + 8228 (See Figure 1.4).

Table 1.1. Control and Bus Signals

1.2 INTERNAL ORGANIZATION OF A MICROPROCESSOR

The internal organization of a typical microprocessor is shown schematically in Figure 1.6. Not all microprocessors have all of the components indicated—in particular, there may be no 'other addressing registers' and no 'other registers'. In some cases a given register may serve both as an arithmetic register and as an addressing register. Some processors have internal units not shown on the diagram, such as a stack of registers or a small ROM, PROM or RAM.

Each connecting line in the diagram represents a number of parallel lines, the number depending on the particular processor.

1.2.1 Power supplies

While some processors require only one power supply (e.g. $+5$ V for the 6800, 8085, Z80, 2650), others require three (e.g. $+12$ V, $+5$ V, -5 V for the 8080 and $+12$ V, $+5$ V, -3 V for the CP1600), by reason of their technology. The power consumption of a microprocessor is usually between 1 and $1\frac{1}{2}$ W and sometimes much less (e.g. 525 mW for the 2650).

1.2.2 Clock

Most microprocessors at present require to be driven by an external *clock* (source of regular pulses). However, some have internal clock circuitry and require only an external crystal to define the clock frequency.

Of those using an externally generated clock, the Z80 requires a single-phase TTL (Transistor–transistor Logic) square wave; the 6800 requires two interleaved pulse trains at TTL levels; while the 8080 requires two interleaved pulse trains each with 12 V amplitude. However, in this last case a special clock generator IC (8224) is available which requires only an external crystal.

In most cases, the clock pulse width and frequency must be kept steady, but within a reasonably wide range (e.g. CP 1600, $\frac{1}{2}$ MHz to 5 MHz). Some (e.g. 2650) allow the clock rate to be taken right down to manual speeds—this greatly simplifies the problem of 'single-shot' operation.

1.2.3 Timing and control unit

This is, logically, a synchronous sequential circuit driven by the clock. Its primary signals are:

(i)   external control signals, such as 'reset' for initialization, 'ready' from peripheral devices and 'hold' and 'interrupt' requests from such devices;

(ii) outputs from the 'instruction decoder' (below), which determine each particular instruction cycle.

Its output signals are:

(i)   internal control signals, which trigger other internal units, and establish data paths and time data transfers within the microprocessor;

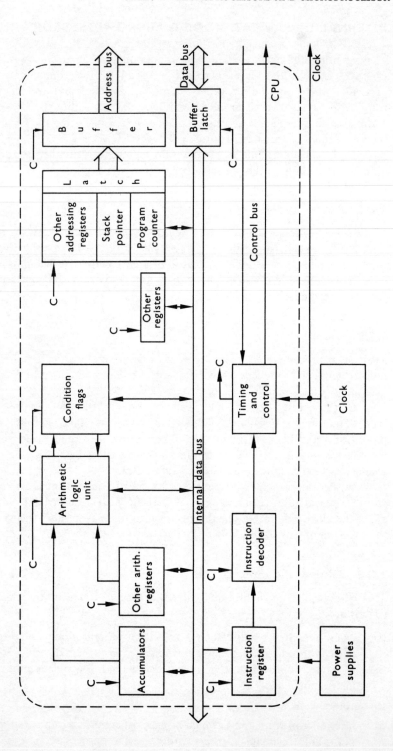

Figure 1.6. Internal organization of a typical microprocessor.

(ii) external control signals, such as 'enable' and 'acknowledge' signals for 'hold' and 'interrupt' requests; bus timing pulses; and signals giving information about processor and bus states for use by external components.

The external control signals are taken to and from the rest of the system along the lines of the *control bus*. The internal control signals, indicated on Fig. 1.6 by 'C', are distributed to all of the other internal components of the processor.

The normal function of the timing and control unit is to respond to each decoded instruction by issuing signals which, in activating the registers, arithmetic units and external devices concerned, ensure the *execution* of that instruction. As examples of this operation:

(i) If the decoded instruction is an inter-register transfer, a path will be opened from the source register, along the internal data bus, to the destination register by suitable enabling or gating signals, and the transfer will be effected by a timing signal (strobe pulse).

(ii) For an arithmetic operation, control signals admit data into the *arithmetic–logic unit* (below) from the registers (or register and store location) containing the operands; they ensure the required operation, and allow the result to go to an accumulator or other result register, or even back to store.

(iii) For an operation involving a read from, or write into, the store, the appropriate address will be held in an *addressing register* (for example, *index register* or *stack pointer*) and this will be released to the address bus. In addition, the *data register* concerned will be connected to the *data bus* and the transfer along the data bus between register and store will be effected by a timing pulse as before.

As well as controlling the execution of each instruction, the timing and control unit must advance or replace the contents of the *program counter* so that it will hold the address of the next instruction to be executed. It can then cause this instruction to be fetched from store to the *instruction register*.

1.2.4 Instruction register and decoder

The instruction register receives each instruction in turn, and holds it during its execution. The instruction decoder is in principle a combinational circuit—and thus no different from any other decoder. Its outputs are used by the timing and control unit in determining the course of execution of the instruction in the instruction register.

1.2.5 Arithmetic–logic unit (ALU)

This unit contains circuitry for performing a number of (combinational) operations, each on one or two operands. The operations include addition, subtraction and various Boolean operations applied in parallel to all the bits of the single operand or all the pairs of corresponding bits of the two operands. In most cases there is a *result* to be held in an *accumulator*; in nearly all cases the *condition flags* will be affected.

1.2.6   Condition flags

Most, if not all, arithmetic and logical operations affect one or more *condition flags*. Each flag may be regarded as a single flip-flop whose set and reset conditions are determined by the result of the last executed arithmetic–logic operation (though in the 6800 simple data transfers also affect them). Thus one flag will record whether the last result was zero or non-zero, another whether it was positive or negative (i.e. whether its most significant bit was 0 or 1). Condition flags are used to determine the outcome of *conditional jump* instructions. The set of condition flags can in most processors be treated as a register ('condition code register', 'condition flag register') in the sense that instructions are provided for copying their bit-values into another register or into store and for restoring them when required. In addition, some or all of them can be set or reset individually by special instructions without regard to ALU operations.

1.2.7   Accumulators

An accumulator is basically a register which can receive and hold the arithmetic sum of its previous contents and some other number. In other words it can be used to build up an accumulated sum. By extension, the word is used to describe a register associated in the same way with operations other than addition. All microprocessors have at least one accumulator, and it is usual for an accumulator to be the register concerned in data transfers to and from the processor along the data bus.

1.2.8   Program counter

This is a register which contains the address of the instruction to be executed next. Normally this address is arrived at by adding the length of the current instruction (one, two, three, or four (bytes)) to the address of that current instruction. However, in an *unconditional jump* instruction, the program counter contents are *replaced* by a specified address (and this replacement constitutes the execution of the jump). For a *conditional jump*, the replacement occurs if the specified condition flag (or function of condition flag values) has the specified value: otherwise normal incrementation takes place. For a *relative jump* (or *branch*) a number specified in the jump instruction is *added* to the program counter.

   The contents of the program counter are also affected by subroutine calls, interrupts, and return instructions. Some processors provide for explicit operations on the program counter.

1.2.9   Stack pointer

Stack operation is a feature of many microprocessors. Typically, the stack itself is established in the store by putting its base address into the stack point register. Every time a new item is put on the stack, the stack pointer value is advanced and every time an item is removed the stack pointer value is retarded. Usually 'advance' means decrementing and 'retard' means incrementing so that the base address is a high number and the stack grows 'downwards' in the address space. There are usually instructions for explicit operations on the stack pointer, and there may be provisions for preserving the stack pointer value through an interrupt or subroutine execution.

1.2.10   Other addressing registers

By an *addressing register* is meant a register whose contents can be used as an address in a store read or write operation. An *index register* is one with associated 'increment' or 'decrement' operations and which can be used in obtaining access to consecutive store locations.

1.3   THE STORE

1.3.1   Main store and secondary store

The store of a large system will consist of two parts: (i) the *main store* and (ii) the *secondary* (or backing) *store*. A small system will have only a main store.

Secondary storage includes such things as magnetic tapes and cassettes, discs, and paper tape or punched cards. Access to secondary storage is through a peripheral device.

The *main store* of a microprocessor system is normally made up of semiconductor devices, integrated circuits each capable of storing several thousand bits. Each byte in main store has a unique address, and with a 16-bit address bus, up to 65536 bytes may be addressed by the processor.

For the microprocessor to operate at the full speed allowed by its clock frequency, it is necessary that the *access time* of the storage device should be properly matched with the clock frequency. If the access time is too long, it will mean that the timing signal which takes data into the processor can occur before the store has been able to make the data available. This problem can sometimes be overcome by interfering with the clock, or by causing the processor cycle to pass through 'waiting states', but it is far preferable to choose storage devices appropriate to the situation. Sufficient varieties are certainly available.

Although microprocessors have been designed to work most efficiently with semiconductor stores, it is possible to use magnetic cores as main store, but the timing difficulties mentioned above are likely to occur and must be overcome.

1.3.2   Semiconductor storage

Semiconductor storage is available in the form of integrated circuits in standard dual-in-line packages. Each such package is described as containing a number of *bits*, almost always a power of two. These bits may be accessed singly, or in groups of 4 or 8. So we may find one type holding 1024×1 bits, another 256×4, another 128×8. Each holds 1024 bits, but

(i)   The 1024×1 device has 10 address pins, and requires a 10-bit address to specify each individual bit;

(ii)   The 256×4 device has 8 address pins, and requires an 8-bit address to specify each group of 4 bits;

(iii) The 128×8 device has 7 address pins, and requires a 7-bit address to specify each byte.

There are three main types of semiconductor storage—ROM, PROM and RAM.

1.3.2.1 ROM ('read only memory')

This term is applied to a semiconductor store containing fixed information which has been built into it during the last stage of manufacture. This information cannot be altered, and when the device is installed in a system, it can only be *read* by the processor. It follows that the applications of ROM are rather specialized—for example, it may be used to hold standard code-conversion tables. Some ROMs containing programs are available, but the reader is warned: a program in ROM cannot be corrected.

A typical ROM, 1024×8, will have 10 address pins and 8 data pins. The latter can be connected directly to the data bus; there are tri-state[4] buffers in the ROM whose outputs are normally in the high-impedance state but which can be enabled by a signal, a timing pulse from the processor, to a 'chip enable' pin. A chip must be enabled only when the data required is in the chip itself, and not in another chip. So the enable signal may have to be gated with a combination of (in this case) the 6 high-order address bits. Some ROMs facilitate this by providing 'chip select' pins, each of which has to be at a specified logic level before the chip can be enabled.

1.3.2.2 PROM ('programmable read only memory')

When it is installed in a system, this device behaves exactly like a ROM, and is used in a similar way. The significant difference between a ROM and a PROM is that the latter can be 'reprogrammed'; that is, it can be detached from the computer system, the information in it erased, and new information put into it. The 're-programming' process requires specially designed apparatus (for example, a source of ultra-violet radiation for erasure and a source of relatively high-voltage pulses for rewriting). The information in a PROM cannot be destroyed or overwritten by the normal signals of the microprocessor system.

(The words 'programmable', 'reprogramming', 'programming', etc. in this context are unfortunate, because a 'program' is a set of instructions which a computer has to execute and 'programming' is writing programs. Some users have been misled into thinking that only PROM can be used for holding programs.)

Clearly, the PROM can be used for the same kind of information as the ROM. But its additional features make it ideally suited to the permanent storage of programs, and even for less permanent storage of programs under development, provided a suitable 'PROM programmer' and 'PROM eraser' are accessible. The software described later in this book was developed in PROMs and is now held in PROMs.

---

[4]A tri-state (or three-state) buffer is, for our purposes here, the electronic equivalent of a mechanical make–break switch. When it is *enabled*, by a control signal, its output has the same logic value, 0 or 1, as its data input; when it is *disabled* its output is independent of its data input. In this latter condition, the 'third state', a *high impedance* is interposed between data input and output which has the same practical effect as a physical break.

1.3.2.3   RAM ('random access memory')[5]

This is the form of semiconductor storage which corresponds most closely to magnetic cores. Information can be *written* into it under system (program) control, and *read* from it. At the present time most available RAMs lose their information when power is switched off. Some, however, have a 'standby' condition in which they retain information, but cannot be read or written into, under considerably reduced power. RAMs able to hold information indefinitely for no power are under development.

All RAM packages have address pins which are used, as in the ROM and PROM, to select the particular bit positions required. In some cases there are two sets of data terminals, one for writing and one for reading. It has, however, become usual to have one set only, to be connected directly to the data bus. In this case the output stage will certainly be three-state.

The control signals normally necessary are:

(i)   a read/write signal to define the next operation;
(ii)   an enable signal (pulse) to control the timing of the transfer;
(iii)   one or more 'select' signals, which must have specified levels for (i), (ii) to be effective.

There are two main types of RAM: static and dynamic. *Static* RAM is (still) more expensive than dynamic, and is slower—though fast enough for many microprocessor applications. Information in static RAM, once written, is held indefinitely as long as the power supply is maintained. *Dynamic* RAM has a higher information density than static (4K bits dynamic RAM, 1K bits static RAM are the commonest sizes available), which is an important point when a large store is required. However, it loses information within a matter of a few milliseconds of writing unless action is taken to 'refresh' it. This is because a capacitative effect is used as the means of storage and the charges leak; they have to be 'topped up' before a 1 becomes indistinguishable from a 0. In most cases the store is organized as an array of rows and columns, and it is arranged that any read or write operation on any bit refreshes *all* the bits in the same column. Thus the 'refresh problem' is that of ensuring that every column is accessed within every period of 2 milliseconds (or whatever period is prescribed). In a microprocessor system this can be done by forcing the processor to wait while the complete RAM is gone through in a 'burst', or by using machine cycles in which the processor does not require normal access to the RAM to achieve 'column-at-a-time' refreshing. The Z80 has circuitry for this latter form of refreshing within the processor. For other processors a special integrated circuit can be used. Designed in TTL, a refreshing circuit can be rather bulky.

In programming practice there is usually no need to consider the difference between static and dynamic RAM. However, the Z80 has a 'refresh register', a counter containing the current 'refresh address' which is put out to a dynamic RAM, if any. This register may be copied to the accumulator, or assigned the value in the

---

[5]The term 'random access memory' for read–write stores is inappropriate since not only RAM but also ROM and PROM are 'random access' in the same sense that all bit positions are equally accessible through the addressing mechanism.

accumulator for test purposes, and instructions for these operations exist in the instruction set. These instructions are not used in ordinary programs.

1.3.3 Address buffering and decoding

Consider a small system in which there are to be 4K bytes of PROM and 1K bytes of RAM. The PROM is to occupy addresses 0000–0FFF (hexadecimal) and the RAM addresses 1000–13FF (hexadecimal). For PROM, four packages each of 1024×8 bits are to be used, and for RAM eight packages each of 128×8 bits. How can these be connected to the address bus so that (i) every byte can be addressed independently of the others and (ii) the store can be expanded without disturbing existing connections?

The problem is simplified by the use of a 3–8 decoder with the layout and truth table indicated in Figure 1.7.

A solution is given in Figure 1.8. (Enabling signals, and read/write signals for the RAMs, have been omitted.) With this arrangement every byte in PROM and RAM has a unique address as specified and the unconnected outputs of the decoders 1 and 2 are available for expansion of the store up to the full complement of 65536 bytes. This expansion is possible without disturbing any existing wiring.

There is a temptation which many designers—including those of commercially available kits—have fallen into, and that is to skimp the address decoding. Given the specification of this small system, they might omit decoder 1 altogether. The effect of this is to limit the space for expansion to 3K (represented by the unused outputs of decoder 2). The reason is that three address bits, A_{15}, A_{14}, A_{13} being ignored, the address bus is reduced to 13 bits. A bus of 13 bits can address only 2^{13} (8192) bytes.

Since any system almost inevitably has to expand at some stage, it is surely wise to allow fully for expansion at the outset. The cost—in components or space, power dissipation or money—is so insignificant compared with that of even a small system that it seems foolish to do otherwise.

From Figure 1.8 it will be clear to anyone with a little experience in logic design that a store of any size is going to impose considerable loading on the address bus,

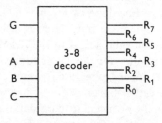

G	A	B	C	R_0	R_1	R_2	R_3	R_4	R_5	R_6	R_7
0	x	x	x	0	0	0	0	0	0	0	0
1	0	0	0	1	0	0	0	0	0	0	0
1	0	0	1	0	1	0	0	0	0	0	0
1	0	1	0	0	0	1	0	0	0	0	0
1	0	1	1	0	0	0	1	0	0	0	0
1	1	0	0	0	0	0	0	1	0	0	0
1	1	0	1	0	0	0	0	0	1	0	0
1	1	1	0	0	0	0	0	0	0	1	0
1	1	1	1	0	0	0	0	0	0	0	1

Figure 1.7.   3 to 8 decoder.

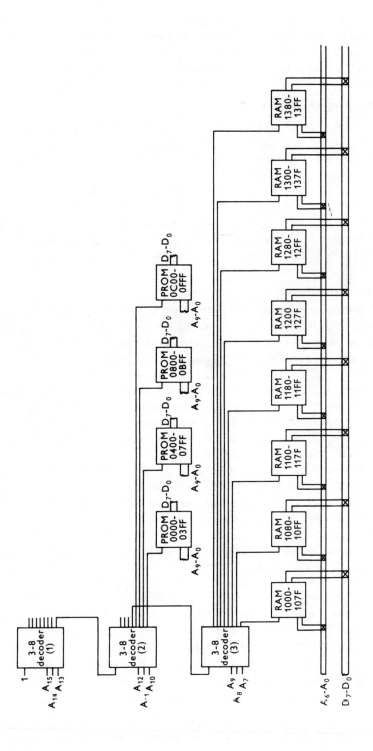

Figure 1.8 Illustration of address decoding.

particularly on its lower bits. For this reason, *buffering*[6] of the address bus is essential in any but the smallest configuration. This is a very simple matter with, for example, the Intel 8212; two of these can be placed next to the processor with their control signals arranged so that they act as straight-through buffers.

1.4   PERIPHERAL DEVICES

Even the simplest microprocessor system will include at least one input device and one output device. These may be no more than a set of switches and a set of lamps, or they may be combined in the form of a teletype or a visual display unit (VDU) with a keyboard and monitor screen.

Additional peripherals may include devices for secondary storage (cassette recorder, floppy disc drive, etc.), devices for special input or output of information (paper tape reader, graphics unit, etc.), mechanisms for controlling or obtaining information from other systems (relays, analogue–digital converters, etc.), or auxiliary devices useful to the computer system itself (such as a PROM programmer).

1.4.1   Interfaces

All peripherals present the system designer with the problem of matching the speed and timing of the device to the speed and timing of the computer. In addition there may be problems of matching signal characteristics, and of managing serial-to-parallel and parallel-to-serial conversions. The circuitry designed to stand between the computer system and the device in order to overcome these problems is called an *interface*. Interface design is a considerable subject in itself, and is outside the scope of this book. However, the microprocessor manufacturers have developed integrated circuits which simplify the task in many cases. For example, for a 'parallel interface', where sets of bits are to be transmitted across the interface simultaneously ('in parallel'), the Motorola 6820 (peripheral interface adapter, PIA), Intel 8255 (programmable peripheral interface, PPI) and Zilog Z80PIO (parallel input–output) are available. A teletype or VDU receives and transmits information in *serial* form, one bit after another. The interface here requires to transform sets of eight bits (as presented by the data bus) into serial form for the peripheral device, and to transform sequences of eight bits (as presented by the keyboard) into parallel sets of bits for the system data bus. The Motorola 6850 (asynchronous communications interface adapter, ACIA), Intel 8251 (programmable communication interface—universal synchronous/asynchronous receiver/transmitter, USART), and Zilog Z80SIO (serial input–output) can effect these transformations very conveniently.

It is usually possible to design the interface for a given peripheral in any of a number of different ways. The *programming* of transfers of information through the interface will vary according to the actual interface used. Three ways of interfacing a teletype or VDU are discussed in Section 2.8, together with their implications for the programmer.

----

[6]The terms 'loading' and 'buffering' are used here in their engineering, not programming, sense. A programmer unfamiliar with them may visualize 'load' as the stress on the source of a signal due to its use as an input. Then a 'buffer' is a device which, given a (strained or weak) input, generates a logically identical output which is capable of bearing a substantial load.

2

Instructions

2.1   BASIC IDEAS

We have seen that a microprocessor operates by repeating a cycle in which an instruction is fetched from store, executed, and succeeded. The successor instruction is normally that occupying the 'next' location in store, but in some cases—jumps, subroutine calls and returns, interrupts—it is elsewhere in store.

Each instruction consists basically of one machine word, which for the 6800, 8080, 8085 and Z80 is one byte—8 bits. Many instructions—notably those for inter-register transfer and many arithmetic–logic operations—require only one byte, but others are always followed immediately by one or two additional bytes which form an 'immediate operand' (number or address), and these additional bytes are usually regarded as part of the instruction. In all these cases, the first byte is often called the 'operation code'. Exceptionally, the Z80 has instructions four bytes in length which will be described later.

If there are 8 bits in an operation code, there are $2^8 = 256$ possible different operations which are to be distinguished by the instruction decoder in the microprocessor. In fact, for the 6800 only 197 have defined executions; for the 8080, 244; for the 8085, 246; while for the Z80 all 256 have defined executions, and indeed 4 of them are interpreted as implying a further operation code byte.

The different defined operations constitute the *instruction set* of the processor. A *program* is a sequence of instructions for execution by the processor to enable it to accomplish some task. It is important to remember that there are two *orders* of the instructions of a program. The *static order* is the order in which they are held in store. The *dynamic order* is the order in which they are executed. This order will be determined by the jumps, calls, interrupts, etc., and will normally involve skipping and repetition. It is not usually possible to predict the dynamic order of a program without executing it, since the outcome of conditional jumps depends on the results of computation, which in turn depend on the data read from input devices.

A program is often regarded as defining a *procedure* or *process* to be carried out on *information* (or *data*); hence the term *information* (or *data*) *processing* for the result of executing a program, and the more recent terms *processor* and *microprocessor* for instruments of information processing. The term *computation* suggests the processing of *numerical* information, but a *computer* nowadays seems to be anything from a simple control mechanism to a large information processing system. For our present purposes a (micro)computer is taken to be a system made up of a microprocessor, its store, and peripheral devices.

2.2   REPRESENTATION OF INSTRUCTIONS

In the computer, whether in store or in the instruction register of the microprocessor, an instruction is simply an ordered set of bits. Obviously an instruction can be represented in writing by an ordered set of ones and zeroes, and there are indeed occasions when this is convenient. But normally a more compact notation is preferable.

Consider the byte 01010011.

In the *octal* (scale of eight) convention the bits are grouped in threes ($8=2^3$) from the right, and each group is represented by a digit standing for the value of that group. The byte is written as 123 or 123_8. Note that the left-most (most significant) octal digit can only be 0, 1, 2 or 3 because it stands for only 2 bits.

In the *hexadecimal* (scale of sixteen) convention the bits are grouped in fours ($16=2^4$) from the right. The byte is written as 53 or 53_{16} or 53H. The sixteen values 0000, 0001, . . . 1001, 1010, . . . 1111 are written as 0, 1, . . . 9, A, . . . F.

Further examples:

Binary	Octal	Hexadecimal
10101100	254	AC
11111111	377	FF
00000000	000	00
01010101	125	55

Throughout the remainder of this book the hexadecimal convention will be used in writing instructions unless specified otherwise in particular cases.

A table of equivalence of 8-bit, octal, hexadecimal, and decimal values is given in Table 2.1.

Clearly, any set of bits—whether instruction, operation code or number—can be written in hexadecimal or octal form.

Now, although hexadecimal notation is a very compact way of writing down what is to go into the system, and has the advantage of inducing fewer transcription errors than 'ones and zeroes', it still has one very great disadvantage: what is written gives no suggestion as to the meaning of an instruction.

The byte 01010011 (53), if it gets into the instruction register of the 6800, causes all the bits of an accumulator (B) to be inverted. The same byte, if it gets into the instruction register of the 8080, 8085 or Z80, causes the contents of one register (D) to be replaced by a copy of the contents of another register (E). Neither of these operations is even suggested by '53', still less by '01010011'.

| | | Decimal | | | | Decimal | | | | Decimal | | | | Decimal | |
Hex.	Oc-tal	Signed	Un-signed	Hex.	Oc-tal	Signed	Un-signed	Hex.	Oc-tal	Signed	Un-signed	Hex.	Oc-tal	Signed	Un-signed
00	000	(+)0	0	40	100	+64	64	80	200	−128	128	C0	300	−64	192
01	001	+1	1	41	101	+65	65	81	201	−127	129	C1	301	−63	193
02	002	+2	2	42	102	+66	66	82	202	−126	130	C2	302	−62	194
03	003	+3	3	43	103	+67	67	83	203	−125	131	C3	303	−61	195
04	004	+4	4	44	104	+68	68	84	204	−124	132	C4	304	−60	196
05	005	+5	5	45	105	+69	69	85	205	−123	133	C5	305	−59	197
06	006	+6	6	46	106	+70	70	86	206	−122	134	C6	306	−58	198
07	007	+7	7	47	107	+71	71	87	207	−121	135	C7	307	−57	199
08	010	+8	8	48	110	+72	72	88	210	−120	136	C8	310	−56	200
09	011	+9	9	49	111	+73	73	89	211	−119	137	C9	311	−55	201
0A	012	+10	10	4A	112	+74	74	8A	212	−118	138	CA	312	−54	202
0B	013	+11	11	4B	113	+75	75	8B	213	−117	139	CB	313	−53	203
0C	014	+12	12	4C	114	+76	76	8C	214	−116	140	CC	314	−52	204
0D	015	+13	13	4D	115	+77	77	8D	215	−115	141	CD	315	−51	205
0E	016	+14	14	4E	116	+78	78	8E	216	−114	142	CE	316	−50	206
0F	017	+15	15	4F	117	+79	79	8F	217	−113	143	CF	317	−49	207
10	020	+16	16	50	120	+80	80	90	220	−112	144	D0	320	−48	208
11	021	+17	17	51	121	+81	81	91	221	−111	145	D1	321	−47	209
12	022	+18	18	52	122	+82	82	92	222	−110	146	D2	322	−46	210
13	023	+19	19	53	123	+83	83	93	223	−109	147	D3	323	−45	211
14	024	+20	20	54	124	+84	84	94	224	−108	148	D4	324	−44	212
15	025	+21	21	55	125	+85	85	95	225	−107	149	D5	325	−43	213
16	026	+22	22	56	126	+86	86	96	226	−106	150	D6	326	−42	214
17	027	+23	23	57	127	+87	87	97	227	−105	151	D7	327	−41	215
18	030	+24	24	58	130	+88	88	98	230	−104	152	D8	330	−40	216
19	031	+25	25	59	131	+89	89	99	231	−103	153	D9	331	−39	217
1A	032	+26	26	5A	132	+90	90	9A	232	−102	154	DA	332	−38	218
1B	033	+27	27	5B	133	+91	91	9B	233	−101	155	DB	333	−37	219
1C	034	+28	28	5C	134	+92	92	9C	234	−100	156	DC	334	−36	220
1D	035	+29	29	5D	135	+93	93	9D	235	−99	157	DD	335	−35	221
1E	036	+30	30	5E	136	+94	94	9E	236	−98	158	DE	336	−34	222
1F	037	+31	31	5F	137	+95	95	9F	237	−97	159	DF	337	−33	223
20	040	+32	32	60	140	+96	96	A0	240	−96	160	E0	340	−32	224
21	041	+33	33	61	141	+97	97	A1	241	−95	161	E1	341	−31	225
22	042	+34	34	62	142	+98	98	A2	242	−94	162	E2	342	−30	226
23	043	+35	35	63	143	+99	99	A3	243	−93	163	E3	343	−29	227
24	044	+36	36	64	144	+100	100	A4	244	−92	164	E4	344	−28	228
25	045	+37	37	65	145	+101	101	A5	245	−91	165	E5	345	−27	229
26	046	+38	38	66	146	+102	102	A6	246	−90	166	E6	346	−26	230
27	047	+39	39	67	147	+103	103	A7	247	−89	167	E7	347	−25	231
28	050	+40	40	68	150	+104	104	A8	250	−88	168	E8	350	−24	232
29	051	+41	41	69	151	+105	105	A9	251	−87	169	E9	351	−23	233
2A	052	+42	42	6A	152	+106	106	AA	252	−86	170	EA	352	−22	234
2B	053	+43	43	6B	153	+107	107	AB	253	−85	171	EB	353	−21	235
2C	054	+44	44	6C	154	+108	108	AC	254	−84	172	EC	354	−20	236
2D	055	+45	45	6D	155	+109	109	AD	255	−83	173	ED	355	−19	237
2E	056	+46	46	6E	156	+110	110	AE	256	−82	174	EE	356	−18	238
2F	057	+47	47	6F	157	+111	111	AF	257	−81	175	EF	357	−17	239
30	060	+48	48	70	160	+112	112	B0	260	−80	176	F0	360	−16	240
31	061	+49	49	71	161	+113	113	B1	261	−79	177	F1	361	−15	241
32	062	+50	50	72	162	+114	114	B2	262	−78	178	F2	362	−14	242
33	063	+51	51	73	163	+115	115	B3	263	−77	179	F3	363	−13	243
34	064	+52	52	74	164	+116	116	B4	264	−76	180	F4	364	−12	244
35	065	+53	53	75	165	+117	117	B5	265	−75	181	F5	365	−11	245
36	066	+54	54	76	166	+118	118	B6	266	−74	182	F6	366	−10	246
37	067	+55	55	77	167	+119	119	B7	267	−73	183	F7	367	−9	247
38	070	+56	56	78	170	+120	120	B8	270	−72	184	F8	370	−8	248
39	071	+57	57	79	171	+121	121	B9	271	−71	185	F9	371	−7	249
3A	072	+58	58	7A	172	+122	122	BA	272	−70	186	FA	372	−6	250
3B	073	+59	59	7B	173	+123	123	BB	273	−69	187	FB	373	−5	251
3C	074	+60	60	7C	174	+124	124	BC	274	−68	188	FC	374	−4	252
3D	075	+61	61	7D	175	+125	125	BD	275	−67	189	FD	375	−3	253
3E	076	+62	62	7E	176	+126	126	BE	276	−66	190	FE	376	−2	254
3F	077	+63	63	7F	177	+127	127	BF	277	−65	191	FF	377	−1	255

Table 2.1. Eight bit equivalence table—hexadecimal, octal, signed and unsigned decimal

The manufacturers of these machines, and by now many of their users, express these instructions by means of combinations of letters and other symbols euphemistically called 'mnemonics'. For the examples:

6800:	53 is COMB	'complement B'
8080, 8085:	53 is MOV D,E	'move E to D' (sic)
Z80:	53 is LD D,E	'load E into D' (sic)

The operation 'add the number in register B into register A' $(A:=A+B)$ is carried out by a single-byte instruction in all four processors. The manufacturers' mnemonics are:

6800 (hexadecimal 1B)	ABA
8080, 8085 (hexadecimal 80)	ADD B
Z80 (hexadecimal 80)	ADD A, B.

Three different notations for the same thing!

'Mnemonics' are a legacy of the large systems of the nineteen sixties. They were not a very happy feature of those systems; they had to be learnt, and programs written in them were difficult to understand.

In this book mnemonics of this kind will not be used. Instead, instructions will be expressed in a notational system which is described below. There are two obvious disadvantages to this approach: (i) it is yet another notation, and (ii) no one of consequence uses it. It is possible that the second disadvantage may be overcome in time in the light of the advantages which are claimed for it:

(i)　within the limitations of the character set provided with most ASCII-coded keyboards, it allows instructions to be expressed consistently and compactly;

(ii)　the notation, which is based on ideas contained in the working papers of the (IFIP) ALGOL group, can be read and understood, with very little explanation, by any literate programmer;

(iii)　where the same operation exists on more than one machine the same notation is used;

(iv)　the notation has shown itself in practice to be a good basis for programming languages. Such languages for the machines under discussion are described later. An assembler for the 8080, occupying $2\frac{1}{4}$K of PROM, has been in use since March 1977. Its full text is given in Chapter 8. This can be improved to give the same facilities in 2K, or extended to provide further facilities in 3K or 4K. Corresponding assemblers for the 6800 and Z80 are under development. An ALGOL W cross-assembler for the 6800 was made by a student in three weeks. See Chapter 7 for a discussion of 'higher-level' possibilities;

(v)　A 'back-assembler' or 'disassembler'—that is, a program for printing out a program (held in the machine) in the notation—can be written quite compactly (less than 1K each for 8080, 8085 and 6800—see Sections 6.1, 8.4). This is an extremely useful 'monitor' facility, enabling programs to be printed in an easily readable form.

2.3 GENERAL NOTATIONS

2.3.1 The bytes of an instruction

Unless it is a Z80 instruction beginning with CB, DD, ED, FD:

(i) The first byte of an instruction is denoted by I. We suppose it to be stored at location n in the main store.

(ii) The second byte of a 2- or 3-byte instruction is denoted by J. It is stored at location $(n+1)$.

(iii) The third byte of a 3-byte instruction is denoted by K. It is stored at location $(n+2)$.

For Z80 instructions beginning with CB, DD, ED, FD only:

(i) The first byte is denoted by I_0; its location is n.

(ii) The second byte is denoted by I_1; its location is $(n+1)$.

(iii) The third byte, if any, is denoted by J; its location is $(n+2)$.

(iv) The fourth byte, if any, is denoted by K; its location is $(n+3)$.

(*Note:* the symbols I, J, K are also used with other meanings—respectively 'interrupt flag', 'jump', 'carry flag'—but the context will always remove any possible ambiguity.)

2.3.2 Registers

A single-length (8-bit) register, or its contents, is denoted by a single letter *identifier*. For example, for the 8080, the identifiers A, B, C, D, E, H, L each stand for an 8-bit register or the value held in that register.

A double-length (16-bit) register, or its contents, is denoted by a two-letter identifier. For example, for the 6800 we have IX, SP, PC.

2.3.3 Assignment (copying or transfer of information)

The symbol ':=' ('becomes') implies that the register, flag, store location or output device specified on its left is to receive a copy of the value specified on its right.

E.g., A:=B means 'register A is to receive a *copy* of the information held in B'. The information previously held in A will be lost, and the information in B will remain in B. Briefly, 'A becomes B'.

A:=12 means 'register A is to receive the value 12'. The information previously held in A will be lost. (12 is a hexadecimal value—see below.)

(On the 6800, though not on the 8080, 8085 and Z80, these operations have the further effect of setting certain condition flag values. See 'Condition flags' below, and the description of the 6800 instruction set in 3.2.)

2.3.4 Interchange

The symbol ':=:' implies a mutual exchange of contents by the registers or store locations specified on its left and right.

E.g., HL:=:DE means 'HL is to contain what was in DE, and DE is to contain what was in HL'. This operator is commutative. Without it an auxiliary store and three assignments would be needed to achieve the same effect; thus

$$
\left.\begin{array}{l} XY:=DE \\ DE:=HL \\ HL:=XY \end{array}\right\} \quad \text{or} \quad \left\{\begin{array}{l} XY:=HL \\ HL:=DE \\ DE:=XY \end{array}\right.
$$

Interchange operators are available on the 8080, 8085 and Z80.

2.3.5 Values

A value is a set of one or more bits. Each bit may be 0 or 1. A set of four bits (sometimes called a 'nibble') can be expressed as a single *hexadecimal* (Hex) *digit*, thus:

Bits	Hex	Bits	Hex	Bits	Hex	Bits	Hex
0000	0	0100	4	1000	8	1100	C
0001	1	0101	5	1001	9	1101	D
0010	2	0110	6	1010	A	1110	E
0011	3	0111	7	1011	B	1111	F

A *byte* is 8 bits (2 nibbles) and this is a *machine word*.[1] A byte can be expressed as a pair of hexadecimal digits:

e.g.	01001110	4E
	00000000	00
	11111111	FF

(Note: after the assignment C:=12, register C holds 00010010; after the assignment C:=BC, register C holds 10111100.

The second example is unambiguous, for, although there is a double-length register whose identifier is BC, since we have the identifier of a single-length register on the left we must have a single-byte value on the right.)

The individual bits of a byte are numbered 0–7 from the right.

The Z80 has instructions which refer to individual bits.

---

[1] The machine word is 8 bits in the 6800, 8080, 8085 and Z80 because that is the usual length of operand. Other processors have words of other lengths—4, 12, 16, 24, 27 (sic), 32, 40, 48, for example. The term 'byte' now seems exclusively used to mean 8 bits, though it has in the past sometimes meant 6 bits.

The notation for specifying a particular bit or bit position is a point followed by the bit number.

E.g., A.0:=1   means 'assign 1 to the right-most bit position in register A (without disturbing the other contents of A)'.

A.7:=0   means 'assign 0 to the left-most bit position of A'.

A.0, A.7   will be written as A_0, A_7 in tables and explanations where this more compact notation is suitable.

A *double-length* (16 bits, 2 bytes) value can be expressed as four hexadecimal digits.

E.g., after SP:=147A, SP contains 0001010001111010.

Unless specifically indicated, all explicit single-length and double-length values will be expressed in hexadecimal digits. (A table of equivalence with octal and decimal notations is given in Table 2.1.) Leading zeroes will invariably be shown, so a single-length number is always 2 digits and a double-length number always 4 digits.

2.3.6 Addresses and storage locations

A given 16-bit address refers uniquely to one of 2^{16} (65536 in decimal notation) *storage locations.*

If the given *address* is 1234, the corresponding *location* is denoted by M1234 (M stands for 'main store' or, in North American, 'memory'[2]).

In an actual system, some storage locations will be empty (that is, unoccupied by a storage device), some will be occupied by ROM or PROM, and some by RAM.[3]

A:=M1234   means '*copy* the value held at location M1234—the location whose address is 1234—*into* register A'. This operation is possible if that location is occupied by ROM, PROM or RAM.

M1234:=A   means '*copy* the value held in register A *into* the storage location whose address is 1234'. This 'write' operation is possible if the location is in RAM, but not if it is in ROM or PROM.

A:=M[DE]   means '*copy* the value held in the storage location whose address is the value held in the double-length register DE into register A'. (DE:=1234 followed by A:=M[DE] is equivalent to DE:=1234 followed by A:=M1234.)

The notation MM1234 stands for the *pair* of locations M1234 and M1235. Thus:

HL:=MM2345   means 'copy the double-length value held in locations M2345 and M2346 into the double-length register HL'.

MM2345:=IX   means 'copy the double-length value held in the double-length register IX into the pair of locations M2345, M2346'.

---

[2]See Note 1 of Chapter 1.
[3]But see also Section 2.8, 'Input and output'.

In operations of this kind, which half of the register is associated with which of the two locations depends on the processor. The bits of a single-length register are numbered 0 (right-most) to 7 (left-most), as are those of a storage location. In single-length assignments a bit from the 'source' is copied into the corresponding bit position in the 'destination'. The bits of a double-length register are numbered 0 (right-most) to 15 (left-most). Bits 0–7 are the 'lower byte' and bits 8–15 are the 'upper byte'.

HL:=MM2345 is an 8080, 8085 or Z80 instruction. The double-length register HL is actually formed of the two single-length registers H and L, H being the upper ('high') byte and L the lower byte. The double-length assignment is equivalent to the two single-length assignments[4] H:=M2346 and L:=M2345. Note that the *upper* byte is associated with the location with the *higher* address.

MM2345:=IX is a 6800 instruction. If we denote the upper and lower halves of IX by IX_U and IX_L respectively, the double-length assignment is equivalent to the two single-length assignments[5] M2345:=IX_U and M2346:=IX_L. Note that here the *upper* byte is associated with the *lower* address.

There are arguments for and against both these conventions, and it is unfortunate (and infuriating to the programmer!) that the processors are different in this respect.

All the examples given in this section are three-byte instructions, except for A:=M[DE] which is a one-byte instruction. The table below gives each with its machine-code equivalent for the processors for which it can be written. In all the examples except A:=M[DE] the store is said to be *directly addressed*; the address is part of the instruction (bytes J and K) and appears explicitly in the written form. In the example A: = M[DE] the store is said to be *indirectly addressed*, since the address is not given by the instruction itself but has to be taken from a register (DE is an 'addressing register', cf. Section 1.2.10).

Written form of instruction	Processor	Machine code		
		I	J	K
A:=M1234	6800	B6	12	34
	8080/8085/Z80	3A	34	12
M1234:=A	6800	B7	12	34
	8080/8085/Z80	32	34	12
A:=M[DE]	8080/8085/Z80	1A	—	—
HL:=MM2345	8080/8085/Z80	2A	45	23
MM2345:=IX	6800	FF	23	45

(*Warning:* The instruction HL:=MM2345 must not be confused with HL:=2345. The latter means 'assign the *value* 2345 to the double-length register HL.')

A special form of direct addressing is provided on the 6800, in addition to the normal kind described above. The operation A:=M0012 can be achieved by the three-byte instruction 'B6 00 12', but it can also be achieved by the two-byte instruction '96 12' written here as 'A:=MZ12'. An address in the range 0000 to 00FF (256

----
[4]These do not exist as separate instructions.
[5]See Note 4.

(decimal) locations) is *privileged* in the sense that operation codes are provided which supply the two leading zeroes, leaving only 2 hex digits (one byte) to be written explicitly (stored as J). Thus

M0034:=A stands for B7 00 34—ordinary direct addressing;[6]
MZ34:=A stands for 97 34   —privileged direct addressing.[7]

A further form of addressing possible in some microprocessors is *indexed addressing*. Here the required address is the *sum* (see 2.4.3.4) of the value held in an *index register* and a value given explicitly (byte J or K). For example, for the 6800 and Z80, the notation M12X is used here to mean 'the storage location whose address is the sum of the contents of the index register IX and the explicitly given value 12'.

Consider the sequence of instructions IX:=3456; M23X:=A. The result of executing these instructions in this order is that location 3479 (3479=3456+23) contains a copy of the contents of register A, and the index register IX contains the value 3456. The contents of A remain unchanged. The two values added together to form an *indexed address* are sometimes called 'base address' and 'displacement' or 'offset'. Which is which is a matter for the programmer himself.

Addresses in *jump instructions* require separate discussion. The *program counter* is a 16-bit register which contains the address of the location at which the next instruction to be executed is to be found. Normally the value in the program counter is *incremented* by a number equal to the number of bytes in the instruction currently being executed to give the address of the next instruction. But the execution of an *unconditional jump*, or of a *conditional jump* when the condition is satisfied, requires the *replacement* of the value in the program counter by a new value.

This new value may be one given in the jump instruction itself (analogous to direct addressing) or one obtained from a register (analogous to indirect addressing). A further possibility (and analogous to indexed addressing) is that it may be obtained by adding a positive or negative value (see 2.4.3.4 below), given in the jump instruction, to the incremented value in the program counter. This is *relative addressing*. The next instruction in the dynamic order will be so many bytes forward or backward from the 'normal' next instruction (that following in the static order).

If for some reason a block of instructions is copied to another part of the store, to be executed from the new locations, then all jumps to instructions of the block will have to be altered, *including* jumps from one instruction of the block to another if these are direct or indirect jumps, but *excluding* any *relative* jumps within the block.

The notations used here for these forms of jump addresses are illustrated by the following examples:

J2345   Jump unconditionally to the instruction held at address 2345.
J[HL]   Jump unconditionally to the instruction whose address is in the register HL.
J+12   Jump unconditionally to the instruction whose address is 12 more than the address of the next instruction in the static order. (*Note:* J+00 is a dummy instruction!)

---

[6]Called 'extended addressing' by the manufacturer.
[7]Called 'direct addressing' by the manufacturer.

If we assume that normal incrementation of the program counter (PC) by the length of the instruction occurs before execution proper—which is the case with the micro-processors—we can represent the actions of these instructions as follows:

Instruction	Normal incrementation	Execution proper	Net effect
J2345	PC:=PC + 3	PC:=2345	PC:=2345
J[HL]	PC:=PC + 1	PC:=HL	PC:=HL
J+12	PC:=PC + 2	PC:=PC + 12	PC:=PC + 14
(cf. A:=B	PC:=PC + 1	A:=B	PC:=PC + 1;A:=B)

If we were to express jumps by writing 'PC:= . . .' as in the last column here—which could of course be done consistently—then we should have to express the normal incrementation of the program counter in all other instructions. Not only is it more convenient to avoid expressing normal incrementation by use of the 'J' notation, but the 'J' notation makes jump instructions instantly recognizable as such on the printed page. J for jump—always the first symbol of a written instruction—should not be confused with J for second byte.

2.3.7 Condition flags

A *condition flag* is a one-bit store (flip-flop) which is set (to 1) or reset (to 0) during the execution of certain machine instructions.

Each condition flag will be denoted by a single-letter identifier; e.g., Z stands for the 'zero' condition flag. Z=1 usually means that the last arithmetic or logical operation executed produced a zero result (one whose bits were all zero), and Z=0 indicates that it produced a non-zero result (at least one of its bits was a 1). There may well be machine instructions which assign specific values to individual flags. Different processors treat condition flags differently. For example the instruction 'A:=00' on the 8080, 8085 or Z80 does not affect any condition flag, but on the 6800 it does, and in particular it sets Z to 1. The treatment of the condition flags, and hence their exact significance, is something which the programmer has to study carefully for each microprocessor. (Perhaps a microprocessor should be judged by the way it treats its flags.)

The set of condition flags (less than 8 in number) may be regarded as forming a *condition flag register*. Instructions exist for copying them, or assigning to them, as a set.

For example, in the 6800 the six condition flags H, I, N, Z, V, K, together with two constant bits, form a single-length register C, and the 6800 instruction set includes the operations A:=C and C:=A.

The prefix N means the complement of a condition flag value. E.g., NZ stands for $\bar{Z}$ (zero flag not set).

2.4 ARITHMETIC AND LOGICAL OPERATIONS

2.4.1 Meanings of a byte

A byte in a storage location or in a register may be treated by the processor or regarded by the programmer as representing any of a number of different kinds of quantity, including:

(i)   eight independent bits;
(ii)   an unsigned binary integer in the range 0 to 255 (decimal);
(iii)   a signed binary integer in the range -128 to $+127$ (decimal);
(iv)   an operation code;
(v)   half of a 16-bit address;
(vi)   a peripheral device number;
(vii)   a character in the character code appropriate to some peripheral device.

We cannot tell simply by looking at a byte in an arbitrary location how it will eventually be treated by the machine. If a copy of it gets into the instruction register, it will be treated as an operation code. If it gets into an accumulator it may be treated as a number. If it gets into an addressing register it will be treated as half of an address. And so on. An incorrectly written jump instruction might cause the program to jump to what was intended to be the second or third byte of an instruction—if this happens the program will have lost its way and the consequences will be unpredictable. This is a point to be borne in mind during program-testing.

The bits making up a byte are identified thus:

d_7	d_6	d_5	d_4	d_3	d_2	d_1	d_0

In *assignment operations* (e.g. A:=B, M12X:=A) the bits forming the copied value maintain their relative positions.

2.4.2 Signed and unsigned values

As an *unsigned binary integer* the value represented by a byte is

$$\sum_{i=0}^{7} d_i 2^i$$

E.g. 10101100 (AC) represents $2^7 + 2^5 + 2^3 + 2^2 = 128 + 32 + 8 + 4 = 172$ (decimal)
      00000000 (00) represents   0 (decimal)
      01111111 (7F) represents 127 (decimal)
      10000000 (80) represents 128 (decimal)
      11111111 (FF) represents 255 (decimal).

As a *signed binary integer* the value represented by the byte is

$$-d_7 2^7 + \sum_{i=0}^{6} d_i 2^i.$$

Thus 10101100 (AC) represents $-2^7 + 2^5 + 2^3 + 2^2 = -128 + 32 + 8 + 4 = -84$ (dec.)
      00000000 (00) represents   0 (decimal)
      01111111 (7F) represents 127 (decimal)
      10000000 (80) represents -128 (decimal)
      11111111 (FF) represents $-$ 1 (decimal)

Here d_7 is called the *sign bit;* if $d_7=1$ the value is negative; if $d_7=0$ the value is positive. This convention for signed numbers is called *twos-complement* representation. It has considerable advantages over another, perhaps more obvious, convention called 'sign and modulus', where the value represented is

$$\sum_{i=0}^{6} d_i 2^i \text{ if } d_7=0, \text{ or } -\sum_{i=0}^{6} d_i 2^i \text{ if } d_7=1.$$

'Sign and modulus' convention is not used in the microprocessors under consideration.

If a byte represents a number, signed or unsigned, d_7 is its 'most significant bit' (m.s.b.) and d_0 its 'least significant bit' (l.s.b.).

A pair of bytes can represent an unsigned or signed binary integer. The bits of the byte forming the upper half (cf. 2.3.6) are renamed, the m.s.b. of the upper half becoming d_{15} and the l.s.b. of the upper half becoming d_8.

Then, if it is an *unsigned binary integer*, the value represented by the pair of bytes is

$$\sum_{i=0}^{15} d_i 2^i \text{ (range 0 to 65,535, decimal).}$$

If it is a *signed binary integer*, the value represented by the pair of bytes is

$$-d_{15}2^{15}+ \sum_{i=0}^{14} d_i 2^i \text{ (range } -32,768 \text{ to } +32,767, \text{ decimal).}$$

Note that in this case the sign bit is the m.s.b. of the upper half.

Thus 1010101111001101 (ABCD)

as an *unsigned* number represents 43,981 (decimal),
while as a *signed* number it represents $-21,555$ (decimal).

(*Note:* AB represents 171 (unsigned, decimal) or -85 (signed, decimal).
CD represents 205 (unsigned, decimal) or -51 (signed, decimal).
Therefore as an unsigned number:
ABCD represents $171 \times 2^8 +205=43,776+205=43,981$ (decimal)
and as a signed number:
ABCD represents $-85 \times 2^8 +205=-21,760+205=-21,555$ (decimal).
ABCD does *not* represent $-85 \times 2^8 -51$. Only the upper half can be a signed number because only the most significant bit of the complete number can be the sign bit.)

Clearly, 'multiple-length numbers' can be formed of any number of bytes. If such a number is signed the sign bit will be the m.s.b. of the most significant byte.

2.4.3 Addition

2.4.3.1 Addition (single-length)

(*i*) *Addition of two unsigned single-length numbers.* Each number is in the range 0 to 255 (decimal), and so their sum is in the range 0 to 510 (decimal). This range requires 9 bits. Eight bits can be accommodated in a single-length register (an *accumulator); the ninth (most significant) bit is held by the *carry flag* K. If, after addition, K=0, the sum is in the range 0 to 255 (i.e. it is single-length). If K=1, the sum is in the range 256 to 510, and the accumulator contains a number 256 less than the sum.

(ii)   Addition of two signed single-length numbers. Each number is in the range -128 to $+127$ (decimal) and so their sum is in the range -256 to $+254$. The processor will add them as if they are unsigned, using the accumulator and carry flag as described above. We must investigate the circumstances in which the result in the accumulator is the byte which represents the signed number which is the true mathematical sum, and the circumstances in which it is not. We must also consider the significance of the carry flag.

(a)   If the two operands are *both positive*, the mathematical sum is positive. However, if this sum exceeds $+127$ (it cannot exceed $+254$), the result in the accumulator will appear to be negative (because its m.s.b. is 1). In any case the carry flag will be 0. Therefore the occurrence of a 1 in the d_7 position of an accumulator when the numbers added are both positive indicates *overflow*—the result cannot be held in a single-length register.

Most microprocessors have a condition flag N ('negative'), which is set (N:=1) when the result of an operation has 1 in the d_7 position and reset (N:=0) when the result has 0 in the d_7 position. The 6800 and Z80, but not the 8080 and 8085, have another flag V ('overflow'), which would be set (V:=1) in the case of overflow, as described here, and reset (V:=0) otherwise.

(b)   If the two operands are both negative, the mathematical sum is negative, and in the range -256 to -2. If this sum is in the range -128 to -2, that value will appear correctly in the single-length register and the carry flag will be set (K:=1). If, however, the mathematical sum is in the range -256 to -129, the carry flag will be set (K:=1), but the accumulator will contain an apparently positive number (N:=0). Thus the occurrence of 0 in the d_7 position of the accumulator when the numbers added are both negative indicates overflow (V:=1).

(c)   If the operands are one positive and one negative, the mathematical sum must be in the range -128 to $+126$, and the accumulator will contain the correct result. The carry flag will be set (K:=1) if the result is positive (≥ 0) and reset (K:=0) if the result is negative (<0). The overflow flag, if it exists, will be reset (V:=0).

In summary, if the sum of two signed single-length numbers is a signed single-length number, the single-length accumulator will give the correct result. If the sum is outside signed single-length range—which can happen only if both operands have the same sign—the incorrectness of the result is indicated by the sign bit of the accumulator (or, equally, by the N flag) being different from the sign bit of the operands, or, if there is an overflow flag, by this flag being set.

The symbol '+' will be used to denote addition. The symbol ':+' will denote addition into an accumulator.

Thus A:+B (which is in fact a contraction of A:−A+B) means 'add the contents of the accumulator A and the value held by B; replace the contents of A by this sum' or in brief 'add B into A'. The 'side-effects' of the operation, namely the setting of the appropriate condition flags and the incrementing of the program counter, are implied.

A:+B   represents a one-byte instruction; the second operand is in a register (B).

A:+43 represents a two-byte instruction; the second operand, 43, is held in the J byte and is called an *immediate operand*.

2.4.3.2 Addition (double-length)

(i) Addition of two 16-bit unsigned numbers. A double-length number p can be represented by two unsigned single-length numbers p_1 and p_0 such that $p = 2^8 p_1 + p_0$. Here p_1 is the upper byte, p_0 the lower byte.

If $p = 2^8 p_1 + p_0$ and $q = 2^8 q_1 + q_0$ then $r = p + q$; $2^8(p_1 + q_1) + (p_0 + q_0) = 2^8 r_1 + r_0$.

Now r requires, in general, seventeen bits, for since $0 \leq p, q \leq 2^{16} - 1, 0 \leq p + q \leq 2^{17} - 2$.

If we form $p_0 + q_0$ we obtain a nine-bit result. Clearly r_0 is the bottom 8 bits—the accumulator contents after a single-length addition. The ninth bit, the value held in the carry flag, k_0 say, will have to be taken into account when we form r_1. We need to form the sum $p_1 + q_1 + k_0$. The bottom eight bits of this sum—the accumulator contents—are the bottom eight bits of r_1, and the ninth bit, the value held in the carry flag, k_1, say, will be the ninth bit of r_1, that is the seventeenth bit of r.

This procedure can be summarized as follows.

$2^8 k_0 + r_0$ is the sum of p_0 and q_0
$2^8 k_1 + r_1$ is the sum of p_1 and q_1 and k_0
$r = 2^{16} k_1 + 2^8 r_1 + r_0$, where r_1, r_0 are single-length.

To facilitate double- (and multiple-) length addition, there is an instruction called 'Add with carry'. The operation will be denoted by ': + +' and as an example of an instruction carrying out this operation we have A:+ +B.

A:+ +B (a contraction of A:=A+B+K) means 'add B and K into A'.

With this operation available, double-length addition can be achieved by the following sequence of instructions:

A:=p_0
A:+q_0 (A contains r_0, K contains k_0 after this instruction.)
r_0:=A
A:=p_1 } These instructions do not affect K.
A:+ +q_1 (A contains r_1, K contains k_1 after this instruction.)
r_1:=A

(If K is set ($k_1 = 1$), the result is outside double-length range.)

(ii) Addition of two 16-bit signed numbers. A signed number has only one sign-bit no matter how long it is. A signed double-length number p can be represented by a *signed* single-length number p_1 and an *unsigned* single-length number p_0 such that

$$p = 2^8 p_1 + p_0. \quad \text{For, if } p = -2^{15} d_{15} + \sum_{i=0}^{14} d_i 2^i$$

$$\text{then } p_1 = -2^7 d_{15} + \sum_{i=0}^{6} d_{i+8} 2^i \quad \text{(the signed part)}$$

$$\text{and } p_0 = \sum_{i=0}^{7} d_i 2^i \quad \text{(the unsigned part)}.$$

The range of signed double-length numbers is $-2^{15} \leq p \leq +2^{15}-1$ (in decimal, $-32,768 \leq p \leq +32,767$).

If the mathematical sum of two signed double-length numbers p,q is within this range, then the program given above for unsigned double-length addition will give the correctly signed double-length result $r = p+q$. If the sum is out of range, the fact will be shown by the overflow flag if there is one, or by the outcome of the 'add with carry' on the signed parts of the operands.

The instructions used in the program in (i) above are all, subject to particular restrictions as to the locations of p_0, p_1, q_0, q_1, available on the 6800, 8080, 8085 and Z80. The 8080, 8085 and Z80 have a single instruction for double-length addition, an example of which is HL:+DE. The seventeenth bit of the result is in the carry flag K.

If two double-length integers are in store at MM1234, MM1236 respectively and it is required to store their sum at MM1238, then one or other of the following sequences of instructions will be found effective:

(i)   (6800): A:=M1235
       A:+M1237
       M1239:=A
       A:=M1234
       A:++M1236
       M1238:=A
       (18 bytes—uses A)

(ii)   (6800): IX:=1234
       A:=M01X
       A:+M03X
       M05X:=A
       A:=M00X
       A:++M02X
       M04X:=A
       (15 bytes—uses A, IX)

(iii) (8080, 8085, Z80): HL:=MM1234
       HL:=:DE   (see 2.3.4)
       HL:=MM1236
       HL:+DE
       MM1238:=HL
       (11 bytes—uses D, E, H, L)

2.4.3.3 Addition (multiple-length)

This can be achieved by a straightforward extension of the program for double-length addition. The sum of the pair of least-significant bytes is formed by simple addition, and for each other pair of corresponding bytes (working towards the most significant bytes) addition with carry is used. (Logic designers will see that 'simple addition' is analogous to the action of a half adder and 'addition with carry' to that of a full adder.)

The Z80 has a double-length add-with-carry instruction which can halve the number of steps required for a long addition. An example is HL:++BC.

2.4.3.4 Addition of numbers of unequal length

Examples of the addition of numbers of unequal length occur in the evaluation of addresses.

(i)   In *indexed addressing* a double-length number (in the index register) and a single-length number (the J byte) are added together to form an address. Both are essentially unsigned. The operation can be seen as extending the single-length number to double length by giving it an upper half consisting of eight 0-bits and then carrying out a normal double-length addition.

(ii)   In *relative addressing* the single-length number is regarded as signed, so that both forward (positive J) and backward (negative J) jumps can be provided. The addition operation can be seen as extending the single-length number to double length by giving it an upper half consisting of eight copies of the most significant bit of the given byte, and then carrying out a normal double-length addition.

In general, two numbers of unequal length can be added if the shorter is extended to the length of the longer by putting a sufficient number of 'filler bits' on its left. If this is signed, the filler bits will be copies of the most significant given bit (see 4.5.1).

2.4.4 Inversion and negation

In the unsigned convention the byte $d_7d_6d_5d_4d_3d_2d_1d_0$ represents the number

$$p = \sum_{i=0}^{7} d_i 2^i.$$

Consider now the word $\overline{d_7d_6d_5d_4d_3d_2d_1d_0}$ formed by logically inverting each bit of the given byte (i.e. by changing each 0 to 1 and each 1 to 0).
The number represented by this byte is

$$\bar{p} = \sum_{i=0}^{7} \overline{d_i} 2^i = \sum_{i=0}^{7} (1-d_i)2^i = (2^8-1)-p.$$

In the *signed* convention the original byte represents

$$q = -2^7 d_7 + \sum_{i=0}^{6} d_i 2^i$$

and the inverted byte represents

$$\bar{q} = -(1-d_7)2^7 + \sum_{i=0}^{6} (1-d_i)2^i$$

$$= -2^7 + (2^7-1) + 2^7 d_7 - \sum_{0}^{6} d_i 2^i$$

$$= -1 - q.$$

This inversion operation, on the contents of an accumulator, is provided by an instruction (one byte) in each of the microprocessors. This instruction will be written as

$$A:\# \quad (\text{meaning } A:=\bar{A}).$$

Now suppose 01 (hexadecimal) is added to the inverted byte. In the unsigned convention we have now

$$\bar{p}+1=(2^8-1)-p+1=2^8-p$$

and the carry flag will not be set unless the original byte was 00 (hexadecimal).

In the signed convention we have after the addition

$$\bar{q}+1=-1-q+1=-q$$

and this result is within single range unless the original byte was 80 (hexadecimal; -128 decimal). In this case the result appears unchanged (for 80 inverted gives 7F and adding 01 gives 80), but there is an overflow condition, and the overflow flag if it exists will be set. Thus A:# followed by A:+01 *negates* the signed number given in A, unless its value was 80 (-128 in decimal). The same sequence operating on an unsigned value gives that value's complement with respect to 2^8 (i.e. 2^8-p given p) unless the given value was 00, in which case the carry flag is set.

The 6800 and Z80 (but not the 8080 and 8085) have a single-byte instruction written here as A:− (contraction of A:= −A) whose effect is that of A:# followed by A:+01.

Negation of a number of double length or longer can be done by inverting each byte and adding 1 to the number so produced. (*Warning:* all the inversions must be done *before* the 1 is added.)

2.4.5 Subtraction

2.4.5.1 Subtraction (single-length)

(i)   Subtraction of two unsigned single-length numbers. Each number p,q is in the range 0–255 (decimal). Thus the difference $p-q$ is in the range -255 to $(+)255$. The subtraction operation in the processor uses an accumulator and the carry flag. If $0 \le p-q \le 255$, the correct result is left in the accumulator and the carry flag is reset (K:=0).

If $-255 \le p-q \le -1$, an amount 256 (2^8) is 'borrowed' and $p-q+256$ is left in the accumulator. Since $-255 \le p-q \le -1$, we have $(+)\,1 \le p-q+256 \le (+)255$ and this quantity is within unsigned single-length range. The fact of borrowing is recorded by setting the carry flag (K:=1).

(ii)   Subtraction of two signed single-length numbers. Each number p,q is in the range -128 to $+127$ (decimal). Thus the difference $p-q$ is in the range -255 to $+255$. We consider the possibilities as for signed single-length addition. The machine will operate as if p and q are unsigned.

(a)   If p,q are both positive then $-127 \le p-q \le +127$ and the accumulator will contain the correct result. The carry flag will be set if the result is negative and reset if the result is positive.

(b)   If p is positive and q is negative then $+1 \le p-q \le +255$. If $+1 \le p-q \le +127$ the accumulator will contain the correct result, but if $+128 < p-q \le +255$ the accumulator will contain an apparently negative number ($p-q\ -256$) and the overflow flag, if there is one, will be set.

(c)   If p is negative and q is positive then $-255 \leq p-q \leq -1$. If $-128 \leq p-q \leq -1$ the accumulator will contain the correct result, but if $-255 \leq p-q \leq -129$ the accumulator will contain an apparently positive number ($p-q+256$) and the overflow flag, if there is one, will be set.

(d)   If p,q are *both negative*, then $-127 \leq p-q \leq +127$ and the accumulator will contain the correct result. The carry flag will be set if the result is negative and reset if the result is positive.

In summary, if the difference of two signed single-length numbers is a signed single-length number, the single-length accumulator will give the correct result. If the difference is outside signed single-length range—which can happen only if the operands are of opposite signs—the incorrectness of the result is indicated by the sign-bit of the accumulator (or, equally, the N flag) being the same as that of the subtracted number (q), or, if there is an overflow flag, by this flag being set.

The symbol '$-$' will be used to denote subtraction. The symbol '$:-$' will denote subtraction 'into' an accumulator. Thus $A:-B$ (a contraction of $A:=A-B$) means 'subtract the value held in B from the value held in A; replace the value in A by this difference'. (In contrast, $A-B$ means only 'form the difference without assigning it to either A or B'. See 'Test and compare operations', 2.4.7.) As in all arithmetic operations, the 'side-effects' on the flags and program counter are implied.

> $A:-B$ represents a one-byte instruction; the second operand is in a register, B.
> $A:-43$ represents a two-byte instruction; the second operand, 43, is held in the
>   J-byte and is an immediate operand.

2.4.5.2   Subtraction (double-length)

(i)   *Subtraction of two 16-bit unsigned numbers.* Using the notation of the corresponding section on double-length addition, and writing $s = p-q = 2^8 s_1 + s_0$, subtracting q_0 from p_0 gives $-2^8 k_0$ carry flag) and $+2^8 k_0 + p_0 - q_0$ (in the accumulator). In the second phase, we need to subtract both q_1 and the carry flag value from p_1. So, by 'subtracting with carry' (also called 'subtracting with borrow') we obtain $-2^8 k_1$ (carry flag) and $+2^8 k_1 + p_1 - q_1 - k_0$ (in the accumulator).

Thus $s_0 = 2^8 k_0 + p_0 - q_0$

$\qquad s_1 = 2^8 k_1 + p_1 - q_1 - k_0$

and so $s = -2^{16} k_1 + 2^{16} k_1 + 2^8 p_1 - 2^8 q_1 - 2^8 k_0 + 2^8 k_0 + p_0 - q_0$

$\qquad\quad = 2^8 (p_1 - q_1) + (p_0 - q_0)$

$\qquad\quad = p-q$ as required.

The operation 'subtract with carry' or 'subtract with borrow' is provided by the microprocessors. It will be denoted here by '$--$' and as an example of an instruction carrying out this operation we have $A:--27$ (a contraction of $A:= A-K-27$). With this type of instruction available, the double-length subtraction can be achieved by the following sequence of instructions:

$A:=p_0$

$A:-q_0$ (A contains s_0, K contains k_0 after this instruction.)

$s_0:=A$ $\left.\begin{matrix} \\ \\ \end{matrix}\right\}$ These instructions do not affect K.

$A:=p_1$

A: $--q_1$ (A contains s_1, K contains k_1 after this instruction.)

$s_1 := A$ (If K is set, $k_1 = 1$—the result is outside double-length range.)

(ii)   *Subtraction of two 16-bit signed numbers.* If the mathematical difference $p-q$ of two signed double-length numbers p,q is within signed double-length range, then the program given above for unsigned double-length subtraction will give the correctly signed double-length result $s = p-q$. If the difference is out of range, the fact will be shown by the overflow flag, if there is one, or by the outcome of the 'subtract with carry' on the signed parts of the operands.

The instructions used in the program in (i) above are all available in the 6800, 8080, 8085 and Z80. The Z80 also has an instruction for 'double-length subtract with borrow', an example of which is HL: $--$ BC (hexadecimal ED 42). This instruction can also be used for simple double-length subtraction if it is ensured that the carry flag is reset before it is executed (HL: $-$ BC does not exist). The value in K after its execution is the same as the value which would be set by the program of (i) above and so is the value in V.

2.4.5.3   Subtraction (multiple-length)

This is exactly analogous to multiple-length addition (2.4.3.3).

2.4.5.4   Subtraction of numbers of unequal length

The remarks in the final paragraph on addition of numbers of unequal length apply equally to subtraction (2.4.3.4).

2.4.6   Logical (Boolean) operations

The Boolean operations of inversion (NOT), conjunction (AND), disjunction (OR) and non-equivalence (exclusive OR) are defined as follows. X, Y are Boolean variables (single bits).

Inversion	X	NOT X	
	0	1	
	1	0	(written $\neg$ X or $\overline{X}$ in most texts)

Conjunction	X	Y	X AND Y	
	0	0	0	
	0	1	0	
	1	1	1	
	1	0	0	(often written $X \wedge Y$ or XY or X.Y or X&Y)

Disjunction	X	Y	X OR Y	
	0	0	0	
	0	1	1	
	1	1	1	
	1	0	1	(often written $X \vee Y$ or $X+Y$)

Non-equivalence   X   Y   X XOR Y
                  0   0   0
                  0   1   1
                  1   1   0
                  1   0   1   (often written $X \not\equiv Y$ or $X \oplus Y$ or
                                                $X \neq Y$ or $X \not\equiv Y$)

Such an operation applied to 8-bit words is defined as eight parallel operations on the individual bits (NOT) or on the pairs of corresponding bits (AND, OR, XOR), thus:

If	p	is	10110010	(B2)
and	q	is	00101111	(2F)
then	$\bar{p}$	is	01001101	(4D)
	$p \wedge q$	is	00100010	(22)
	$p \vee q$	is	10111111	(BF)
	$p \not\vee q$	is	10011101	(9D)

The microprocessors have these 8-bit Boolean operations available in single instructions, using an accumulator, which *replace* the contents of the accumulator by the result of the operation.

Thus, for NOT we have $A := \bar{A}$
for AND we have $A := A \wedge q$
for OR   we have $A := A \vee q$
for XOR we have $A := A \not\vee q$

where A stands for the accumulator and q may be another register or an immediate operand value.

None of the symbols $\wedge$, $\vee$, $\not\vee$, $\oplus$, $\neg$ is available on ordinary console keyboards, nor is overlining; and $+$ is used in its arithmetic sense. So the following notations will be used here:

A:#   for $A := \bar{A}$
A:&q   for $A := A \wedge q$
A:Uq   for $A := A \vee q$
A:#q   for $A := A \not\vee q$

The 8080, 8085 and Z80 have an instruction for inverting the value of the carry flag. This instruction will be written

K:#

2.4.7 'Test' and 'compare' operations

The single-length arithmetic instructions described above can all affect the carry flag K and (6800, Z80) the overflow flag V. They will also affect two other flags, Z (zero) and N (negative). After any of these operations,

Z = 1   if the result of the operation is zero (00000000);
Z = 0   if the result is non-zero;
N = 1   if the result is negative, that is if $d_7 = 1$;
N = 0   if the result is positive or zero (non-negative, $d_7 = 0$).

These flags may also be affected by the logical operations of the last section, but the processors differ—for example, the instruction $A:\neq$ on the 8080, 8085 and Z80 does not affect them, but on the 6800 it does. The programmer should refer to the specific descriptions (Chapter 3) for details in each case.

Now it frequently happens that we wish to know whether some relationship holds between two quantities—whether two bytes are identical, or whether one number is greater than another, for example.

Suppose we have computed a signed number in A and somewhere we have another signed number q. If the number in A is less than q, we have to continue the program with the computed value; if it is greater than or equal to q, we have to continue with q in A. This requirement would be expressed in a 'high-level' language such as ALGOL by

$$if \ A \geq q \ then \ A:=q; \hspace{3cm} \text{(i)}$$

One way to manage this (each line stands for one microprocessor instruction) is:

$A:-q$ Subtract q 'into' A

—Jump if $N=1$ Jump if result is negative

$A:=q$ Put q into A

—Jump   Jump unconditionally

→$A:+q$ Restore original value in A

→ (continue)

Another way:

$B:=A$

$A:-q$

—Jump if $N=1$

$B:=q$

→$A:=B$

(continue)

These solutions are awkward because the actual value of the difference between the computed value q has to be accommodated. But we are not concerned with the *value* of this difference, only in its sign. The awkwardness is overcome by means of the so-called 'compare' operation. This operation carries out the subtraction, and sets the condition flags accordingly, *but it does not assign the value of the result to the accumulator.*

With the use of an instruction for this operation, provided by all the micro-processors, the example reduces to:

$A - q$ Set flags according to value of $A - q$

   ┌—Jump if $N = 1$

   │ $A := q$

   └→(continue)

The reader should compare this final version with the high-level expression, (i).

The notation $A - q$ (no colon) makes the point that no assignment is made to A, and so the value in A remains what it was before the operation. It has the advantage over abbreviations of 'compare A,q' that it leaves no doubt that the difference concerned is $A - q$, not $q - A$.

The reader must be reminded that N gives a correct indication of the sign of $A - q$ only if the value of $A - q$ is within signed single-length range—see 2.4.5.1 above. If the values of A, q are *unsigned*, then the sign of the difference $A - q$ is given by K ($K = 0$ if the difference is positive or zero, $K = 1$ if the difference is negative) rather than by N.

On the 6800 and Z80 the overflow flag V is available; the relative jumps on the conditions $K \vee Z$, $N \veebar V$, $Z \vee (N \veebar V)$ and their complements in the 6800 should be noted. After a signed subtraction, the condition $N \veebar V$ is true ($N \veebar V = 1$) if and only if the true difference is negative (less than zero) (Chapter 3).

There is no overflow flag on the 8080 or 8085. In signed arithmetic, K and N are insufficient to give the sign of $A - q$ if this value can be out of range. One 'trick', which avoids the need for double-length subtraction, is to form $A + 80$ and $q + 80$; then after the comparison $(A + 80) - (q + 80)$ the carry flag will be set ($K = 1$) if $A - q$ is negative, and reset ($K = 0$) otherwise. (The flag N is still correct only if $A - q$ is within single-length range.)

Other operations for setting the condition flags according to some value are provided in the 6800.

In the 6800 instructions written in the form 'A&q' the value 'A&q' is formed but not assigned to A. The flags N, Z are affected.

In a 'test' instruction, written simply as, for example, A or as M1234, the flags N, Z are set according to the specified value (here that in A or that at M1234), V and K are cleared, and the other flags are unchanged.

There is also 'compare index register', written here for conciseness as $IX - q$, which, the reader should be warned, does not involve a double-length subtraction. Writing IX_U and IX_L for the upper and lower halves of IX, and q_U and q_L for the upper and lower halves of the value q, the execution of the instruction is as if the two single-length differences $IX_U - q_U$ and $IX_L - q_L$ were evaluated. Then Z is set if *both* differences are zero; N is set if $IX_U - q_U$ is negative, and V is set if there is overflow in the evaluation of $IX_U - q_U$; the other flags are unaffected. In practice, therefore, only Z gives directly usable information about the double-length difference $IX - q$.

2.4.8 'Shift' and 'rotate' operations

The experienced programmer accustomed to shifting 32- and 64-bit numbers through n places in either direction by single instructions may well feel somewhat disconcerted by the fact that in these microprocessors a shift instruction will move a number only one place (or, exceptionally, four places). And he may well wonder what application there is for a nine-bit single-place cyclic shift. The facilities available in any given microprocessor may still seem arbitrary after a good deal of programming; but at least they are usable and appear capable of achieving any reasonable objective, even if recourse to counting loops is sometimes necessary.

The four processors—6800, 8080, 8085, Z80—have between them nine different types of shift or rotate operations. The nine types are described below, and this description is followed by a table indicating the availability of each type on each processor.

In all four processors the carry flag K plays an important part.

1   *Arithmetic shift up (single-length multiplication by 2)*

Here the sign-bit d_7 is copied into the carry flag; the d_6 bit is moved into the d_7 position; the d_5 bit into the d_6 position; . . . ; the d_0 bit into the d_1 position; and finally a '0' is introduced into the d_0 position (see diagram above). If, after the shift, the carry-bit and the sign-bit are equal, the result is a signed value equal to twice the original value. If the original value was regarded as an unsigned number, the condition $K = 1$ means that the doubled value exceeds single-length range.

Applied to a single-length quantity q, this operation will be written as $q:*2$.

2   *Arithmetic shift down (single-length truncated division by 2)*

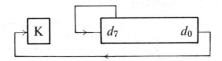

Here the d_0 bit is copied into the carry flag; the d_1 bit into the d_0 position; . . . ; the d_7 bit into the d_6 position; and the d_7 position is left undisturbed (after the operation $d_7 = d_6$).

This operation is equivalent *in the signed convention* to dividing by 2; the quotient has replaced the original signed number and the remainder (0 or 1) is in the carry flag. Since the remainder is necessarily positive we have, for example,

$$3 \text{ divided by 2 gives quotient } \quad 1 \text{ remainder } 1$$
$$-3 \text{ divided by 2 gives quotient } -2 \text{ remainder } 1$$
$$-1 \text{ divided by 2 gives quotient } -1 \text{ remainder } 1$$
$$-2 \text{ divided by 2 gives quotient } -1 \text{ remainder } 0$$

The quotient is always single-length. Applied to a single-length quantity q, this operation will be written as $q:/2$.

3 'Logical' shift right

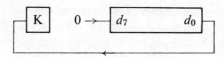

Here the operation is like 2 above, except that at the end a '0' bit is placed in the d_7 position.

If the shifted quantity was an unsigned integer, the operation is equivalent to division by 2, replacing the original number by the quotient and leaving the remainder (0 or 1) in the carry flag.

The operation is perhaps more frequently used in contexts in which the shifted quantity is regarded simply as a set of bits; it enables successive bits to be 'picked off'.

Applied to a single-length quantity q, this operation will be written as $q:->$.

4 Cyclic shift (rotation) left

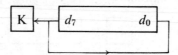

In this operation K receives a copy of the original d_7, and all the 8 bits of the operand are displaced one position to the left, the d_0 position receiving the bit originally in d_7 (see diagram above).

Applied to a single-length quantity q, this operation will be written as $q:@L$. (The symbol @ is, for some long-forgotten reason, in the ASCII code and available on teletypes and other console devices. Its form may suggest to the reader the idea of a cyclic shift or rotation.)

5 Cyclic shift (rotation) right

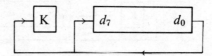

In this operation, K receives a copy of the original d_0, and all the 8 bits of the operand are displaced one position to the right, the d_7 position receiving the bit originally in d_0 (see diagram).

Applied to a single-length quantity q, this operation will be written as $q:@R$.

(Exercise: What is the effect of (i) $q:@L$ followed by $q:@R$?

(ii) $q:@R$ followed by $q:@L$?)

6 Nine-bit cyclic shift left

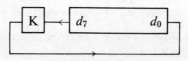

Here K is treated as the ninth bit of the operand, between d_7 and d_0. All bits move one place left, the K bit going to the d_0 position and the d_7 bit going to the carry flag.

Applied to a single-length quantity q and to K, this will be written as $qK:@L$.

7 Nine-bit cyclic shift right

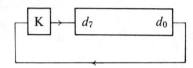

This, as indicated in the diagram, is the exact opposite of the 9-bit cyclic shift left.

Applied to a single-length quantity q, and to K, this will be written as $qK:@R$.

8 Nibble shift left (Z80 only)

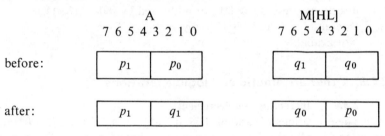

In this operation, and in the 'nibble shift right', we are concerned with two single-length quantities p (in register A) and q (in store at the address held in HL). The effect is that the upper 'nibble' of p, p_1 in the diagram, is left undisturbed while the other three nibbles undergo a cyclic shift to the left through four bit-positions. The instruction will be written as A3M:@4L (intended to suggest bits 0 to 3 of A and (all bits of) M[HL] shifted cyclically 4 places left).

9 Nibble shift right (Z80 only)

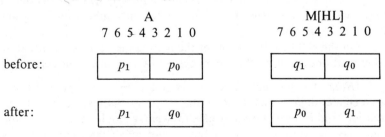

This is the converse operation to 'nibble shift left', as indicated in the diagram. The instruction will be written as A3M:@4R.

Availability

		6800	8080/8085	Z80
1.	$q:*2$	(i)	(ii)	(iv)
2.	$q:/2$	(i)	—	(iv)
3.	$q:->$	(i)	—	(iv)
4.	$q:@L$	—	(iii)	(iv)
5.	$q:@R$	—	(iii)	(iv)
6.	$qK:@L$	(i)	(iii)	(iv)
7.	$qK:@R$	(i)	(iii)	(iv)
8.	$A3M:@4L$	—	—	(v)
9.	$A3M:@4R$	—	—	(v)

(i) q may be in either accumulator (A,B) or in any store location addressed directly (JK) or by index (IX).

(ii) Not available as such, but effect obtainable by $A:+A$ (single-length add) or $HL:+HL$ (double-length add).

(iii) q must be in accumulator register A.

(iv) q may be in any single-length register (A,B,C,D,E,H,L,) or in a location indirectly addressed (by HL) or addressed by index (IX, IY).

(v) Operands in A and M[HL] only.

— Not available.

2.4.9 Other arithmetic and logic operations

2.4.9.1 Increment and decrement

The operations of 'adding 1' and 'subtracting 1' (that is, of 'counting up' and 'counting down') are required so frequently that all our microprocessors have special instructions for them on all registers, and indeed (subject to addressing constraints) on all storage locations.

Here the operations will be written as ':+1' and ':−1' respectively. Examples of instructions using them are:

```
6800            A:+1 (4C)    SP:−1 (34)    M1234:−1 (7A 12 34)
8080/8085/Z80   B:−1 (02)    HL:+1 (23)    M:+1 (1C, M[HL]:+1)
Z80             M12Y:−1 (FD 35 12)    IX:+1 (DD 23)
```

The 8080, 8085 and Z80 increment and decrement instructions on single-length quantities affect the usual flags but not K; on double-length registers they do not affect the flags at all.

On the 6800 the treatment of the flags is the same, except that an increment or decrement operation on the index register IX may affect the zero flag Z.

(*Note:* The instruction $A:+01$ (where the second operand is expressed as two hexadecimal digits which become the J-byte of the instruction) stands for a normal addition, and its execution may affect the carry flag K. The instruction $A:+1$ (single-digit) has the same effect on A but cannot affect the carry flag. A similar remark applies to $A:-01$ and $A:-1$, and to corresponding pairs of instructions concerning other single-length or double-length accumulators.)

2.4.9.2 Decimal adjustment

This curious and somewhat complicated operation is available through a 1-byte instruction on each of the four processors. It is intended to assist in 'binary-coded-decimal (BCD) arithmetic' (also known as 'packed-decimal arithmetic'). In BCD arithmetic, a decimal digit is represented by a nibble (4 bits) holding one of the values 0000 (0) to 1001 (9), and so two such digits can be held in a single-length register. Suppose we have two such pairs of digits, each pair standing for an unsigned decimal integer in the range 0 to 99. How can they be added together to produce the BCD sum? First let us examine the effect of simple (binary) addition of the given BCD words.

$$\begin{array}{rll} \text{If } p \text{ is} & 01010011 & (53) \\ \text{and } q \text{ is} & 01000110 & (46), \quad \text{then binary addition} \\ \text{gives} & 10011001 & (99) \quad\;\; \text{which is correct.} \end{array}$$

$$\begin{array}{rll} \text{But if } p \text{ is} & 00110101 & (35) \\ \text{and } q \text{ is} & 01000110 & (46), \quad \text{then binary addition} \\ \text{gives} & 01111011 & (7B), \quad \text{which is not the desired} \\ \text{result} & 10000001 & (81). \end{array}$$

$$\begin{array}{rll} \text{Again, if } p \text{ is} & 00111001 & (39) \\ \text{and } q \text{ is} & 01011000 & (58), \quad \text{then binary addition} \\ \text{gives} & 10010001 & (91), \quad \text{which is not the desired} \\ \text{result} & 10010111 & (97). \end{array}$$

$$\begin{array}{rll} \text{Finally, if } p \text{ is} & 10011001 & (99) \\ \text{and } q \text{ is} & 01100111 & (67), \quad \text{then binary addition} \\ \text{gives} & (1)00000000 & (K,00), \quad \text{which is not the} \end{array}$$

desired result (1)01100110 (K,66), where the carry flag would indicate an overflow of 100 (one hundred).

In all these cases the transformation of the result of simple binary addition into the desired BCD result is accomplished by executing the 'decimal adjust' instruction immediately after the binary addition. The adjustment operation depends on the existence of a special condition flag H (half-carry), which indicates whether the binary addition has generated a carry between the d_3 and the d_4 of the accumulator. It also depends on K, the (full) carry flag. Consequently a binary number fetched into the accumulator, or derived by any process other than the addition of two BCD numbers, will not in general be converted to BCD by decimal adjustment alone.

The 'decimal adjust' instruction of the Z80 (but not that of the 6800, 8080 or 8085) can also be applied after subtraction (with or without borrow) or negation. This is made possible by the provision of a further flag (here called S) which is set by subtraction instructions and reset by all others.

The significance of the carry flag K after a valid decimal adjustment is analogous to that after *unsigned* binary addition or subtraction.

If K = 0 the result in the accumulator is correct.

If K = 1 after adjusted addition, the true result is 100 (one hundred) *more* than the result in the accumulator.

If K = 1 after adjusted subtraction (Z80 only), the true result is 100 *less* than the result in the accumulator, and is therefore negative.

The process of decimal adjustment can be summarized as follows. In all cases the value to be adjusted is in accumulator A. We write a_1, a_0 for the upper and lower nibbles of A.

The required adjustment after binary addition is:

$$if \ \ a_0 > 9 \lor H \ \ then \ \ A:+06;$$
$$if \ \ a_1 > 9 \lor K \ \ then \ \ A:+60.$$

The required adjustment after binary subtraction is:

$$if \ \ H \ \ then \ \ A:-06;$$
$$if \ \ K \ \ then \ \ A:-60.$$

If K has been set by the binary addition or subtraction it will remain set throughout the adjustment process. If K is clear before adjustment, it may well be set by one or other of the adjustment steps, and once set it will not be cleared.

(Readers unfamiliar with the 'ALGOL-like' notation above may find a translation useful: after addition, if either $a_0 > 9$, or H is set, add 06 (hex) into A; if now $a_1 > 9$ or K is set, add 60 (hex) into A; both corrections may be necessary. After subtraction, if H is set, subtract 06 in to A; if now K is set, subtract 60 into A; both corrections may be necessary.)

It will be found useful to work through the adjustment steps for the examples of addition at the beginning of this section, and for similar examples of subtraction.

The written form of the instruction here is DEC.

Further BCD operations are discussed in 4.7.

2.5   STACK OPERATIONS

The idea of the stack is very simple, but it is an idea that has had fundamental and far-reaching influence both in computer design and in programming. A programmer with experience in the use of stacks would find his style severely cramped without them. It is not possible here to do more than describe the mechanics of stacks and their implementation, and in later chapters to illustrate their application.[8]

For our purposes a *stack* is a pile of objects represented as numbers. A new number can be put *on to* the stack; the number at the top of the stack can be taken *off*. A number in the stack is not accessible until all the numbers above it have been taken off one by one. The rule is 'last in—first out'.

A stack for single-length numbers can be implemented in the main store (RAM) with the help of an addressing register, which will serve as the 'stack pointer'. First the *base* of the stack is defined by assigning a value to the stack pointer. It is usual for this to be a high-valued address and for the stack to grow towards the lower-valued addresses. The operation of putting a number on to the stack ('push') is then

(i)   assign the number to the location whose address is the stack pointer value;

(ii)   decrease the stack pointer value by 1.

To take a number off the stack ('pop', 'pull') and put it into, say, an accumulator,

(i)   increase the stack pointer value by 1;

[8]The IEEE journal *Computer* devoted much of its May 1977 issue (Vol. 10, No. 5) to a survey of stack computers.

(ii)   assign the contents of the location whose address is in the stack pointer register to the accumulator.

Thus if the stack pointer register is SP and the accumulator to be used is A, and if the base of the stack is to be (arbitrarily) 7FFF, then:

The stack is established by   SP: = 7FFF
The 'push' operation is   M[SP]: = A; SP: − 1
The 'pop' or 'pull' operation is   SP: + 1; A: = M[SP].

Note that with this arrangement the stack pointer always points to the location 'above' the top of the stack—free space to which the next new element will be assigned.[9]

The 6800 has exactly this arrangement. It has a 16-bit register SP for the stack pointer, and 'push' and 'pop' instructions for each of the two accumulators A, B.

An instruction written SP: = 7FFF (hex 8E 7F FF) assigns the specified value to the stack pointer.

S:= A ((hex 36), meaning 'put contents of A on to stack') has the effect of M[SP]: = A; SP: − 1.

A: = S ((hex 32), meaning' move top value of stack into A') has the effect of SP: + 1; A: = M[SP].

For accumulator B, S:= B (hex 37) and B:= S (hex 33) are provided.

On the 8080, 8085 and Z80 the stack arrangements are rather different. The major difference is that stack operations are concerned with *double-length* quantities, not single bytes. 'Pop' and 'push' instructions to and from each double-length register (except the program counter) are provided. Each of these instructions increases or decreases the stack pointer value by 2. The other difference from the 6800 arrangement is that the stack pointer always points to the actual top element of the stack rather than to the first free space 'above' it.

Thus we have

SP: = 17F4 (hex 31 F4 17) to assign the specified value to the stack pointer;
ST: = BC (hex C5), 'push', equivalent to SP: − 2; MM[SP]: = BC;
BC: = ST (hex C1), 'pop', equivalent to BC: = MM[SP]; SP: + 2.

and similar instructions for the other double-length registers.

These machines also have an interchange operation (see 2.3.4) involving the top element of the stack.

The instruction HL: = :ST (hex E3) interchanges the value in HL and that on the top of the stack. It has no net effect on the value of the stack pointer.

All the machines have 'increment' and 'decrement' instructions operating on the stack pointer. In all cases the value of the increment or decrement is 1.

At the entry to every subroutine (see 2.7), a value (the return address) is placed on the stack. This value is removed on exit from the subroutine. The use of *a* stack for return addresses is right, but it is unfortunate that there is no special stack or stack pointer for this purpose. Consequently, the stack cannot be used conveniently to pass values into or out of a subroutine, and the use of several stacks in a program with subroutines requires extreme care.

___

[9]The reader who, perhaps through familiarity with some other realization of the stack concept, finds it difficult to associate *removing* a stack element with *incrementing* the stack-pointer value should imagine the stack as depicted on a page whose lines are conventionally numbered, with the lowest number at the top and the highest number at the foot.

2.6   JUMPS

Examples of *unconditional jump* instructions were used to illustrate the section on 'addresses' (2.3.6). The effect of such an instruction is to assign a new value to the program counter; this causes the next instruction for execution to be taken from the location whose address is this new value, rather than from the next location in the static order. The new value for the program counter may be given in the instruction itself (bytes JK) for a direct jump, or in a register (*indirect*) or be found by adding a signed value (byte J) to the old value (*relative* jump).

A *conditional jump* has this effect if some specified condition is satisfied, usually if a particular flag has a specified value. If that condition is not satisfied, the conditional jump instruction does nothing except allow the program counter to receive a normal increment, and it is then succeeded by the next instruction in the static order.

Examples of conditional jumps:

JZ1234   If Z = 1, jump to 1234 (PC: = 1234);
              otherwise, do nothing (PC: + 3)
JNK + 12   If K = 0, jump forward 12 bytes (18 in decimal!) (PC: + 14);
              otherwise, do nothing (PC: + 2).

(See Section 2.3.6.)

2.7   SUBROUTINES

A subroutine is a piece of program that may be executed at any time during the execution of the program proper. For example, since the microprocessors have no multiplication instruction, multiplication has to be achieved by using a subroutine (but see 4.5.3). We might have a piece of program which, given two single-length numbers in single-length registers, computes their product in a double-length register. Then, at any point where multiplication is required, the main program can put the two factors into the two single-length registers and then jump to the beginning of the multiplication subroutine. After this is executed, there will have to be a jump back to the instruction statically following the 'jump to subroutine'. This instruction will be the first of a sequence which makes use of the product left in the double-length register.

There is one copy of the subroutine in store. There is no difficulty in jumping to its first instruction from several points in the main program. The problem is in getting back to the right place in the main program after each 'call' of the subroutine. The solution adopted by the microprocessors makes use of the *stack*. Immediately before jumping to the first instruction of a subroutine, the program puts the 'normal' value of the program counter on to the stack. This value is the address of the instruction following the jump instruction in the static order—that is, of the instruction to which the dynamic sequence must pass after the subroutine execution. The subroutine must end, therefore, by 'popping' this *return address* into the program counter (PC: = ST).

Each microprocessor has special instructions for jumping to (calling) a subroutine. For example, JS1234 stored at 0123 has the effect of putting the value 0126 (0123+3) on to the stack and then jumping to 1234.

Each microprocessor also has special instructions for returning from a subroutine. For example, if the subroutine beginning at 1234 goes on to execute the instruction RET (return), the value on the stack (0126) will be assigned to the program counter—equivalent to a jump to 0126.

This can perhaps best be illustrated by writing a short program. We require $x = a \times b + c \times d + e \times f$, where a, b, c, d, e, f are single-length numbers and x is the double-length result. The machine is the 8080, and there is a subroutine whose first instruction is stored at 1234, and which multiplies together the numbers given to it in registers B and C, leaving their product in HL. The subroutine ends (dynamically) with RET. The program must start at 2000.

1234: —

—

—

—   } multiplication subroutine (HL: = B × C)

—

—

RET

. . .

. . .

2000:B: $= a$	
C: $= b$	
JS1234	Form $a \times b$
HL: $=$:DE	Put $a \times b$ in DE
B: $= c$	
C: $= d$	
JS1234	Form $c \times d$
HL: $+$ DE	Form $a \times b + c \times d$
HL: $=$:DE	Put $a \times b + c \times d$ in DE
B: $= e$	
C: $= f$	
JS1234	Form $e \times f$
HL: $+$ DE	Form $a \times b + c \times d + e \times f$
x: $=$ HL	Store result.

(What has the writer of the program assumed about the subroutine? That it does not disturb the contents of DE.)

There are variations on the simple 'jump to subroutine' described above. The 6800 has a subroutine call in which the address is *relative* and one in which the call is to an *indexed* address. The 8080, 8085 and Z80 subroutine calls use *direct* addressing only, but there is in each a set of *conditional subroutine calls* corresponding to the conditional jumps, and a set of *conditional returns*. These machines also have eight *privileged addresses* (0000, 0008, 0010, 0018, 0020, 0028, 0030, 0038). A subroutine whose first instruction is at one of these addresses may be called by a single-byte instruction. Thus JSS1 (hex CF, 1 byte) is equivalent to JS0008 (CD 08 00, 3 bytes).

For some unaccountable reason, these special subroutine calls are called 're-start' instructions in manufacturer's manuals.

(See 2.9).

The simple program above has not explained why a stack is used for the return address. In programs of any complexity subroutines themselves may need to call other subroutines, and these subroutines may call others. At any time the return address at the top of the stack is that appropriate to the call of the subroutine most recently entered. Return addresses below the top of the stack will be 'exposed' one by one as they are required.

It can now be seen why a second stack pointer, out of the programmer's reach, should have been provided for return addresses. The actual arrangement makes it difficult to use the stack to pass values into and out of a subroutine, and the presence of return addresses on the stack makes any re-assignment to the stack pointer fraught with danger.

With the second stack pointer, return addresses would take care of themselves in a stack of their own, and the programmer would have at the same time complete freedom to pass values to and from subroutines by way of any of a number of stacks which the nature of the problem might require.

2.8   INPUT–OUTPUT

There are no special instructions for input or output in the 6800 instruction set. This does not mean that peripheral devices cannot be used with the 6800. What it does mean is that a peripheral device has to be *interfaced* to the 6800 system in such a way that it appears to the processor as part of the store, occupying one or more storage locations. When this is done, *input* can be effected by executing instructions (such as A: = M1234) which copy the value presented at the addresses of these locations into a processor register. Conversely, *output* can be effected by assigning values to these locations (by, for example, instructions like M1234: = A).

In the discussion on semiconductor storage (1.3.2), the importance of matching the access time of PROMS and RAMS to the clock rate of the processor was emphasized. The first problem with peripheral devices is that they work at their own slow speeds, or even (as do keyboards) at human speeds. The second problem is that the nature of the information to be communicated between the system and the outside world may imply adaptation to the nature of information within the system—based on 8-bit bytes.

Consider the question of a teletype keyboard, to be used for input to the system.

Figure 2.1 shows a general arrangement as it affects the programmer. On the microprocessor's side of the interface, the requirement for the execution of a read instruction (e.g. A: = M1234) is that the address (1234) should appear on the address bus, and that a timing signal (control signal) should be accepted by the interface. The information at the data bus terminals of the interface will then be read.

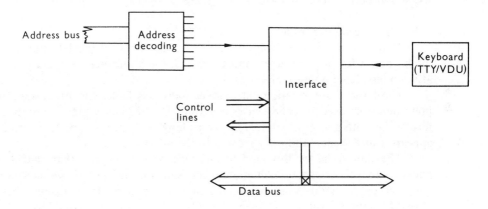

Figure 2.1   Schematic of keyboard interface.

On the keyboard side, every time a key is operated the interface will receive a sequence of bits from the keyboard. Typically, these will be one start bit, eight information bits and two stop bits, at the *baud rate* (110–330 bits per second). Between key operations nothing will be received.

Full discussion of the interface design belongs elsewhere.[10] Several approaches are possible, with different consequences for programming.

(i)   'Bit by bit'

Here the function of the interface is to make all the bits (including the start and stop bits) received from the keyboard available, in sequence, each as one of the data bus bits. A subroutine, called every time a character is to be read, will begin with a loop of instructions. This loop will read (by e.g. A: = M1234) the interface—only one of the eight bits assigned to A will be significant. This bit will be tested, and until it indicates the arrival of the start bit, a conditional jump will cause the loop to be repeated. The loop is left when the start bit is detected. The first information bit will then be expected some milliseconds (3 or 9) later, and so there will be a 'time delay' loop of instructions, killing time. Then the interface will be read again—and the first information bit will be in A. This bit will be put into another register for safety, and then the 'time delay' loop will be repeated and the second information

---

[10]See D. Zissos, *System Design with Microprocessors*. London: Academic Press, 1978.

bit read. This bit will be put next to the first, and the process will continue until 8 information bits have been assembled into a byte in the second register. After this, there must be further 'time delay' to account for the stop bits. The subroutine can then end, and can be entered again immediately or at any time to deal with a further expected incoming character.

This subroutine is not easy to write—or to test. But once written it will be held permanently in a read-only store, and thereafter reading a character is a simple matter of calling a subroutine.

An interface of this kind, designed by Motorola for the MEK6800 kit, has a ROM subroutine of 65 bytes for reading one character.

(ii) 'Serial to parallel'

Here the interface is designed to receive and hold all the bits transmitted by the keyboard for one character, and to present the 8 information bits to the system at the interface data terminals.

Until the 8 information bits are actually available, the processor must be prevented from executing the read instruction. The 'read character' subroutine therefore begins with a loop which is repeated as long as a bit, meaning 'data ready', and appearing at a second address allocated to the interface, is zero.

The subroutine for this kind of interface is much simpler than that described under (i) above, correspondingly more work being allotted to the interface hardware. An interface with this kind of specification designed by Intel around their 8251 USART requires a subroutine of only eight bytes, as does a similar Motorola interface using the 6850 ACIA. These represent the most usual way for a microprocessor system to receive and transmit serial data.

(iii) A 'wait' interface

Here the interface hardware takes over all the work, and the program requires no subroutine, only a single read instruction (e.g. A: = M1234), to read a character. The 'data ready' bit of (ii) above, instead of being presented on the data bus to be read by the processor, is an input signal to a circuit which holds the processor in 'suspended animation' as long as its value is zero. As soon as the 'data ready' signal changes to 1 the processor is released and the read instruction can be executed. Immediately after the execution of the read instruction, the 'data ready' signal is reset to prevent the same character being read a second time.[11]

Interfaces of these kinds can be made for the 8080, 8085 and Z80 as well as the 6800, and addresses can be used in the same way on all the machines. Interfaces of types (ii) and (iii) can be designed to present up to 16 bits (two successive bytes) to be read by a double-length read instruction. Similar interfaces can be designed operating 'in reverse' for output peripherals such as teletype printers and v.d.u. screens.

An additional feature of the 8080, 8085 and Z80 allows up to 256 special addresses ('peripheral device numbers') beyond the 65,536 normal addresses provided

[11]ibid.

by the 16-bit address bus. These special addresses are made available in the execution of the 'input' and 'output' instructions of the processors. Each special address can be occupied by an input–output port or 'gateway'. An instruction, to be written here as A: = G23 (hex DB 23), meaning 'assign to A the value appearing at gateway 23', is executed as follows. The special address is put out on the address bus, but, instead of a timing pulse for a 'memory read', a timing pulse for 'input read' is issued by the processor. Thus no store location is affected, but the input byte is admitted from the input port to the register A.

The converse operation, written G24: = A (hex D3 24), outputs a byte to output port (gateway) 24.

Further instructions provided only on the Z80 allow the special address to be specified *indirectly* through a single-length register (C) and at the same time the data register may be any register, including A. The 'step' and 'loop' operations of the Z80 (described below in 2.10) allow direct transfers between an input–output port and a store location or block of store locations. For each transfer both port and store location are indirectly addressed.

2.9 INTERRUPTION

Suppose there are two programs, A and B, in store. Program A is being executed, and program B is not. Suddenly, for some reason outside the microprocessor system, there is a need for B to be executed as soon as possible, but of course without the loss of the work so far done by A. The problem is to *interrupt* the execution of A, to execute B, and then to resume A at the point of interruption.

Now the processor is a clocked sequential circuit and its execution of either program must necessarily proceed in phase with the clock, which will itself be un-affected by the interruption. But it operates by repeating an instruction cycle of a variable number of states. If interruption is allowed at *any* clock pulse, that is at any phase in the instruction cycle, then there will be the extremely difficult problem of arranging the resumption of a partially executed instruction—any instruction, inter-rupted at any stage. Clearly, if B can be made to wait until the current instruction cycle is complete before taking over the processor, the problem will be much simplified.

We can envisage the basic process of interruption as follows.

(i)   A signal indicates to the processor that the program it is executing is to be interrupted.

(ii)   The processor completes the execution of its current instruction cycle.

(iii)   The processor stores away the contents of the program counter (puts the return address on the stack?).

(iv)   The processor receives (from the data bus) information (address of first instruc-tion of program B), enabling it to begin the execution of the interrupting program B.

(v)   Execution of B can now proceed normally. If B ends with a 'return' instruction, the interrupted program will be resumed immediately after the point of inter-ruption.

This process is analogous to a subroutine call with A as the main program and B as the subroutine—except for the fact that the call of B is provoked not by an instruction of A but by an external signal. If it is to cause no damage to A it must be arranged that all the information belonging to A—register contents, states of flags—which may be required to enable A to continue correctly after the interruption must be preserved throughout the execution of B and restored before A is resumed.

In certain circumstances it may be undesirable to allow a program—or a particular section of a program—to be interrupted. For example, if the execution of the 'bit-by-bit' subroutine described under (i) in the 'Input–output' section above were interrupted, several bits of the character in transmission from the keyboard would be lost to the subroutine. On resumption the subroutine would try to read the last bits, but too late. The interruption process must be modified to take account of this possibility. If there is a flip-flop (I) in the processor which can be set and reset by program instructions it can be used to allow or defer interruptions as follows.

(i)   An external signal *requests* the interruption of the program currently being executed

(ii)   If $I = 1$ the program can be interrupted; the execution of the current instruction cycle is completed and steps (iii), (iv) and (v) above can be taken. If, however, $I = 0$ when the request for interruption is received, the request must be refused, and only when I has been set to 1 by program A can the interruption be allowed to take effect.

This outline represents the treatment of interruptions by the 8080. In that machine there is an 'interrupt flag' I which can be set ($I: = 1$, hex FB) to 'enable interrupts' (in English, to allow interruptions to take place) and reset ($I: = 0$, hex F3) to 'disable interrupts' (in English, to prevent interruptions from taking place). The state of this flag is shown by an output signal of the processor, INTE ('interrupts enabled'). The interruption request signal, INT, is received by the processor and, if and when $I = 1$, a signal INTA ('interrupt acknowledged') is given out by the processor at the end of the instruction cycle. The presence of this signal allows an *instruction* (normally a subroutine call—one or three bytes) to be forced on to the data bus. This instruction is taken into the instruction register and the interrupting program begins its execution.

The instructions $I: = 0$ and $I: = 1$ are the only instructions in the 8080 set concerned with interruption, but see reference to 'HALT' below. It is the programmer's responsibility to ensure that an interrupting routine preserves and restores all information necessary for the correct resumption of the interrupted program.

If, as suggested in (iii) above, and in fact implemented in the microprocessors, a (the) stack is used for the return address, then in principle an interrupting program can itself be interrupted, as a subroutine can itself call a subroutine. This suggests the possibility of requests for interruption coming from more than one source, and with that the possibility of several such requests waiting for attention while $I = 0$. When interruptions become possible again ($I: = 1$), in what order are these to be dealt with? In order of arrival time (queue?) or according to some notion of relative priority? The answer will have to be built into hardware which, taking in requests for interruption from the several sources, produces the 'INT' signal for the processor and puts the right instruction on to the data bus to enable the first interruption to take effect.

There are several possibilities for the relationship between the interrupted program A and the interrupting program B.

(i)   They may be independent programs and use disjoint parts of the store for working space—though they are very likely to call the same subroutines.

(ii)   B may work on results obtained by A. For example, the purpose of B could be to print and report on the progress of A at the request of the operator.

(iii)   A may work on results obtained from B. For example, the purpose of B could be to provide A with new information which A needs as soon as it is available. If this information is available from its source (perhaps a peripheral device connected to an instrument monitoring some chemical process) for only a very short time, the request for interruption can be very urgent—if the request is not granted quickly enough, the opportunity will be lost.

In case (i), the program A can be written without regard to the question of interruptions. Program B must be written so that it leaves the processor, and any storage locations it uses and which are also used by A, as it finds them. In cases (ii) and (iii), program A should be written with the activities of B in mind. For example, in (ii), if A computes successive *sets* of results, it may be desirable to allow B to report the progress of A only when a new complete set is available, and not in the middle of the computation of a set. This would be managed by the use of the flag I. In case (iii) there may be periods when A is able to receive new information and periods when it is not. Flag I, again, can be used to control this. But with the possibility of urgent requests logical difficulties can arise.

Programming can become very difficult indeed when all the possibilities are combined—interrupted interruptions, requests of different degrees of urgency, mutual dependence of programs—and a full discussion is outside the scope of an elementary book.

The 6800, 8085 and Z80 have rather more elaborate provision for interruptions in their instruction sets than does the 8080.

In the 6800 there is a condition flag I but its significance is the opposite of that of I in the 8080. In the 6800, $I = 0$ means that requests for interruption will be granted; $I = 1$ means that ordinary requests will not. Ordinary requests are those received at the terminal 'IRQ' ('interrupt request'). A request received at another terminal 'NMI' ('non-maskable interrupt') will be granted at the end of the current instruction cycle irrespective of the state of I and will, moreover, be given priority over a request at IRQ. This brings both advantages and difficulties in programming.

The action of the 6800 processor in accepting an interruption is more complicated than that of the 8080. As well as the return address, the contents of all the registers—accumulators A, B, the condition flag register C and the index register IX—are stacked. Correspondingly, for use at the end of an interruption, there is an instruction 'return from interrupt', RI (hex 3B) which reassigns the stacked values to the registers before jumping to the stacked return address.

The interruption process, having stacked the register contents, ends (cf. step (iv) above) with a jump (indirect) to the address which is held at locations MMFFF8 (IRQ) or MMFFFC (NMI). Thus MMFFF8 or MMFFFC must be made to deliver the address of the first actual instruction of the interrupting routine.

A program such as A in case (iii) above may find itself unable to continue until program B has interrupted it and provided it with new information. The 6800 designers have anticipated this difficulty by giving an instruction 'wait for interrupt', WI (hex 3E). This instruction effectively holds the program in suspended animation until an interruption has been made and completed. In outline its action is as follows. First, it stacks the address of its (static) successor as the return address, and then it stacks the contents of the registers. Then the processor is held in a waiting state until the expected request (IRQ) is received. As soon as this happens the execution of WI is completed by a jump to the address held at locations MMFFF8.

In similar circumstances on the 8080, a HALT (hex 76) instruction would be used. The execution of this instruction is to put the machine into a state from which it will not proceed until an input signal (RESET, INT, HOLD) is received. If INT is received while the machine is halted, the interruption will be allowed and after its completion the interrupted program will resume at the instruction (statically) after the HALT.

The 6800 has a further feature which must be mentioned here, the so called 'software interrupt' caused by the instruction SI (hex 3F). This is not an interruption in the ordinary sense. It should be thought of rather as a special form of subroutine call. The execution of SI is to stack a return address and the register contents and then jump to the address held in the pair of locations MMFFFA. The subroutine entered by this jump should end not with the ordinary return instruction RET(39) but with RI(3B) since the register contents have to be unstacked.

The Z80 has two interruption request input terminals—INT for ordinary requests for interruption, and NMI (as on the 6800) for urgent requests. Its response to a request at NMI is to complete the current instruction and then, regardless of the state of I, to stack the return address in the usual way and jump to 0066 (always 0066). Its response to a request at INT depends on its current 'interrupt mode'. The 'interrupt mode' can be 0, 1, or 2. On RESET, it is set to 0; at any other time one of the instructions IM: = 0 (hex ED 46), IM: = 1 (ED 56), IM: = 2 (ED 5E) can be used to set it as required.

In mode 0, the processor's response to a request at INT is the same as that of the 8080; that is, if $I = 1$, the return address is stacked and the instruction (any instruction) put into the data bus by the interrupting device is executed.

In mode 1, if $I = 1$ the return address is stacked, and a jump made to address 0038.

In mode 2, if $I = 1$ the return address is stacked, and a jump made to the address held in location MM[Q∥p], where p is an even-valued byte put on to the data bus by the interrupting device. (Q is a special single-length register to which assignment can be made from register A—see Z80 instruction set, Chapter 3. Q∥p means the 16-bit value whose upper half is the value in Q and whose lower half is p.)

If $I = 0$, a request at INT is ignored. The HALT instruction (76) is the same as that in the 8080.

8085 interruptions. The 8085 has five interruption request terminals, namely INTR, RST 5.5, RST 6.5, RST 7.5, and TRAP. In every instruction cycle these five are inspected, in effect in the order TRAP, RST 7.5, RST 6.5, RST 5.5, INTR.

A request at TRAP is granted irrespective of the state of I, and its effect is to stack the return address and jump to 0024. Requests at the RST terminals may be *masked* (that is prevented) by setting the corresponding bits of the 'interrupt mask' IM (see Chapter 3). Only if $I = 1$ and the mask bit is 0 will an RST request be granted. Then the effect is to stack the return address and jump to 003C (RST 7.5), 0034 (RST 6.5), or 002C (RST 5.5). A request at INTR is treated exactly as a request at INT of the 8080. When an interruption request is granted, $I: = 0$.

2.10 OTHER INSTRUCTIONS (Z80 ONLY)

Auxiliary registers

In addition to the registers A, B, C, D, E, F, H, L, the Z80 has an auxiliary set A', B', C', D', E', F', H', L'. In connection with these auxiliary registers two interchange instructions (cf. 2.3.4 above) are provided:

$AF := :XX$ (hex 08) has the effect $A := :A'$; $F := :F'$
$BL := :XX$ (hex D9) has the effect $B := :B'$; $C := :C'$; $D := :D'$;
$E := :E'$; $H := :H'$; $L := :L'$.

No other instructions are concerned with the auxiliary registers. Their principal application, therefore, is as providing a 'safe place' for the contents of the ordinary registers during the execution of a subroutine or interruption or other sequence of instructions requiring the use of the ordinary registers.

Operations involving individual bits

The notation $q.i$ for bit i of register or location q was introduced in Section 2.3.5. In the following, q may be any of A, B, C, D, E, H, L or M (standing for M[HL]), or $Mj_1 j_0 X$ or $Mj_1 j_0 Y$ (locations with indexed addresses—see 2.3.6 above).

$Z: = \# q.i$ sets the zero flag to 1 if $q.i = 0$.
                  or to 0 if $q.i = 1$.
$q.i: = 0$ sets $q.i$ to 0 without affecting the other bits of q.
$q.i: = 1$ sets $q.i$ to 1 without affecting the other bits of q.

A counting jump

The pair of instructions $B: -1$; $JNZ + j_1 j_0$ (occupying three bytes) can be replaced on the Z80 by a single instruction occupying two bytes only and with the same effect. This insruction is most likely to be used in counting repetitions of a 'loop' of instructions, and the amount of the jump is therefore likely to be negative.

The instruction will be written here as

$$B: -1, \ JNZ + F8$$

(where the comma indicates that we have one instruction, not two, and F8 is an example of a J-byte value).

There are no similar instructions involving registers other than B or conditions other than NZ.

Step and block instructions

The Z80 has a group of 16 instructions, which are considered below in groups of four, for use in operations on sets of consecutive locations. Each of these instructions has a two-byte operation code (I_0, I_1) and no J or K bytes.

(i) *Copy.* The instruction hex ED B0 has the following effect:

$$W:M[DE]:=M[HL];$$
$$DE:+1;$$
$$HL:+1;$$
$$BC:-1;$$
$$\text{if } BC \neq 0000 \text{ then go to } W;$$

Thus, if the original value in BC was n ($1 \leq n \leq 65{,}535$, decimal), n bytes will have been copied from one 'block' of consecutive locations to another. (If BC was zero originally, the loop will have been executed 65,536, not zero, times!)

The instruction hex ED B8 has the same effect except that the values in DE and HL are each *decreased* by 1 each time through the loop.

The instruction hex ED A0 effects a single step of ED B0, thus:

$$M[DE]:=M[HL];$$
$$DE:+1;$$
$$HL:+1;$$
$$BC:-1.$$

The instruction hex ED A8 effects a single step of ED B8.

(ii) *Search.* The instruction ED B1 has the effect

$$W:A-M[HL];$$
$$HL:+1;$$
$$BC:-1;$$
$$\text{if } BC \neq 0000 \wedge Z \text{ then go to } W.$$

If, after the execution of this instruction, the flag $Z = 0$, we will have $BC = 0000$; none of the n locations examined holds a value equal to that in A.

If, however, $Z = 1$ after execution, this means that a location has been found which contains the same value as A. The address of this location can be obtained by subtracting 1 from the value in HL.

The instruction hex ED B9 has the same effect except that the value in HL is *decreased* by 1 at each step, and so we have a 'backward' search through the block of storage locations.

The instruction hex ED A1 effects a single step of ED B1:

$$A-M[HL];$$
$$HL:+1;$$
$$BC:-1.$$

After the execution of this instruction, the flags N,Z are as set by the subtraction. The flag P (normally overflow) is set (1) if $BC \neq 0$ and reset (0) if $BC = 0$ after execution.

The instruction ED A9 effects a single step of ED B9.

(iii) **Input.** The instruction hex ED B2 has the effect

W:M[HL]: = G[C];
   HL:+1;
   B:−1;
   if B ≠ 0 **then go to** W.

If the original value in B was n, $1 \leq n \leq 255$, then n bytes will have been read from input port C (that is, whose device number is in C) and assigned to consecutive locations in store. If originally B held 00, then 256 bytes will have been read and assigned.

This instruction must be used with extreme caution, as must the other instructions in the 'input' and 'output' groups. At the full clock frequency of 4MHz, the time interval between successive read operations will be $5\frac{1}{4}$ microseconds. A teletype can deliver a character only once every 100,000 or 33,333 microseconds, and a 1000 c.p.s. paper tape reader only once every 1000 microseconds. Unless the peripheral at port C can produce a new valid value every $5\frac{1}{4}$ microseconds, if this instruction is to be used either a 'wait' interface as described in 2.8 above will have to be provided, or the execution will have to be interrupted as mentioned below.

The instruction ED BA has the same effect except that the value in HL is *decreased* by one at each step.

The instruction ED A2 effects a single step of ED B2:

M[HL]: = G[C];
   HL:+1;
   B:−1;

and the instruction ED AA represents a single step of ED BA.

(iv) **Output.** The instruction hex ED B3 has the effect

W:G[C]: = M[HL];
   HL:+1;
   B:−1;
   if B ≠ 0 **then go to** W.

This is the converse of ED B2.

Hex ED BB is the same except that the HL value is *decreased* by one in each step.

The instruction ED A3 effects a single step of ED B3:

G[C]: = M[HL];
   HL:+1;
   B:−1;

and ED AB effects a single step of ED BB.

A warning similar to that for the 'input' instructions above applies to these instructions.

Interruption

The eight block instructions ED B0, ED B1, ED B2, ED B3, ED B8, ED B9, ED BA, ED BB are exceptional in that the execution of any of them can be interrupted after any step. A request for interruption received during the execution of one of these instructions will be granted as soon as the current step is complete; after the return the execution of the interrupted instruction will be resumed. The question of interruption of the block input and block output requires particularly careful consideration.

Notations

Compact forms consistent with previous notations for expressing in detail the actions of each of these instructions are tabulated below. They are, however, too long to be used as programming-language instructions. For this purpose it may be more convenient to use three-letter groups made up of single letters with the following meanings: C—copy; S—search; I—input; O—output; S—step; B—block; U—up; D—down. Such groups are shown in the right-hand column.

Machine code	Action	3-letter group
ED A0	$M[DE:+1]:=M[HL:+1],BC:-1$	CSU
ED A1	$A-M[HL:+1],BC:-1$	SSU
ED A2	$M[HL:+1]:=G[C],B:-1$	ISU
ED A3	$G[C]:=M[HL:+1],B:-1$	OSU
ED A8	$M[DE:-1]:=M[HL:-1],BC:-1$	CSD
ED A9	$A-M[HL:-1],BC:-1$	SSD
ED AA	$M[HL:-1]:=G[C],B:-1$	ISD
ED AB	$G[C]:=M[HL:-1],B:-1$	OSD
ED B0	**repeat** $M[DE:+1]:=M[HL:+1],BC:-1$ **until** $BC=0000$	CBU
ED B1	**repeat** $A-M[HL:+1],BC:-1$ **until** $BC=0000\vee Z$	SBU
ED B2	**repeat** $M[HL:+1]:=G[C],B:-1$ **until** Z	IBU
ED B3	**repeat** $G[C]:=M[HL:+1],B:-1$ **until** Z	OBU
ED B8	**repeat** $M[DE:-1]:=M[HL:-1],BC:-1$ **until** $BC=0000$	CBD
ED B9	**repeat** $A-M[HL:-1],BC:-1$ **until** $BC=0000\vee Z$	SBD
ED BA	**repeat** $M[IIL:-1]:=G[C],B:-1$ **until** Z	IBD
ED BB	**repeat** $G[C]:=M[HL:-1],BC:-1$ **until** Z	OBD

3

Instruction sets

3.1 EXPLANATION

This chapter is devoted to complete descriptive listings and tabulations of the instruction sets of the four microprocessors 6800, 8080, 8085 and Z80 in a common form and using a common notation.

In each case the description begins with a list of the registers and flags as seen by the programmer. In cases where a register is made up of flags, or of other registers, this is indicated. (The symbol ‖ means concatenation or juxtaposition so, for example, $HL \equiv H\|L$ means that HL is the same as H joined to L so that H_0 is immediately to the left of L_7.) Any special notations are then defined.

A large table is then given in which the binary form of each instruction is shown together with its written form as used in this book (and by the software already constructed or projected), and a description of its effect. The effect has in general three components: (i) the effect on registers, stores, ports and isolated flags; (ii) the effect on the flags in the flag register; (iii) the increment applied to the program counter. The next column contains references to the explanatory material of Chapter 2. The rows of the table have been arranged according to what is perhaps an arbitrary classification given in the extreme right-hand column of the table.

In the binary form there are many places where a group of 1, 2, 3 or 4 bit-positions is covered by a symbol such as m, r′, op or cond. An auxiliary table for each of these symbols gives a substitution which must be made for that symbol in the written form or in the description for each possible combination of bits that may appear in place of that symbol. For example, in the 6800 table we have

| I | | | Written | Description of |
7 6 5 4 3 2 1 0	Hex		instruction	operation
0 0 1 1 0 0 1 r	3 –		r: = S	SP: +1; r: = M[SP]

and in the auxiliary, or substitution, table:

r	Written	Descr.
0	A	A
1	B	B

Therefore the single line in the main table stands for the two lines:

| 0 0 1 1 0 0 1 0 | 32 | A: = S | SP: +1; A: = M[SP] |
| 0 0 1 1 0 0 1 1 | 33 | B: = S | SP: +1; B: = M[SP] |

These are the 'pull', 'pop' or 'unstack' operations (2.5).

Throughout, j_1 and j_0 stand respectively for the upper and lower halves (hexadecimal digits) of the J-byte of the instruction, and k_1 and k_0 stand for the upper and lower halves of the K-byte. Substitution in the 'binary' column will be of a set of 4 bits; in the other columns it will be of the corresponding hexadecimal digit (see 2.3.1, 2.3.5).

Where there is insufficient space in the table, references are given to explanatory notes following the tables. In the column concerned with flags, a quantity with a 'prime', e.g. A_7', means that the flag takes the value of the *resultant* specified bit; without the prime it refers to the value before execution of the instruction.

The notes are followed by a Karnaugh map representation of each instruction set. The layout of these maps is shown in Table 3.1. The value in any 'cell' differs in one bit-position only from that in each of the adjacent cells and from that in each of its 'reflections' in the axes of the diagram. (By way of illustration, the reader should locate 00 and the eight values which differ from it by one bit, 01, 02, 04, 08, 10, 20, 40, 80; and also some other set such as AF with AE, AD, AB, A7, BF, 8F, EF, 2F.) This arrangement shows up the structure of the instruction set very clearly, in bringing together groups of related instructions. It has been found very useful in practice as a compact summary for reference while writing programs.

After the Karnaugh map is a listing of the instructions in numerical order of operation code (I) with the written form. The occurrence of '12' in a written form, intended to represent a typical one-byte value, implies that the instruction has a further byte J. Clearly '12' can be replaced by any hexadecimal value from 00 to FF inclusive. Similarly, '1234', a typical two-byte value, implies bytes J and K; it can be replaced by any value of four hexadecimal digits. This listing also has been found to be a useful reference during programming.

The extensive instruction set of the Z80 has made it necessary to give its main table in a fuller format than that of the others. Also, the Z80 Karnaugh map is in five parts—a main part (the 8080 map with the gaps filled in) and a part for each of the 'I_0' values CB, DD, ED, FD.

Finally, there is an alphabetical 'dictionary' of all of the instructions of all of the processors.

The reader may well find the appearance of these tables and lists overwhelming at first, though in time they should become a conveniently accessible set of reference material. For each processor the large table is the primary description; the Karnaugh map and numerical listing are merely summaries in forms each of which will be convenient to some readers for some purposes. The 'dictionary' presents a summary in yet another form which will be found useful, and contains timing information which cannot easily be accommodated elsewhere. The reader's actual use of this reference material will vary with the development of his experience and interest.

$I_5I_4I_3$	$I_6=0$, $I_2I_1I_0$								$I_6=1$, $I_2I_1I_0$							
	000	010	110	100	101	111	011	001	001	011	111	101	100	110	010	000
$I_7=0$																
000	00	02	06	04	05	07	03	01	41	43	47	45	44	46	42	40
010	10	12	16	14	15	17	13	11	51	53	57	55	54	56	52	50
110	30	32	36	34	35	37	33	31	71	73	77	75	74	76	72	70
100	20	22	26	24	25	27	23	21	61	63	67	65	64	66	62	60
101	28	2A	2E	2C	2D	2F	2B	29	69	6B	6F	6D	6C	6E	6A	68
111	38	3A	3E	3C	3D	3F	3B	39	79	7B	7F	7D	7C	7E	7A	78
011	18	1A	1E	1C	1D	1F	1B	19	59	5B	5F	5D	5C	5E	5A	58
001	08	0A	0E	0C	0D	0F	0B	09	49	4B	4F	4D	4C	4E	4A	48
$I_7=1$																
001	88	8A	8E	8C	8D	8F	8B	89	C9	CB	CF	CD	CC	CE	CA	C8
011	98	9A	9E	9C	9D	9F	9B	99	D9	DB	DF	DD	DC	DE	DA	D8
111	B8	BA	BE	BC	BD	BF	BB	B9	F9	FB	FF	FD	FC	FE	FA	F8
101	A8	AA	AE	AC	AD	AF	AB	A9	E9	EB	EF	ED	EC	EE	EA	E8
100	A0	A2	A6	A4	A5	A7	A3	A1	E1	E3	E7	E5	E4	E6	E2	E0
110	B0	B2	B6	B4	B5	B7	B3	B1	F1	F3	F7	F5	F4	F6	F2	F0
010	90	92	96	94	95	97	93	91	D1	D3	D7	D5	D4	D6	D2	D0
000	80	82	86	84	85	87	83	81	C1	C3	C7	C5	C4	C6	C2	C0

Table 3.1. Karnaugh Map Layout for Eight-bit Operation Codes

3.2   MOTOROLA 6800

Microprocessor 6800   Word: 8 bits   Address: 16 bits

Single-length registers: A, B, C

Double-length registers: IX, SP, PC

Condition flags: $H \equiv C.5$ ('half-word carry')

$I \equiv C.4$ ('interruptions disabled')

$N \equiv C.3$ ('negative')

$Z \equiv C.2$ ('zero')

$V \equiv C.1$ ('overflow')

$K \equiv C.0$ ('carry')

(*Note*: $C.7 \equiv 1$, $C.6 \equiv 1$ both constant)

Stack pointer: SP

Index register: IX

Program counter: PC

Accumulators: A, B

Double-length addressing: $MM[x] \equiv M[x]\|M[x+1]$

Action of RESET signal: $I := 1$; $PC := MMFFFE$

Reserved addresses: FFF8, FFF9: 'interruption request'—note 4 and below.

FFFA, FFFB: 'software interruption'—note 5.

FFFC, FFFD: 'non-maskable interruption'—below.

FFFE, FFFF: 'reset'—above.

Response to interruption request signals:

(i)   IRQ: after completion of the current instruction, if $I = 0$ then:
$MM[SP-1] := PC+1$; $MM[SP-3] := IX$; $M[SP-4] := A$;
$M[SP-5] := B$; $M[SP-6] := C$; $SP: -7$; $I := 1$;
$PC := MMFFF8$

(ii)   NMI: after completion of execution of current instruction:
$MM[SP-1] := PC+1$; $MM[SP-3] := IX$; $M[SP-4] := A$;
$M[SP-5] := B$; $M[SP-6] := C$; $SP: -7$; $I := 1$;
$PC := MMFFFC$

6800 Instruction set—main table

I 76543210	Hex.	Written instruction	Description of operation	H	I	N	Z	V	K	PC:+	References	Class
00000001	01	NULL		·	·	·	·	·	·	1		Null
1r α 0110	–6	r:=α	r:=α	·	·	α_7	α	0	·	1,2,3	2.3	
1r α'0111	–7	α':=r	α':=r	·	·	r_7	r	0	·	1,2,3	2.3	
00010110	16	B:=A	B:=A	·	·	A_7	A	0	·	1	2.3	
00010111	17	A:=B	A:=B	·	·	B_7	B	0	·	1	2.3	
01 β 1111	–F	β:=0	β:=0	·	·	0	1	0	0	1,2,3	2.3	Assignment / Single-length, Flag St-reg. ack
00000111	07	A:=C	A:=C	·	·	·	·	·	·	1	2.3	
00000110	06	C:=A	C:=A	A_5	A_4	A_3	A_2	A_1	A_0	1	2.3	
0011001r	3–	r:=S	SP:+1;r:=M[SP]	·	·	·	·	·	·	1	2.5	
0011011r	3–	S:=r	M[SP]:=r; SP:–1	·	·	·	·	·	·	1	2.5	
1ρ γ 1110	–E	ρ:=γ	ρ:=γ	·	·	γ_{15}	γ	0	·	1,2,3	2.3, 2.5	Double-length
1ρ γ'1111	–F	γ':=ρ	γ':=ρ	·	·	ρ_{15}	ρ	0	·	1,2,3	2.3, 2.5	
00110000	30	IX:=SP+1	IX:=SP+1	·	·	·	·	·	·	1	2.3, 2.5	
00110101	35	SP:=IX–1	SP:=IX–1	·	·	·	·	·	·	1	2.3, 2.5	
0000101b	0–	V:=b		·	·	·	·	b	·	1	2.3.7	Flags
0000110b	0–	K:=b		·	·	·	·	·	b	1	2.3.7	
0000111b	0–	I:=b		·	b	·	·	·	·	1	2.9	
01 β 1100	–C	β:+1	β:+1	·	·	β_7'	β'	β'	·	1,2,3	2.4.9	Increment/decrement / Single l'gth
01 β 1010	–A	β:–1	β:–1	·	·	β_7'	β'	β'	·	1,2,3	2.4.9	
00001000	08	IX:+1	IX:+1	·	·	·	IX'	·	·	1	2.4.9	Double-length
00001001	09	IX:–1	IX:–1	·	·	·	IX'	·	·	1	2.4.9	
00110001	31	SP:+1	SP:+1	·	·	·	·	·	·	1	2.4.9	
00110100	34	SP:–1	SP:–1	·	·	·	·	·	·	1	2.4.9	
01 β 0011	–3	β:#	β:=¬β	·	·	β_7'	β'	0	1	1,2,3	2.4.4	Unary
01 β 0000	–0	β:–	β:=–β	·	·	β_7'	β'	①	②	1,2,3	2.4.4	
1r α op	—	ropα	ropα	⑤	·	r_7'	r'	r'	r'	1,2,3	2.4	Binary Special / Arithmetic-logic
00010001	11	A–B	A–B	·	·	√	√	√	√	1	2.4.7	
00011011	1B	A:+B	A:+B	A'	·	A_7'	A'	A'	A'	1	2.4.3.1	
00010000	10	A:–B	A:–B	·	·	A_7'	A'	A'	A'	1	2.4.5.1	
00011001	19	DEC	(note 2)	·	·	A_7'	A'	A'	④	1	2.4.9	
01 β 1101	–D	β		·	·	β_7	β	0	0	1,2,3	2.4.7	
10 γ 1100	–C	IX–γ	(note 7)	·	·	⑦	√	·	·	1,2,3	2.4.7	
01 β 0100	–4	β:– >		·	·	0	β'	③	β_0	1,2,3	2.4.8	Shifts and rotations
01 β 1000	–8	β:*2		·	·	β_6	β'	③	β_7	1,2,3	2.4.8	
01 β 0111	–7	β:/2	} (note 6)	·	·	·	β'	③	β_0	1,2,3	2.4.8	
01 β 1001	–9	βK:@L		·	·	β_6	β'	③	β_7	1,2,3	2.4.8	
01 β 0110	–6	βK:@R		·	·	K	β'	③	β_0	1,2,3	2.4.8	
01101110	6E	Jj₁j₀X	PC:=IX+J	·	·	·	·	·	·	–	2.6	Jump Call Return / Control transfer
01111110	7E	Jj₁j₀k₁k₀	PC:=JK	·	·	·	·	·	·	–	2.6	
0010cond	2–	Jcond+j₁j₀	(note 8)	·	·	·	·	·	·	–	2.6	
10001101	8D	JS+j₁j₀	(note 9)	·	·	·	·	·	·	–	2.7	
10111101	BD	JSj₁j₀k₁k₀	(note 10)	·	·	·	·	·	·	–	2.7	
10101101	AD	JSj₁j₀X	(note 11)	·	·	·	·	·	·	–	2.7	
00111001	39	RET	(note 12)	·	·	·	·	·	·	–	2.7	
00111011	3B	RI	(note 3)	(note 3)						–	2.9	Special
00111110	3E	WI	(note 4)	·	⑥	·	·	·	·	–	2.9	
00111111	3F	SI	(note 5)	·	⑥	·	·	·	·	–	2.7	

6800   Substitution tables

r	Written	Descr.
0	A	A
1	B	B

ρ	Written	Descr.
0	SP	SP
1	IX	IX

b	Written	Descr.
0	0	0
1	1	1

α	Written	Descr.
00	$j_1 j_0$	J
01	$MZj_1 j_0$	$M[0\|J]$
10	$Mj_1 j_0 X$	$M[IX+J]$
11	$Mj_1 j_0 k_1 k_0$	$M[JK]$

α'	Written	Descr.
00		(undefined)
01	$MZj_1 j_0$	$M[0\|J]$
10	$Mj_1 j_0 X$	$M[IX+J]$
11	$Mj_1 j_0 k_1 k_0$	$M[JK]$

β	Written	Descr.
00	A	A
01	B	B
10	$Mj_1 j_0 X$	$M[IX+J]$
11	$Mj_1 j_0 k_1 k_0$	$M[JK]$

γ	Written	Descr.
00	$j_1 j_0 k_1 k_0$	JK
01	$MMZj_1 j_0$	$MM[0\|J]$
10	$MMj_1 j_0 X$	$MM[IX+J]$
11	$MMj_1 j_0 k_1 k_0$	$MM[JK]$

γ'	Written	Descr.
00		(undefined)
01	$MMZj_1 j_0$	$MM[0\|J]$
10	$MMj_1 j_0 X$	$MM[IX+J]$
11	$MMj_1 j_0 k_1 k_0$	$MM[JK]$

Note: In the above tables, $0\|J$ means eight zero bits followed by the eight bits of J. $IX+J$ stands for $IX+0\|J$.

cond	Written	Descr.
0000		1
0001		(undefined)
0010	NKZ	$\neg(K \vee Z)$
0011	KZ	$K \vee Z$
0100	NK	$\neg K$
0101	K	K
0110	NZ	$\neg Z$
0111	Z	Z
1000	NV	$\neg V$
1001	V	V
1010	NN	$\neg N$
1011	N	N
1100	NY	$\neg(N \veebar V)$
1101	Y	$N \veebar V$
1110	NYZ	$\neg(Z \vee (N \veebar V))$
1111	YZ	$Z \vee (N \veebar V)$

op	Written	Descr.
0000	:−	:−
0001	−	−
0010	:− −	:− −
0011		(undefined)
0100	:&	: $\wedge$
0101	&	$\wedge$
0110		(see r:=α)
0111		(see α':=r)
1000	:#	: $\veebar$
1001	:++	:++
1010	:U	: $\vee$
1011	:+	:+
1100		(see IX−γ)
1101		(see JS..)
1110		(see ρ:=γ)
1111		(see γ':=ρ)

6800 Notes

1 Condition flags: H, N, Z, V, K are affected by each operation as indicated in the table:

√ value determined by result of operation

0,1 actual value after operation, regardless of operand values

· value unchanged by operation

α_7 reference to bit; flag takes the value this bit had before the operation

α_7' reference to bit; flag takes the resultant value of this bit

α reference to value; if this value is zero, then $Z:=1$; if not, $Z:=0$

α' reference to resultant value; flag H, Z, V, K takes value as defined in Chapter 2

① $V:=1$ if and only if $\beta'=80$ (hex.); otherwise $V:=0$

② $K:=1$ if and only if $\beta'=00$ (hex.); otherwise $K:=0$

③ $V=N\not\vee K$ after the shift

④ $K:=K\vee (A>99)$

⑤ H affected by $:+$ and $:++$ only; undisturbed by other operators

⑥ see notes 4 and 5

⑦ see note 7.

2 Hex. 19 (DEC) is, writing $A=2^4a_1+a_0$, equivalent to

if $a_0 > 9 \vee$ H **then** $A:+06$;

if $a_1 > 9 \vee$ K **then** $A:+60$; (see Section 2.4.9).

3 'Return from interruption'—equivalent to:

$SP:+7$; $C:=M[SP-6]$; $B:=M[SP-5]$; $A:=M[SP-4]$; $IX:=MM[SP-3]$;

$PC:=MM[SP-1]$.

4 'Wait for interruption'—equivalent to:

$MM[SP-1]:=PC+1$; $MM[SP-3]:=IX$; $M[SP-4]:=A$; $M[SP-5]:=B$;

$M[SP-6]:=C$; $SP:-7$; (wait for IRQ signal); $I:=1$; $PC:=MMFFF8$.

(Note that the machine cannot receive an IRQ signal unless $I=0$.)

5 'Software interruption'—equivalent to:

$MM[SP-1]:=PC+1$; $MM[SP-3]:=IX$; $M[SP-4]:=A$; $M[SP-5]:=B$;

$M[SP-6]:=C$; $SP:-7$; $I:=1$; $PC:=MMFFFA$.

6 Descriptions of these operations are given in 2.4.8.

7 This operation is described in 2.4.7. Flag N is set to the value of the most significant bit of the result of subtracting the upper half of γ from the upper half of IX. Flag V is set if there is overflow (as discussed in Section 2.4.5) in this same partial subtraction. Flag Z is set if the 16-bit value of γ is the same as the value in IX. No other flags are affected.

8 **if** *cond* **then** $PC:=PC+J+2$ **else** $PC:+2$.

9 $MM[SP-1]:=PC+2$; $SP:-2$; $PC:=PC+J+2$.

10 $MM[SP-1]:=PC+3$; $SP:-2$; $PC:=JK$.

11 $MM[SP-1]:=PC+2$; $SP:-2$; $PC:=IX+J$.

12 $SP:+2$; $PC:=MM[SP-1]$.

		06 C:=A		07 A:=C		0? N
10 A:−B		16 B:=A		17 A:=B		1? A
30 IX:=SP+1	32 A:=S	36 S:=A	34 SP:−1	35 SP:=IX−1	37 S:=B	33 B:=S	3? S
20	22 NKZ	26 NZ	24 NK	25 K	27 Z	23 KZ	2?
28 NV	2A NN	2E NYZ	2C NY	2D Y	2F YZ	2B N	2?
		3E WI		3F SI	3B RI	3?
					1B A:+B	1?
08 IX:+1	0A V:=0	0E I:=0	0C K:=0	0D K:=1	0F I:=1	0B V:=1	0?

J cond + [J] { (covering rows 20–27 and 28–2B)

Lower grid with left-hand labels:

label 1	label 2							
JK	J	88	8A	8E	8C	8D JS+[J]		8B	8?
MMZ[J]	MZ[J]	98 A:#α	9A A:Uα	9E SP:=γ	9C IX−γ		9F Y':=SP	9B A:+α
MM[JK]	M[JK]	B8	BA	BE	BC	BD JS[JK]	BF	BB
MM[J]X	M[J]X	A8	AA	AE	AC	AD JS[J]X	AF	AB
MM[J]X	M[J]X	A0	A2	A6	A4	A5	A7	
MM[JK]	M[JK]	B0 A:−α	B2 !:−α	B6 A:=α	B4 A:&α	B5 A&α	B7 α':=A	
MMZ[J]	MZ[J]	90 A:−	92 !:	96 A:	94 A:&	95 A&α	97	
JK	J	80	82	86	84	85		

γ,γ'   α,α'

6800   Karnaugh map

β

43	47		44	46		40	A
53	57		54	56		50	B
73 β:#	77 β:/2		74 β:->	76 βK:@R		70 β:-	M[JK]
63	67		64	66		60	M[J]X
	6F	6D	6C	6E J+[J]	6A	68	M[J]X
	7F β:=0	7D β	7C β:+1	7E J[JK]	7A β:-1	78 β:*2	M[JK]
	5F	5D β	5C β:+1		5A β:-1	58 β:*2	B
	4F	4D	4C		4A	48	A

CB				CE	CA	C8	J	JK
DB	DF B:+α			DE IX:=Y	DA B:Uα	D8 B:#α	MZ[J]	MMZ[J]
FB B:+α	FF γ':=IX			FE IX:=Y	FA B:Uα	F8 B:#α	M[JK]	MM[JK]
EB	EF			EE	EA	E8	M[J]X	MM[J]X
	E7	E5	E4	E6	E2	E0	M[J]X	MM[J]X
	F7 α':=B	F5 B&α	F4 B:&α	F6 B:=α	F2 B:-α	F0 B:-α	M[JK]	MM[JK]
	D7	D5 B&α	D4 B:&α	D6 B:=α	D2 B:-α	D0 B:-α	MZ[J]	MMZ[J]
		C5	C4	C6	C2	C0	J	JK

α,α'　　　γ,γ'

6800 Instructions in numerical order of operation code

Op		Mnemonic	Op		Mnemonic	Op		Mnemonic	Op		Mnemonic
00			40		A:−	80	12	A:−12	C0	12	B:−12
01		NULL	41			81	12	A−12	C1	12	B−12
02			42			82	12	A:−−12	C2	12	B:−−12
03			43		A: #	83			C3		
04			44		A:− >	84	12	A:&12	C4	12	B:&12
05			45			85	12	A&12	C5	12	B&12
06		C:=A	46		AK:@R	86	12	A:=12	C6	12	B:=12
07		A:=C	47		A:/2	87			C7		
08		IX:+1	48		A:*2	88	12	A: #12	C8	12	B: #12
09		IX:−1	49		AK:@L	89	12	A:++12	C9	12	B:++12
0A		V:=0	4A		A:−1	8A	12	A:U12	CA	12	B:U12
0B		V:=1	4B			8B	12	A:+12	CB	12	B:+12
0C		K:=0	4C		A:+1	8C	12 34	IX−1234	CC		
0D		K:=1	4D		A	8D	12	JS+12	CD		
0E		I:=0	4E			8E	12 34	SP:=1234	CE	12 34	IX:=1234
0F		I:=1	4F		A:=0	8F			CF		
10		A:−B	50		B:−	90	12	A:−MZ12	D0	12	B:−MZ12
11		A−B	51			91	12	A−MZ12	D1	12	B−MZ12
12			52			92	12	A:−−MZ12	D2	12	B:−−MZ12
13			53		B: #	93			D3		
14			54		B:− >	94	12	A:&MZ12	D4	12	B:&MZ12
15			55			95	12	A&MZ12	D5	12	B&MZ12
16		B:=A	56		BK:@R	96	12	A:=MZ12	D6	12	B:=MZ12
17		A:=B	57		B:/2	97	12	MZ12:=A	D7	12	MZ12:=B
18			58		B:*2	98	12	A: #MZ12	D8	12	B: #MZ12
19		DEC	59		BK:@L	99	12	A:++MZ12	D9	12	B:++MZ12
1A			5A		B:−1	9A	12	A:UMZ12	DA	12	B:UMZ12
1B		A:+B	5B			9B	12	A:+MZ12	DB	12	B:+MZ12
1C			5C		B:+1	9C	12	IX−MMZ12	DC		
1D			5D		B	9D			DD		
1E			5E			9E	12	SP:=MMZ12	DE	12	IX:=MMZ12
1F			5F		B:=0	9F	12	MMZ12:=SP	DF		MMZ12:=IX
20	12	J+12	60	12	M12X:−	A0	12	A:−M12X	E0	12	B:−M12X
21			61			A1	12	A−M12X	E1	12	B−M12X
22	12	JNKZ+12	62			A2	12	A:−−M12X	E2	12	B:−−M12X
23	12	JKZ+12	63	12	M12X: #	A3			E3		
24	12	JNK+12	64	12	M12X:− >	A4	12	A:&M12X	E4	12	B:&M12X
25	12	JK+12	65			A5	12	A&M12X	E5	12	B&M12X
26	12	JNZ+12	66	12	M12XK:@R	A6	12	A:=M12X	E6	12	B:=M12X
27	12	JZ+12	67	12	M12X:/2	A7	12	M12X:=A	E7	12	M12X:=B
28	12	JNV+12	68	12	M12X:*2	A8	12	A: #M12X	E8	12	B: #M12X
29	12	JV+12	69	12	M12XK:@L	A9	12	A:++M12X	E9	12	B:++M12X
2A	12	JNN+12	6A	12	M12X:−1	AA	12	A:UM12X	EA	12	B:UM12X
2B	12	JN+12	6B			AB	12	A:+M12X	EB	12	B:+M12X
2C	12	JNY+12	6C	12	M12X:+1	AC	12	IX−MM12X	EC		
2D	12	JY+12	6D	12	M12X	AD	12	JS12X	ED		
2E	12	JNYZ+12	6E	12	J12X	AE	12	SP:=MM12X	EE	12	IX:=MM12X
2F	12	JYZ+12	6F	12	M12X:=0	AF	12	MM12X:=SP	EF	12	MM12X:=IX
30		IX:=SP+1	70	12 34	M1234:−	B0	12 34	A:−M1234	F0	12 34	B:−M1234
31		SP:+1	71			B1	12 34	A−M1234	F1	12 34	B−M1234
32		A:=S	72			B2	12 34	A:−−M1234	F2	12 34	B:−−M1234
33		B:=S	73	12 34	M1234: #	B3			F3		
34		SP:−1	74	12 34	M1234:− >	B4	12 34	A:&M1234	F4	12 34	B:&M1234
35		SP:=IX−1	75			B5	12 34	A&M1234	F5	12 34	B&M1234
36		S:=A	76	12 34	M1234K:@R	B6	12 34	A:=M1234	F6	12 34	B:=M1234
37		S:=B	77	12 34	M1234:/2	B7	12 34	M1234:=A	F7	12 34	M1234:=B
38			78	12 34	M1234:*2	B8	12 34	A: #M1234	F8	12 34	B: #M1234
39		RET	79	12 34	M1234K:@L	B9	12 34	A:++M1234	F9	12 34	B:++M1234
3A		RI	7A	12 34	M1234:−1	BA	12 34	A:UM1234	FA	12 34	B:UM1234
3B			7B			BB	12 34	A:+M1234	FB	12 34	B:+M1234
3C			7C	12 34	M1234:+1	BC	12 34	IX−MM1234	FC		
3D			7D	12 34	M1234	BD	12 34	JS1234	FD		
3E		WI	7E	12 34	J1234	BE	12 34	SP:=MM1234	FE	12 34	IX:=MM1234
3F		SI	7F	12 34	M1234:=0	BF	12 34	MM1234:=SP	FF	12 34	MM1234:=IX

3.3   INTEL 8080 AND 8085

Microprocessor 8080   Word: 8 bits   Address: 16 bits

Single-length registers: A, B, C, D, E, F, H, L

Double-length registers: BC $\equiv$ B$\|$C, DE $\equiv$ D$\|$E, HL $\equiv$ H$\|$L, AF $\equiv$ A$\|$F, SP, PC

Condition flags: (i) in F: N $\equiv$ F.7 ('negative')

$\qquad\qquad\qquad\qquad$ Z $\equiv$ F.6 ('zero')

$\qquad\qquad\qquad\qquad$ H $\equiv$ F.4 ('half-word carry')

$\qquad\qquad\qquad\qquad$ P $\equiv$ F.2 ('even parity')

$\qquad\qquad\qquad\qquad$ K $\equiv$ F.0 ('carry')

$\qquad\qquad\qquad\qquad$ (*Note*: F.5 $\equiv$ 0, F.3 $\equiv$ 0, F.1 $\equiv$ 1, all constant)

$\qquad\qquad$ (ii) isolated: I ('interruptions enabled')

Stack pointer: SP

Program counter: PC

Accumulators: A, HL

Double-length addressing: MM[x] $\equiv$ M[$x+1$]$\|$M[x]

Action of RESET signal: I: $=0$; PC: $= 0000$

Response to interruption request signal INT:

After completion of current instruction, if I $=1$ then:

$\qquad$ I: $= 0$; SP:-2; MM[SP]: $=$ PC;

and then the one-byte instruction put on to the data bus at the time of INTA is executed. (Use of the 'system controller', 8228, allows *any* instruction to be put on to the data bus.)

Special addresses, additional to those of M0000 to MFFFF:
    00 to FF for input–output ports ('gateways') G00 to GFF.

8080   Instruction set—main table

I 76543210	Hex.	Written instruction	Description of operation	N	Z	H	P	K	PC :+	Refer- ences	Class
00000000	00	NULL		·	·	·	·	·	1		Null
00 r 110	—	$r:=j_1j_0$	$r:=J$	·	·	·	·	·	2	2.3	
00 ρ 0001	–1	$\rho:=k_1k_0j_1j_0$	$\rho:=KJ$	·	·	·	·	·	3	2.3	
01 r_1 r_2	—	$r_1:=r_2$	$r_1:=r_2$	·	·	·	·	·	1	2.3	Single-length
00110010	32	$Mk_1k_0j_1j_0:=A$	$M[KJ]:=A$	·	·	·	·	·	3	2.3	
00111010	3A	$A:=Mk_1k_0j_1j_0$	$A:=M[KJ]$	·	·	·	·	·	3	2.3	
00000010	02	$M[BC]:=A$	$M[BC]:=A$	·	·	·	·	·	1	2.3	
00001010	0A	$A:=M[BC]$	$A:=M[BC]$	·	·	·	·	·	1	2.3	
00010010	12	$M[DE]:=A$	$M[DE]:=A$	·	·	·	·	·	1	2.3	
00011010	1A	$A:=M[DE]$	$A:=M[DE]$	·	·	·	·	·	1	2.3	Assignment
00100010	22	$MMk_1k_0j_1j_0:=HL$	$MM[KJ]:=HL$	·	·	·	·	·	3	2.3	Double-length
00101010	2A	$HL:=MMk_1k_0j_1j_0$	$HL:=MM[KJ]$	·	·	·	·	·	3	2.3	
11111001	F9	$SP:=HL$	$SP:=HL$	·	·	·	·	·	1	2.3, 2.5	
00110111	37	$K:=1$		·	·	·	·	1	1	2.3.7	Flags
11111011	FB	$I:=1$	(see note 5)	·	·	·	·	·	1	2.9	
11110011	F3	$I:=0$	$I:=0$	·	·	·	·	·	1	2.9	
11011011	DB	$A:=Gj_1j_0$	$A:=G[J]$	·	·	·	·	·	2	2.8	I/O
11010011	D3	$Gj_1j_0:=A$	$G[J]:=A$	·	·	·	·	·	2	2.8	
11ρ'0001	–1	$\rho':=ST$	$\rho':=MM[SP]; SP:+2$	*	*	*	*	*	1	2.5	Stack
11ρ'0101	–5	$ST:=\rho'$	$SP:-2; MM[SP]:=\rho'$	·	·	·	·	·	1	2.5	
11101011	EB	$HL:=:DE$	$HL:=:DE$	·	·	·	·	·	1	2.3.4	Interchange
11100011	E3	$HL:=:ST$	$HL:=:MM[SP]$	·	·	·	·	·	1	2.3.4, 2.5	
00 r 100	—	$r:+1$	$r:+1$	r^7	r'	r'	r'	·	1	2.4.9	Increment/
00 r 101	—	$r:-1$	$r:-1$	r^7	r'	r'	r'	·	1	2.4.9	decrement
00 ρ 0011	–3	$\rho:+1$	$\rho:+1$	·	·	·	·	·	1	2.4.9	
00 ρ 1011	–B	$\rho:-1$	$\rho:-1$	·	·	·	·	·	1	2.4.9	
10 op r	—	$Aopr$	$Aopr$	A^7	A'	A'	A'	A'	1	2.4	
11 op 110	—	$Aopj_1j_0$	$AopJ$	A^7	A'	A'	A'	A'	2	2.4	
00101111	2F	$A:\#$	$A:=\neg A$	·	·	·	·	·	1	2.4.6	Arithmetic-logic
00100111	27	DEC	(see note 2)	A^7	A'	A'	A'	A'	1	2.4.9	Single-length
00000111	07	$A:@L$	⎫	·	·	·	·	A_7	1	2.4.8	
00001111	0F	$A:@R$	⎪	·	·	·	·	A_0	1	2.4.8	
00010111	17	$AK:@L$	⎬ (see note 4)	·	·	·	·	A_7	1	2.4.8	
00011111	1F	$AK:@R$	⎭	·	·	·	·	A_0	1	2.4.8	
00 ρ 1001	–9	$HL:+\rho$	$HL:+\rho$	·	·	·	·	①	1	2.4.3.2	D.L.
00111111	3F	$K:\#$		·	·	·	·	$\bar{K}$	1	2.3.7	Flag
11101001	E9	J[HL]	$PC:=HL$	·	·	·	·	·	–	2.6	
11000011	C3	$Jk_1k_0j_1j_0$	$PC:=KJ$	·	·	·	·	·	–	2.6	
11 cnd 010	—	$Jcndk_1k_0j_1j_0$	(see note 6)	·	·	·	·	·	–	2.6	Jump
11001101	CD	$JSk_1k_0j_1j_0$	(see note 7)	·	·	·	·	·	–	2.7	Call
11 cnd 100	—	$JScndk_1k_0j_1j_0$	(see note 8)	·	·	·	·	·	–	2.7	Return
11 s 111	—	JSSs	(see note 9)	·	·	·	·	·	–	2.7	Control transfer
11001001	C9	RET	(see note 10)	·	·	·	·	·	–	2.7	
11 cnd 000	—	$Rcnd$	(see note 11)	·	·	·	·	·	–	2.7	
01110110	76	HALT	(see note 3)	·	·	·	·	·	(1)	2.9	Special

8080 Substitution tables

r r_1 r_2	Written	Descr.
000	B	B
001	C	C
010	D	D
011	E	E
100	H	H
101	L	L
110	M	M[HL]†
111	A	A

ρ	Written	Descr.
00	BC	BC
01	DE	DE
10	HL	HL
11	SP	SP

ρ'	Written	Descr.
00	BC	BC
01	DE	DE
10	HL	HL
11	AF	AF

†undefined if $r_1=r_2=110$ (see HALT)

op	Written	Descr.
000	:+	:+
001	:++	:++
010	:−	:−
011	:−−	:−−
100	:&	:∧
101	:#	:⊻
110	:U	:∨
111	−	−

cnd	Written	Descr.
000	NZ	¬Z
001	Z	Z
010	NK	¬K
011	K	K
100	NP	¬P
101	P	P
110	NN	¬N
111	N	N

s	Written	Descr.
000	0	0
001	1	1
010	2	2
011	3	3
100	4	4
101	5	5
110	6	6
111	7	7

8080 Notes

1   Condition flags: N, Z, H, P, K are affected by each operation as indicated in the table:

·   value unchanged by operation

*   value unaffected except in AF:=ST (hex. F1)

A_7 flag takes value this bit had before the operation

$A_{\prime}$ flag takes resultant value of this bit

For Z: r' means Z:=1 if $r=00$ after the operation; otherwise Z:=0

For H: r' means H:=1 if the operation produced carry from r_3 to r_4;
         H:=0 otherwise

For P: r' means P:=¬($r'_7 \veebar r'_6 \veebar r'_5 \veebar r'_4 \veebar r'_3 \veebar r'_2 \veebar r'_1 \veebar r'_0$)
         (that is, P:=1 if the result r' of the operation has an *even* number of ones)

For K: r' means K:=1 if the operation produced carry from r_7
         ① means K:=1 if the operation produced carry from H_7

After :#, :U we have K=0 and H=0.

After :& we have K=0 and H=1.

No flag is affected by ρ:+1 or by ρ:−1.

K is not affected by r:+1 nor by r:−1.

Only K can be affected by HL:+ρ.

2   Hex. 27 (DEC) is, writing $A=2^4 a_1 + a_0$, equivalent to
     if $a_0 > 9$ ∨ H **then** A:+06;
     if $a_1 > 9$ ∨ K **then** A:+60;   (see Section 2.4.9).

3   Hex. 76 (HALT): execution of the instruction cycle is stopped until a (hardware) signal— RESET or INT—is received.

4   'Rotations': descriptions of these operations are given in Section 2.4.8.

5   I:=1, after the execution of the next instruction.

6   **if** cnd **then** PC:=KJ **else** PC:+3

7   SP:−2; MM[SP]:=PC+3; PC:=KJ

8   **if** cnd **then begin** SP:−2; MM[SP]:=PC+3;
             PC:=KJ **end**
     else PC:+3.

9   SP:−2; MM[SP]:=PC+1; PC:=8×s.

10   SP:+2; PC:=MM[SP−2].

11   **if** cnd **then begin** SP:+2; PC:=MM[SP−2] **end**
     else PC:+1.

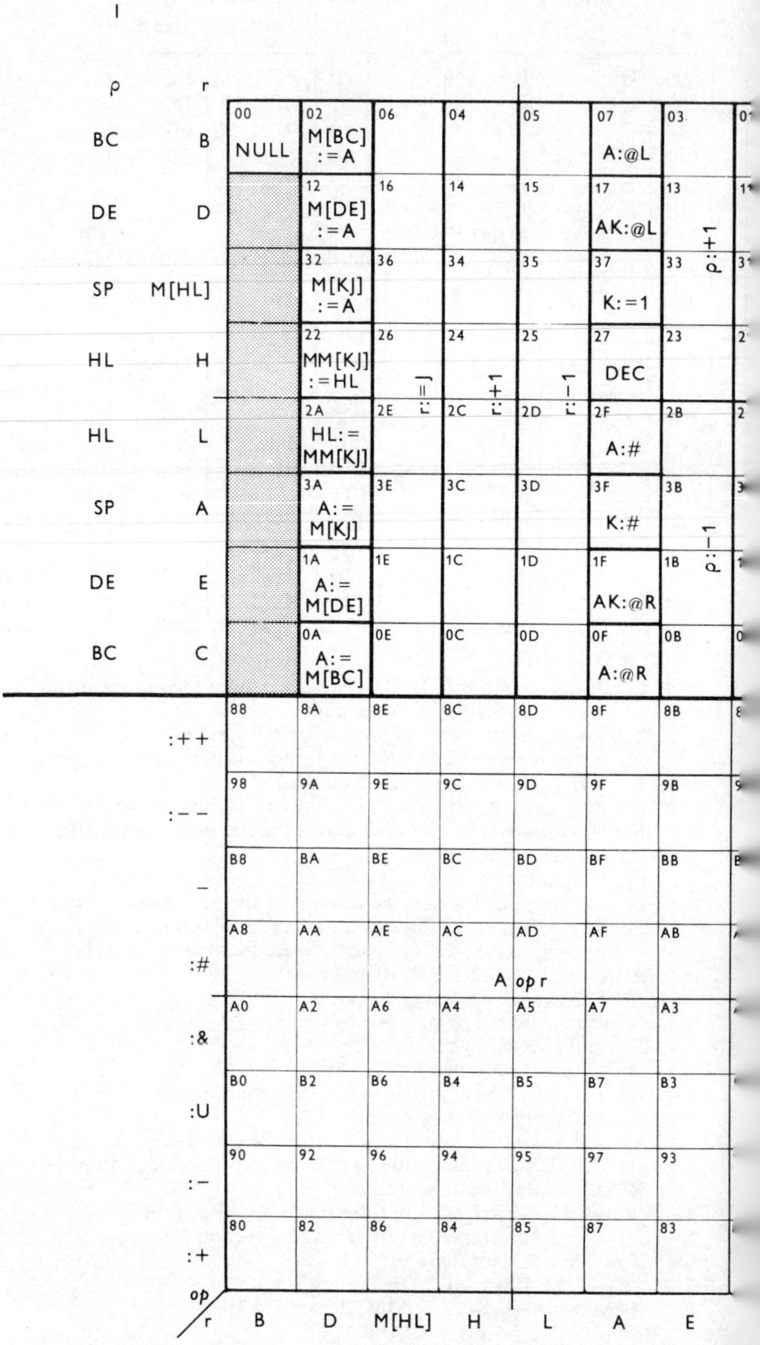

I

ρ	r	00	02	06	04	05	07	03	01
BC	B	NULL	M[BC] :=A	06	04	05	07 A:@L	03	01
DE	D		12 M[DE] :=A	16	14	15	17 AK:@L	13	11
SP	M[HL]		32 M[KJ] :=A	36	34	35	37 K:=1	33	31
HL	H		22 MM[KJ] :=HL	26	24	25	27 DEC	23	2
HL	L		2A HL:= MM[KJ]	2E	2C	2D	2F A:#	2B	2
SP	A		3A A:= M[KJ]	3E	3C	3D	3F K:#	3B	3
DE	E		1A A:= M[DE]	1E	1C	1D	1F AK:@R	1B	1
BC	C		0A A:= M[BC]	0E	0C	0D	0F A:@R	0B	0

Column annotations: `=` `+1` `-1`   ρ:+1   ρ:-1

op	B	D	M[HL]	H	L	A	E
:++	88	8A	8E	8C	8D	8F	8B	8
:--	98	9A	9E	9C	9D	9F	9B	9
-	B8	BA	BE	BC	BD	BF	BB	B
:#	A8	AA	AE	AC	AD	AF	AB	
:&	A0	A2	A6	A4	A5	A7	A3	
:U	B0	B2	B6	B4	B5	B7	B3	
:-	90	92	96	94	95	97	93	
:+	80	82	86	84	85	87	83	

A op r

8080   Karnaugh map

E	A	L	H	M[HL]	D	B	r₂/r₁	
	47	45	44	46	42	40	B	
	57	55	54	56	52	50	D	
	77	75	74	76 HALT	72	70	M[HL]	
	67	65	64	66	62	60	H	
	6F	6D	6C (r₁:=r₂)	6E	6A	68	L	
	7F	7D	7C	7E	7A	78	A	
	5F	5D	5C	5E	5A	58	E	
	4F	4D	4C	4E	4A	48	C	
	CF (1)	CD JS[KJ]	CC	CE	CA	C8	Z	
A:=G[J]	DF (3)		DC	DE	DA	D8	K	
:=1	FF (7)		FC	FE	FA	F8	N	
L:=DE	EF (5)		EC	EE	EA	E8	P	
L:=ST	E7 (4)	E5	E4	E6	E2	E0	NP	HL
:=0	F7 (6)	F5	F4	F6	F2	F0	NN	AF
G[J]:=A	D7 (2)	D5	D4	D6	D2	D0	NK	DE
J[KJ]	C7 (0)	C5	C4	C6	C2	C0	NZ	BC
							cnd	ρ'

JS Ss · ST:=ρ' · JS cnd [KJ] · A op J · J cnd [KJ] · R cnd

(s)

00		NULL	40		B:=B	80		A:+B	C0		RNZ
01	34 12	BC:=1234	41		B:=C	81		A:+C	C1		BC:=ST
02		M[BC]:=A	42		B:=D	82		A:+D	C2	34 12	JNZ1234
03		BC:+1	43		B:=E	83		A:+E	C3	34 12	J1234
04		B:+1	44		B:=H	84		A:+H	C4	34 12	JSNZ1234
05		B:-1	45		B:=L	85		A:+L	C5		ST:=BC
06	12	B:=12	46		B:=M	86		A:+M	C6	12	A:+12
07		A:@L	47		B:=A	87		A:+A	C7		JSS0
08			48		C:=B	88		A:++B	C8		RZ
09		HL:+BC	49		C:=C	89		A:++C	C9		RET
0A		A:=M[BC]	4A		C:=D	8A		A:++D	CA	34 12	JZ1234
0B		BC:-1	4B		C:=E	8B		A:++E	CB		
0C		C:+1	4C		C:=H	8C		A:++H	CC	34 12	JSZ1234
0D		C:-1	4D		C:=L	8D		A:++L	CD	34 12	JS1234
0E	12	C:=12	4E		C:=M	8E		A:++M	CE	12	A:++12
0F		A:@R	4F		C:=A	8F		A:++A	CF		JSS1
10			50		D:=B	90		A:-B	D0		RNK
11	34 12	DE:=1234	51		D:=C	91		A:-C	D1		DE:=ST
12		M[DE]:=A	52		D:=D	92		A:-D	D2	34 12	JNK1234
13		DE:+1	53		D:=E	93		A:-E	D3	12	G12:=A
14		D:+1	54		D:=H	94		A:-H	D4	34 12	JSNK1234
15		D:-1	55		D:=L	95		A:-L	D5		ST:=DE
16	12	D:=12	56		D:=M	96		A:-M	D6	12	A:-12
17		AK:@L	57		D:=A	97		A:-A	D7		JSS2
18			58		E:=B	98		A:--B	D8		RK
19		HL:+DE	59		E:=C	99		A:--C	D9		
1A		A:=M[DE]	5A		E:=D	9A		A:--D	DA	34 12	JK1234
1B		DE:-1	5B		E:=E	9B		A:--E	DB	12	A:=G12
1C		E:+1	5C		E:=H	9C		A:--H	DC	34 12	JSK1234
1D		E:-1	5D		E:=L	9D		A:--L	DD		
1E	12	E:=12	5E		E:=M	9E		A:--M	DE	12	A:--12
1F		AK:@R	5F		E:=A	9F		A:--A	DF		JSS3
20			60		H:=B	A0		A:&B	E0		RNP
21	34 12	HL:=1234	61		H:=C	A1		A:&C	E1		HL:=ST
22	34 12	MM1234:=HL	62		H:=D	A2		A:&D	E2	34 12	JNP1234
23		HL:+1	63		H:=E	A3		A:&E	E3		HL:=:ST
24		H:+1	64		H:=H	A4		A:&H	E4	34 12	JSNP1234
25		H:-1	65		H:=L	A5		A:&L	E5		ST:=HL
26	12	H:=12	66		H:=M	A6		A:&M	E6	12	A:&12
27		DEC	67		H:=A	A7		A:&A	E7		JSS4
28			68		L:=B	A8		A: #B	E8		RP
29		HL:+HL	69		L:=C	A9		A: #C	E9		J[HL]
2A	34 12	HL:=MM1234	6A		L:=D	AA		A: #D	EA	34 12	JP1234
2B		HL:-1	6B		L:=E	AB		A: #E	EB		HL:=:DE
2C		L:+1	6C		L:=H	AC		A: #H	EC	34 12	JSP1234
2D		L:-1	6D		L:=L	AD		A: #L	ED		
2E	12	L:=12	6E		L:=M	AE		A: #M	EE	12	A: #12
2F		A: #	6F		L:=A	AF		A: #A	EF		JSS5
30			70		M:=B	B0		A:UB	F0		RNN
31	34 12	SP:=1234	71		M:=C	B1		A:UC	F1		AF:=ST
32	34 12	M1234:=A	72		M:=D	B2		A:UD	F2	34 12	JNN1234
33		SP:+1	73		M:=E	B3		A:UE	F3		I:=0
34		M:+1	74		M:=H	B4		A:UH	F4	34 12	JSNN1234
35		M:-1	75		M:=L	B5		A:UL	F5		ST:=AF
36	12	M:=12	76		HALT	B6		A:UM	F6	12	A:U12
37		K:=1	77		M:=A	B7		A:UA	F7		JSS6
38			78		A:=B	B8		A-B	F8		RN
39		HL:+SP	79		A:=C	B9		A-C	F9		SP:=HL
3A	34 12	A:=M1234	7A		A:=D	BA		A-D	FA	34 12	JN1234
3B		SP:-1	7B		A:=E	BB		A-E	FB		I:=1
3C		A:+1	7C		A:=H	BC		A-H	FC	34 12	JSN1234
3D		A:-1	7D		A:=L	BD		A-L	FD		
3E	12	A:=12	7E		A:=M	BE		A-M	FE	12	A-12
3F		K: #	7F		A:=A	BF		A-A	FF		JSS7

Microprocessor 8085

The description of the 8080 applies also to the 8085 except as noted below.
Condition flags: there are additionally

> (iii)   3-bit interrupt mask $IM \equiv IM7\|IM6\|IM5$

> (iv)   'serial output data' T, value available at SOD.

RESET signal: the action is

$$I:=0; \; IM:=111; \; T:=0; \; PC:=0000.$$

Response to interruption request signals:

> After completion of current instruction

> **if TRAP then begin** $I:=0$; J S0024 **end**
> **else if I then begin if** $RST7\cdot5 \wedge \overline{IM7}$ **then begin** $I:=0$; JS003C **end**
> **else if** $RST6\cdot5 \wedge \overline{IM6}$ **then begin** $I:=0$; JS0034 **end**
> **else if** $RST5\cdot5 \wedge \overline{IM5}$ **then begin** $I:=0$; JS002C **end**
> **else if** $INTR$ **then begin** $I:=0$; $ST:=PC$;
> $\langle bus \rangle$ **end**
> where JS003C   stands for $SP:-2$; $MM[SP]:=PC$; $PC:=003C$;
> $ST:=PC$ stands for $SP:-2$; $MM[SP]:=PC$;
> and $\langle bus \rangle$ means 'execute the instruction put on to the data bus by the interrupting device'.

Instruction set: as for the 8080 with the following two additions:

00100000	20	$A:=IM$	(note 5)	. . . . .	1
00110000	30	$IM:=A$	(note 6)	. . . . .	1

Substitution tables: as for the 8080.

Notes: As for the 8080 with the following two additions:

5   Effect is:

$$A_0:=IM5; \; A_1:=IM6; \; A_2:=IM7; \; A_3:=I;$$
$$A_4:=RST5\cdot5; \; A_5:=RST6\cdot5; \; A_6:=RST7\cdot5; \; A_7:=SID.$$

6   Effect is:

$$IM5:=IM5 \wedge \bar{A}_3 \vee A_0 \wedge A_3;$$
$$IM6:=IM6 \wedge \bar{A}_3 \vee A_1 \wedge A_3;$$
$$IM7:=(IM7 \wedge \bar{A}_3 \vee A_2 \wedge A_3) \wedge \bar{A}_4;$$
$$T:=T \wedge \bar{A}_6 \vee A_7 \wedge A_6.$$

The two additional instructions 20 ($A:=IM$) and 30 ($IM:=A$) should be inserted in the Karnaugh map and in the instruction list.

Z80 Instruction set—main table

I_0 76543210	I or I_1 76543210	J 76543210	K 76543210	I_0	I or I_1	J	K	Written instruction	Description of operation	N	Z	H	P	S	K	PC :+	References
	0000000				00			NULL		·	·	·	·	·	·	1	2.3
	01 r₁ r₂				–			r:=r2	r:=r₂	·	·	·	·	·	·	1	2.3
	00 r 110	ji jo			–	–	–	r:=jijo	r:=J	·	·	·	·	·	·	2	2.3
	00110010	ji jo	ko		32	–	–	Mk₁kojijo:=A	M[KJ]:=A	·	·	·	·	·	·	3	2.3
	00111010	ji jo	ko		3A	–	–	A:=Mk₁kojijo	A:=M[KJ]	·	·	·	·	·	·	3	2.3
	00000010				02			M[BC]:=A	M[BC]:=A	·	·	·	·	·	·	1	2.3
	00001010				0A			A:=M[BC]	A:=M[BC]	·	·	·	·	·	·	1	2.3
	00010010				12			M[DE]:=A	M[DE]:=A	·	·	·	·	·	·	1	2.3
	00011010				1A			A:=M[DE]	A:=M[DE]	·	·	·	·	·	·	1	2.3
11x11101	00110110	ji jo	ko	–D	36			Mjijox:=k₁ko	M[Ix+J]:=K	·	·	·	·	·	·	4	2.3
11x11101	01 r' 110	ji jo		–D	–			Mjijox:=r'	M[Ix+J]:=r'	·	·	·	·	·	·	4	2.3
11x11101	01110 r'	ji jo		–D	7–			r':=Mjijox	r':=M[Ix+J]	·	·	·	·	·	·	2	2.3
	00 ρ 0001	ji jo	ko		–1			ρ:=k₁kojijo	ρ:=KJ	·	·	·	·	·	·	3	2.3
11x11101	00100001	ji jo	ko	–D	21			Ix:=k₁kojijo	Ix:=KJ	·	·	·	·	·	·	4	2.3
	00100010	ji jo	ko		22			MMk₁kojijo:=HL	MM[KJ]:=HL	·	·	·	·	·	·	3	2.3
	00101010	ji jo	ko		2A			HL:=MMk₁kojijo	HL:=MM[KJ]	·	·	·	·	·	·	3	2.3
1110101	01ρ'''0011	ji jo	ko	ED	–3			MMk₁kojijo:=ρ'''	MM[KJ]:=ρ'''	·	·	·	·	·	·	4	2.3
1110101	01ρ'''1011	ji jo	ko	ED	–B			ρ''':=MMk₁kojijo	ρ''':=MM[KJ]	·	·	·	·	·	·	4	2.3
11x11101	00100010	ji jo	ko	–D	22			MMkijojijo:=Ix	MM[KJ]:=Ix	·	·	·	·	·	·	4	2.3
11x11101	00101010	ji jo	ko	–D	2A			Ix:=MMk₁kojijo	Ix:=MM[KJ]	·	·	·	·	·	·	4	2.3
	11111001				F9			SP:=HL	SP:=HL	·	·	·	·	·	·	1	2.3
11x11101	11111001			–D	F9			SP:=Ix	SP:=Ix	·	·	·	·	·	·	2	2.3
1001011	1b s r			CB	–			r.s:=b	r.s:=b	·	·	·	·	·	·	2	2.10
11x11101	1001011		1b s 110	CB	–			Mjijox.s:=b	M[Ix+J].s:=b	·	·	·	·	·	·	4	2.10
	00110111				37			K:=1	(note 7)	·	·	·	·	·	·	1	2.3.7
	1111b011				F–			I:=b		·	·	·	·	·	·	1	2.9
1001011	01 s r			CB				Z:=#r.s	Z:=¬(r.s)	?	e	1	?	0	·	2	2.10
11x11101	1001011		01 s 110	CB	–			Z:=#Mjijox.s	Z:=¬(M[Ix+J].s)	?	e	1	?	0	·	4	2.10
1110101	11011011			ED	DB			A:=Gijio	A:=G[J]	·	·	·	·	·	·	2	2.8
1110101	11010011			ED	D3			Gijio:=A	G[J]:=A	·	·	·	·	·	·	2	2.8
1110101	01 r' 000			ED	–			r':=G[C]	r':=G[C]	G₇	G	0	0	p	0	2	2.8
1110101	01 r' 001			ED	–			G[C]:=r'	G[C]:=r'	·	·	·	·	·	·	2	2.8
1110101	01000111			ED	47			Q:=A	Q:=A	·	·	·	·	·	·	2	2.9
1110101	01010111			ED	57			A:=Q	A:=Q	Q₇	Q	0	Q	0	I	2	2.9
1110101	01001111			ED	4F			R:=A	R:=A	·	·	·	·	·	·	2	2.10
1110101	01011111			ED	5F			A:=R	A:=R	R₇	R	0	R	0	I	2	2.10
	11 ρ'0001				–1			ρ':=ρ'	ρ':=MM[SP]; SP:+2	*	*	*	*	*	*	1	2.5
	11 ρ'0101				–5			ST:=ρ'	SP:–2; MM[SP]:=ρ'	·	·	·	·	·	*	1	2.5
11x11101	11100001			–D	E1			Ix:=ST	Ix:=MM[SP]; SP:+2;	·	·	·	·	·	*	2	2.5
11x11101	11100101			–D	E5			ST:=Ix	SP:–2; MM[SP]:=Ix	·	·	·	·	·	*	2	2.3, 2.5
	11100011				E3			HL:=:ST	HL:=:MM[SP]	·	·	·	·	·	*	2	2.3, 2.5

Class (Assignment): NULL — Single-length — Double-length — Bit — Flag — Input–output — Special — Stack — Inte[rrupt]

	Arithmetic-logic				Control transfer			
	Single-length	Shift	Double-length Shift	Flag	Jump	Call	Return	Special

Binary	Prefix	Hex	mnemonic	IX:m̄l	2.4.9 / 2.4
10 *op* r		—	A*opr*	A*opr*	2.4
11 *op* 110		—	A*opijo*	A*opJ*	2.4
10 *op* 110	-D	—	A*op*Mjijox	A*op*M[Ix+J]	2.4
00101111		2F	A: #	A:= ¬A	2.4.6
01000100	ED	44	A:-	A:= -A	2.4.4
00100111		27	DEC	(note 2)	2.4.9
00000111		07	A:@L		2.4.8
00001111		0F	A:@R		2.4.8
00010111		17	AK:@L	(note 3)	2.4.8
00011111		1F	AK:@R		2.4.8
00 *shf* r		—	*rshf*		2.4.8
11001011	-D	CB	Mjijox*shf*	(note 3)	2.4.8
01101111	ED	6F	A3M:@4L		2.4.8
01100111	ED	67	A3M:@4R	(note 3)	2.4.8
00 ρ 1001		−9	HL:+ρ	HL:+ρ	2.4.3.2
01 ρ 1010	ED	−A	HL:+ +ρ	HL:+ +ρ	2.4.3.2
01 ρ 0010	ED	−2	HL:- -ρ	HL:- -ρ''	2.4.5.2
00ρ''1001	-D	−9	Ix:+ρ''	Ix:+ρ''	2.4.3.2
00111111		3F	K: #		2.3.7
11000011		C3	JKikojijo	PC:=KJ	2.6
11101001		E9	J[HL]	PC:=HL	2.6
11101001	-D	E9	J[Ix]	PC:=Ix	2.6
00011000		18	J+jijo	PC:=PC+J+2	2.6
11*cnd*010		—	J*cnd*kikojijo	(note 9)	2.6
00100000		20	JNZ+jijo	(note 10)	2.6
00101000		28	JZ+jijo	(note 11)	2.6
00110000		30	JNK+jijo	(note 12)	2.6
00111000		38	JK+jijo	(note 13)	2.6
00010000		10	B:-1,JNZ+jijo	(note 14)	2.6
11001101		CD	JSkikojijo	(note 15)	2.10
11 s 111		—	JSSs	(note 16)	2.7
11*cnd*100		—	JS*cnd*kikojijo	(note 17)	2.7
11001001		C9	RET	(note 18)	2.7
11*cnd*000		—	R*cnd*	(note 19)	2.7
01001101	ED	4D	RI	(notes 4 and 20)	2.9
01000101	ED	45	RNMI	(notes 4 and 20)	2.9
010*im*110	ED	—	IM:=*im*	IM:=*im*	2.9
101qd0gp	ED	—	gpqd	(note 21)	2.10
01110110		76	HALT	(note 5)	2.9

3.4   ZILOG Z80

Microprocessor Z80   Word: 8 bits   Address: 16 bits

Single-length registers: A, B, C, D, E, F, H, L, Q, R
Double-length registers: BC ≡ B‖C, DE ≡ D‖E, HL ≡ H‖L, AF ≡ A‖F,
                            IX, IY, PC, SP, B′C′, D′E′, H′L′, A′F′
Condition flags: (i) in F: N ≡ F.7 ('negative')
                             Z ≡ F.6 ('zero')
                             H ≡ F.4 ('half-word carry')
                             P ≡ V ≡ F.2 ('even parity' or 'overflow', c.q.)
                             S ≡ F.1 ('subtraction')
                             K ≡ F.0 ('carry')
                             (The values of F.5 and F.3 are undefined.)
                        (ii) isolated: I ('interruptions enabled')
                       (iii) isolated, three-valued: IM ('interruption mode')
Stack pointer: SP
Index registers: IX, IY
Program counter: PC
Accumulators: A, HL, IX, IY
Special registers: Q (upper half of indirect address used in interruption mode 2—
                         below)
                      R (7 bits—dynamic RAM refreshing address counter)

Double-length addressing: $MM[x] \equiv M[x+1]\|M[x]$
Special addresses, additional to those of M0000 to MFFFF:

00 to FF for input–output ports ('gateways') G00 to GFF

Action of RESET signal: $I := 0$; $IM := 0$; $Q := 00$; $R := 00$; $PC := 0000$
Response to interruption request signals:

INT: After completion of current instruction, if $I = 1$ then:

$I := 0$; $SP : -2$; $MM[SP] := PC$; then:

if $IM = 0$ the instruction (any instruction) put on to the data bus
by the interrupting device is executed.

if $IM = 1$ $PC := 0038$.

if $IM = 2$ $PC := MM[Q\|p]$ where p is an *even valued* byte put on
to the data bus by the interrupting device.

NMI: After completion of current instruction, regardless of I then:

$SP : -2$; $MM[SP] := PC$; $PC := 0066$.

During this interruption, $I = 0$; I is restored to its previous value on
the return to the interrupted program (RNMI).

Z80   Substitution tables

r r_1 r_2	Written	Descr.
000	B	B
001	C	C
010	D	D
011	E	E
100	H	H
101	L	L
110	M	M[HL]†
111	A	A

r′	Written	Descr.
000	B	B
001	C	C
010	D	D
011	E	E
100	H	H
101	L	L
110		(undef.)
111	A	A

†Undefined if $r_1 = r_2 = 110$ (see HALT).

ρ	Written	Descr.
00	BC	BC
01	DE	DE
10	HL	HL
11	SP	SP

ρ′	Written	Descr.
00	BC	BC
01	DE	DE
10	HL	HL
11	AF	AF

ρ″	Written	Descr.
00	BC	BC
01	DE	DE
10	Ix	Ix
11	SP	SP

ρ‴	Written	Descr.
00	BC	BC
01	DE	DE
10		(undef.)
11	SP	SP

x	Written	Descr.
0	X	X
1	Y	Y

b	Written	Descr.
0	0	0
1	1	1

m	Written	Descr.
0	+	+
1	−	−

im	Written	Descr.
00	0	0
01		(undef.)
10	1	1
11	2	2

s	Written	Descr.†
000	0	0(0000)
001	1	1(0008)
010	2	2(0010)
011	3	3(0018)
100	4	4(0020)
101	5	5(0028)
110	6	6(0030)
111	7	7(0038)

op	Written	Descr.
000	:+	:+
001	:++	:++
010	:−	:−
011	:−−	:−−
100	:&	:∧
101	:#	:⊻
110	:U	:∨
111	−	−

shf	Written	Descr.
000	:@L	⎫
001	:@R	⎪
010	K:@L	⎬ see 2.4.8
011	K:@R	⎪
100	:*2	⎭
101	:/2	
110		(undefined)
111	:−>	see 2.4.8

†The value in parentheses in the table for s is the hexadecimal value of 8 × s, that is the address to which the call is made.

cnd	Written	Descr.
000	NZ	$\neg$Z
001	Z	Z
010	NK	$\neg$K
011	K	K
100	NP	$\neg$P
101	P	P
110	NN	$\neg$N
111	N	N

gp	Written	Descr.
00	C	copy
01	S	search
10	I	input
11	O	output

c	Written	Descr.
0	S	step
1	B	block

d	Written	Descr.
0	U	up
1	D	down

Z80 Notes

1   Condition flags: N, Z, H, P ($\equiv$ V), S, K are affected by each operation as indicated in the table.

    •   value unchanged by operation

    *   value unaffected except in AF:=ST (hex. F1)

    A_7 flag takes value this bit had before the operation

    A_7' flag takes resultant value of this bit

    e   flag takes value of expression to the right of :=

    ?   value of flag after operation undefined

    For N: flag takes value of m.s.b. of result

    For Z: Z:=1 if result is zero; Z:=0 otherwise

      G,Q,R Z:=1 if assigned value is zero; Z:=0 otherwise

    For H: H:=1 if operation produced carry from bit 3 to bit 4;

             H:=0 otherwise

    For P(V) p: P:=1 if result has even number of ones (cf. 8080 note 1);

             P:=0 otherwise

          v: P:=1 if operation produced overflow (Sections 2.4.3–7);

             P:=0 otherwise

    For K: K:=1 if operation produced carry from m.s.b. position;

             K:=0 otherwise

    ①   H:=1 in :& , :# , :U .

    ②   P:=p in :& , :# , :U ; otherwise P:=v .

    ③   S=1 after :− , :− − , − ; otherwise S=0 .

    ④   K=0 after :& , :# , :U .

  See also note 6 below.

  Warning: In a number of instructions the flags H, P are treated differently on the Z80 and 8080. This is indicated by '!' next to the 'Flags' column in the Z80 main table.

2   Hex. 27 (DEC) is, writing $A = 2^4 a_1 + a_0$, equivalent to

        for S=0: **if** $a_0 > 9$ $\lor$ H **then** A:+06;

                  if $a_1 > 9$ $\lor$ K **then** A:+60;

        for S=1: **if** H **then** A:−06;

                  if K **then** A:−60;

  See also 2.4.9.

3   The several 'shift' and 'rotate' operations are described in Section 2.4.8.

  Flags: Note that instructions 07, 0F, 17, 1F differ from the corresponding 8080 instructions in that the Z80 clears H while the 8080 leaves H undisturbed.

    The instructions CB 07, CB 0F, CB 17, CB 1F duplicate the instructions 07, 0F, 17, 1F respectively as far as their principal effects are concerned; but those in the former group affect N, Z, and P whereas those in the latter group do not.

4   Return from interruptions: the execution of either of these instructions is identical with that of RET (C9). However, the Zɪʟᴏɢ Z80PIO and Z80SIO (see 1.4.1) are capable of recognizing their occurrence on the data bus as they are taken into the Z80 microprocessor.

5   Hex. 76 (HALT): execution of the instruction cycle is stopped until a (hardware) signal—RESET, INT or NMI—is received.

6   'Copy' group—ED A0, ED B0, ED A8, ED B8:
           N, Z, K are unaffected. H:=0, S:=0. P=0 after the instruction if BC=0000; P=1
           otherwise.
      'Search' group—ED A1, ED B1, ED A9, ED B9:
           N, Z, H are set according to the result of the (final) subtraction, A−M[HL]. K, however,
           is unaffected. S:=1. P=0 after the instruction if BC=0000; P=1 otherwise.
      'Input' and 'Output' groups—ED A2, ED B2, ED AA, ED BA, ED A3, ED B3, ED AB,
           ED BB: the effect on N, H, P is undefined; K is unaffected; S:=1. Z=1 after the
           instruction if B=00; Z=0 otherwise.
      These instructions are described in 2.10.

7   I:=b (If b=1, the execution is delayed by one instruction cycle).
8   BC:=:B′C′; DE:=:D′E′; HL:=:H′L′.
9   if *cnd* then PC:=KJ else PC:+3.
10   if ¬ Z then PC:=PC+J+2 else PC:+2.
11   if Z then PC:=PC+J+2 else PC:+2.
12   if ¬ K then PC:=PC+J+2 else PC:+2.
13   if K then PC:=PC+J+2 else PC:+2.
14   B:−1; if ¬ Z then PC:=PC+J+2 else PC:+2.
15   SP:−2; MM[SP]:=PC+3; PC:=KJ.
16   SP:−2; MM[SP]:=PC+1; PC:=8×s.
17   if *cnd* then begin SP:−2; MM[SP]:=PC+3; PC:=KJ; end else PC:+3.
18   SP:+2; PC:=MM[SP−2].
19   if *cnd* then begin SP:+2; PC:=MM[SP−2] end else PC:+1.
20   SP:+2; PC:=MM[SP−2].
21   *gp* q d (and see Section 2.10).

ρ	r	00	02	06	04	05	07	03	0(1)
BC	B	NULL	M[BC]:=A	06	04	05	A:@L (07)	03	
DE	D	B:-1, JNZ+[J] (10)	M[DE]:=A (12)	16	14	15	AK:@L (17)	13 :+1	
SP	M[HL]	JNK+[J] (30)	M[KJ]:=A (32)	36	34	35	K:=1 (37)	33 ρ:	
HL	H	JNZ+[J] (20)	MM[KJ]:=HL (22)	26 =	24 :+1	25 :-1	DEC (27)	23	
HL	L	JZ+[J] (28)	HL:=MM[KJ] (2A)	2E =	2C :+1	2D :-1	A:# (2F)	2B	
SP	A	JK+[J] (38)	A:=M[KJ] (3A)	3E	3C	3D	K:# (3F)	3B ρ:-1	
DE	E	J+[J] (18)	A:=M[DE] (1A)	1E	1C	1D	AK:@R (1F)	1B	
BC	C	AF:=:XX (08)	A:=M[BC] (0A)	0E	0C	0D	A:@R (0F)	0B	

op	88	8A	8E	8C	8D	8F	8B
:++	88	8A	8E	8C	8D	8F	8B
:--	98	9A	9E	9C	9D	9F	9B
-	B8	BA	BE	BC	BD	BF	BB
:#	A8	AA	AE	AC	AD	AF	AB
:&	A0	A2	A6	A4	A5	A7	A3
:U	B0	B2	B6	B4	B5	B7	B3
:-	90	92	96	94	95	97	93
:+	80	82	86	84	85	87	83
r	B	D	M[HL]	H	L	A	E

A op r

Z80 Karnaugh map

E	A	L	H	M[HL]	D	B	r₂/r₁	
43	47	45	44	46	42	40	B	
53	57	55	54	56	52	50	D	
73	77	75	74	76 HALT	72	70	M[HL]	
63	67	65	64	66	62	60	H	
6B	6F	6D $r_1:=r_2$	6C	6E	6A	68	L	
7B	7F	7D	7C	7E	7A	78	A	
5B	5F	5D	5C	5E	5A	58	E	
4B	4F	4D	4C	4E	4A	48	C	
CB (I_0)	CF (1)	CD JS[KJ]	CC	CE	CA	C8	Z	
DB A:=G[J]	DF (3)	DD (I_0)	DC	DE	DA	D8	K	
FB I:=1	FF (7)	FD (I_0)	FC	FE	FA	F8	N	
EB HL:=:DE	EF (5)	ED (I_0)	EC	EE	EA	E8	P	
E3 HL:=:ST	E7 (4)	E5	E4	E6	E2	E0	NP	HL
F3 I:=0	F7 (6)	F5	F4	F6	F2	F0	NN	AF
D3 G[J]:=A	D7 (2)	D5	D4	D6	D2	D0	NK	DE
C3 J[KJ]	C7 (0)	C5	C4	C6	C2	C0	NZ	BC
							cnd	ρ'

JSₛ ST:=ρ' JS cnd [KJ] A op J J cnd [KJ] R cnd

(s)

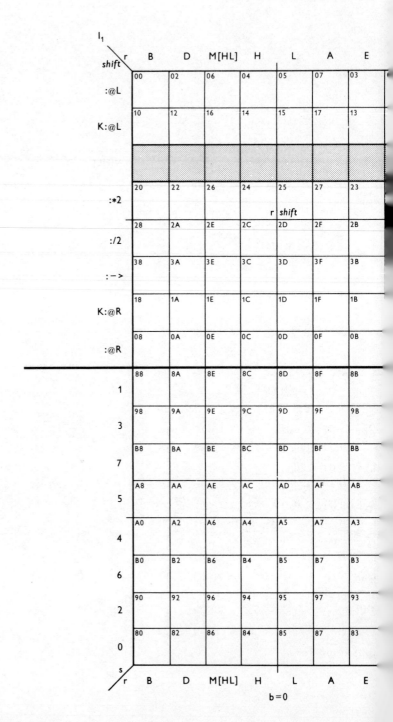

Z80 Karnaugh map for $I_0 = CB$

E	A	L	H	M[HL]	D	B	r/s
43	47	45	44	46	42	40	0
53	57	55	54	56	52	50	2
73	77	75	74	76	72	70	6
63	67	65	64	66	62	60	4
6B	6F	6D	6C	6E	6A	68	5
7B	7F	7D	7C	7E	7A	78	7
5B	5F	5D	5C	5E	5A	58	3
4B	4F	4D	4C	4E	4A	48	1
CB	CF	CD	CC	CE	CA	C8	1
DB	DF	DD	DC	DE	DA	D8	3
FB	FF	FD	FC	FE	FA	F8	7
EB	EF	ED	EC	EE	EA	E8	5
E3	E7	E5	E4	E6	E2	E0	4
F3	F7	F5	F4	F6	F2	F0	6
D3	D7	D5	D4	D6	D2	D0	2
C3	C7	C5	C4	C6	C2	C0	0

$Z := \#\,r.s$

E   A   L   H   M[HL]   D   B   s/r

b = 1

$I_0 = DD, \ x = X$
$I_0 = FD, \ x = Y$
I_1

Z80 Karnaugh map for $I_0 = DD$, $I_0 = FD$

E	A	L	H	D	B	r'/r'
			46			B
			56			D
73 M[J]x:=r'	77	75	74	72	70	
			66			H
			6E			L
			7E r':=M[]x			A
			5E			E
			4E			C
CB (K)						
E3 Ix:=:ST	E5 ST:=Ix					

I_0=DD, x=X; I_1=CB
I_0=FD, x=Y; I_1=CB
K

shift			06			
:@L						
K:@L			16			
:*2			26			
:/2			2E			
:->			3E			
K:@R			1E			
:@R			0E			
1			8E			
3			9E			
7			BE			
5			AE			
4			A6			
6			B6			
2			96			
0			86			
s						

M[J]x shift

M[J]x.s:=0

Z80 Karnaugh map for I_0 = DD, I_0 = FD with I_1 = CB

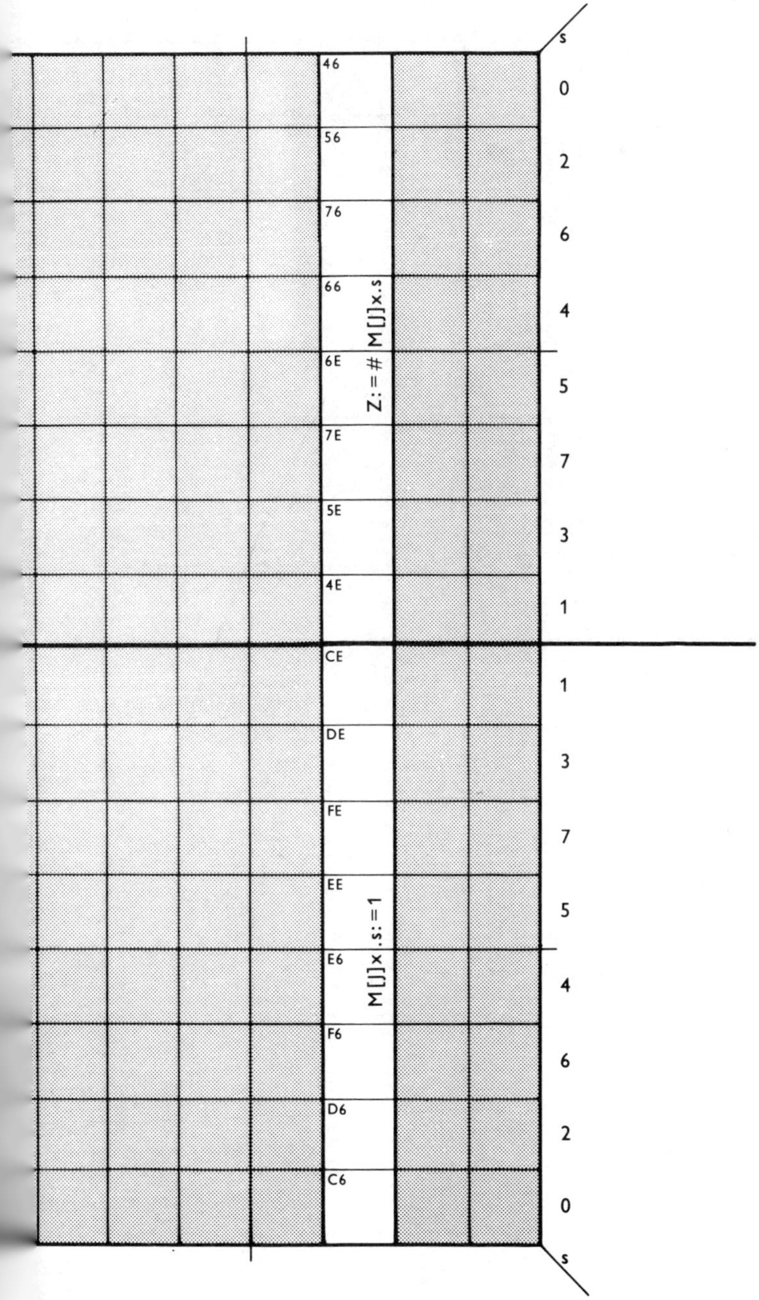
s
46
0
56
2
76
6
66
4
Z: = # M[J]x.s
6E
5
7E
7
5E
3
4E
1
CE
1
DE
3
FE
7
EE
5
M[J]x .s: = 1
E6
4
F6
6
D6
2
C6
0
s

I_1

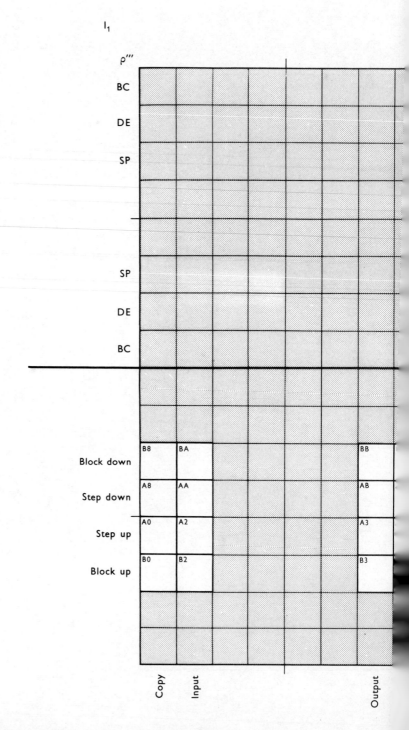

Z80 Karnaugh map for $I_0 = ED$

							r'	ρ
43 ρ'':=ρ''	**47** Q:=A	**45** RNMI	**44** A:-	**46** IM:=0	**42**	**40**	B	BC
53 MM[KJ]:=ρ''	**57** A:=Q			**56** IM:=1	**52** HL:-ρ	**50**	D	DE
73					**72**	**70**		SP
	67 A3M :@4R				**62**	**60** r':=G[C]	H	HL
	6F A3M :@4L				**6A**	**68**	L	HL
7B					**7A** HL:++ρ	**78**	A	SP
5B MM[KJ]	**5F** A:=R			**5E** IM:=2	**5A**	**58**	E	DE
4B ρ'''':=MM[KJ]	**4F** R:=A	**4D** RI			**4A**	**48**	C	BC

Z80   Instructions in numerical order of operation code

The instruction set of the Z80 is that of the 8080 with the following additions:

08		AF: = :XX
10	12	B: −1,JNZ+12
18	12	J+12
20	12	JNZ+12
28	12	JZ+12
30	12	JNK+12
38	12	JK+12
D9		BL: = :XX

CB   00 to CB FF inclusive:

If the second byte (I_1) is expressed in octal (see Section 2.2) and becomes the three octal digits tsr, then:

r represents a register or M[HL]—see substitution table for r—and
if t = 0 the instruction is the shift instruction   r *shf*
where *shf* = s—see substitution table for *shf*.

if t = 1 the instruction is Z: = #r.s
where s is a bit number—see substitution table for s.

if t = 2 the instruction is r.s: = 0
where s is a bit number—see substitution table for s.

if t = 3 the instruction is r.s: = 1
where s is a bit number—see substitution table for s.

(Note that operations are undefined for CB 30 to CB 37 inclusive.)

DD	09			IX:+BC	DD	72	12		M12X: = D
DD	19			IX:+DE	DD	73	12		M12X: = E
DD	21	34	12	IX: = 1234	DD	74	12		M12X: = H
DD	22	34	12	MM1234: = IX	DD	75	12		M12X: = L
DD	23			IX:+1	DD	77	12		M12X: = A
DD	29			IX:+IX	DD	7E	12		A: = M12X
DD	2A	34	12	IX: = MM1234	DD	86	12		A:+M12X
DD	2B			IX:−1	DD	8E	12		A:+ +M12X
DD	34	12		M12X:+1	DD	96	12		A:−M12X
DD	35	12		M12X:−1	DD	9E	12		A:− −M12X
DD	36	12	34	M12X: = 34	DD	A6	12		A:&M12X
DD	39			IX:+SP	DD	AE	12		A:#M12X
DD	46	12		B: = M12X	DD	B6	12		A:UM12X
DD	4E	12		C: = M12X	DD	BE	12		A−M12X
DD	56	12		D: = M12X	(DD	CB	..	..	—see below)
DD	5E	12		E: = M12X	DD	E1			IX: = ST
DD	66	12		H: = M12X	DD	E3			IX: = :ST
DD	6E	12		L: = M12X	DD	E5			ST: = IX
DD	70	12		M12X: = B	DD	E9			J[IX]
DD	71	12		M12X: = C	DD	F9			SP: = IX

DD	CB	12	06	M12X:@L	DD	CB	12	86	M12X.0:=0
DD	CB	12	0E	M12X:@R	DD	CB	12	8E	M12X.1:=0
DD	CB	12	16	M12XK:@L	DD	CB	12	96	M12X.2:=0
DD	CB	12	1E	M12XK:@R	DD	CB	12	9E	M12X.3:=0
DD	CB	12	26	M12X:*2	DD	CB	12	A6	M12X.4:=0
DD	CB	12	2E	M12X:/2	DD	CB	12	AE	M12X.5:=0
DD	CB	12	36		DD	CB	12	B6	M12X.6:=0
DD	CB	12	3E	M12X:->	DD	CB	12	BE	M12X.7:=0
DD	CB	12	46	Z:=#M12X.0	DD	CB	12	C6	M12X.0:=1
DD	CB	12	4E	Z:=#M12X.1	DD	CB	12	CE	M12X.1:=1
DD	CB	12	56	Z:=#M12X.2	DD	CB	12	D6	M12X.2:=1
DD	CB	12	5E	Z:=#M12X.3	DD	CB	12	DE	M12X.3:=1
DD	CB	12	66	Z:=#M12X.4	DD	CB	12	E6	M12X.4:=1
DD	CB	12	6E	Z:=#M12X.5	DD	CB	12	EE	M12X.5:=1
DD	CB	12	76	Z:=#M12X.6	DD	CB	12	F6	M12X.6:=1
DD	CB	12	7E	Z:=#M12X.7	DD	CB	12	FE	M12X.7:=1

ED	40		B:=G[C]	ED	58		E:=G[C]
ED	41		G[C]:=B	ED	59		G[C]:=E
ED	42		HL:=--BC	ED	5A		HL:++DE
ED	43	34 12	MM1234:=BC	ED	5B	34 12	DE:=MM1234
ED	44		A:-	ED	5E		IM:=2
ED	45		RNMI	ED	5F		A:=R
ED	46		IM:=0	ED	60		H:=G[C]
ED	47		Q:=A	ED	61		G[C]:=H
ED	48		C:=G[C]	ED	62		HL:=--HL
ED	49		G[C]:=C	ED	67		A3M:@4R
ED	4A		HL:++BC	ED	68		L:=G[C]
ED	4B	34 12	BC:=MM1234	ED	69		G[C]:=L
ED	4D		RI	ED	6A		HL:++HL
ED	4F		R:=A	ED	6F		A3M:@4L
ED	50		D:=G[C]	ED	72		HL:=--SP
ED	51		G[C]:=D	ED	73	34 12	MM1234:=SP
ED	52		HL:=--DE	ED	78		A:=G[C]
ED	53	34 12	MM1234:=DE	ED	79		G[C]:=A
ED	56		IM:=1	ED	7A		HL:++SP
ED	57		A:=Q	ED	7B	34 12	SP:=MM1234

ED	A0	Copy	Step	Up	ED	B0	Copy	Block	Up
ED	A1	Search	Step	Up	ED	B1	Search	Block	Up
ED	A2	Input	Step	Up	ED	B2	Input	Block	Up
ED	A3	Output	Step	Up	ED	B3	Output	Block	Up
ED	A8	Copy	Step	Down	ED	B8	Copy	Block	Down
ED	A9	Search	Step	Down	ED	B9	Search	Block	Down
ED	AA	Input	Step	Down	ED	BA	Input	Block	Down
ED	AB	Output	Step	Down	ED	BB	Output	Block	Down

FD	...	Substitute FD for DD and Y for X in the list of instructions with $I_0 =$ DD above.

3.5 DICTIONARY OF INSTRUCTIONS

The following is a complete alphabetical listing of all the written forms of instructions of the 6800, 8080, 8085 and Z80 as used in this book. The 'collating sequence', or extended alphabetical order, is defined by the ASCII code in Table 4.1 below.

Machine-code equivalents are given, normally in hexadecimal. As in the previous lists of this chapter, '12' and '1234' are taken as representative one-byte and two-byte values. Here '7' occurs in some instructions as a typical three-*bit* value.

In each such case, one byte of the corresponding machine-code instruction is given in octal and the *middle* octal digit is '7'. These '7s' can be replaced by two copies of any other octal digit, and then the octal byte can be expressed in hexadecimal.

Note that the instruction sets of the 8080 are identical except that the 8085 has two additional instructions, A: = IM and IM: = A.

The *execution times* for each instruction on each machine are given in four separate columns. In all cases the time unit is the *clock period* which will vary from one system to another within the following approximate limits:

6800: 1.0 µs to 10 µs.   8080/8085: 0.32 µs to 2·0 µs.   Z80: 0.25 µs to 2·2 µs.

Where *two* times are given in a particular case, the execution time depends on a *condition*; the longer time refers to the condition being satisfied and the full execution taking place. The execution time for a Z80 'block' instruction, marked by '*' in the listing, is in all cases $21n - 5$ clock periods, where n is the number of executed steps ($n \geq 1$).

The final column gives references to the general discussion of types of instructions in Chapter 2.

Instruction	Machine code			Clock cycles				Reference
	6800	8080/8085	Z80	68 00	80 80	80 85	Z 80	
A	4D			2				↑
A&12	85 12			2				
A&M1234	B5 12 34			4				
A&M12X	A5 12			5				
A&MZ12	95 12			3				
A−12	81 12	FE 12	FE 12	2	7	7	7	
A−A		BF	BF		4	4	4	
A−B	11	B8	B8	2	4	4	4	
A−C		B9	B9		4	4	4	2.4.7
A−D		BA	BA		4	4	4	
A−E		BB	BB		4	4	4	
A−H		BC	BC		4	4	4	
A−L		BD	BD		4	4	4	
A−M		BE	BE		7	7	7	
A−M1234	B1 12 34			4				
A−M12X	A1 12		DD BE 12	5			19	
A−M12Y			FD BE 12				19	
A−MZ12	91 12			3				↓
A.7: = 0			CB 277				8	2.10
A.7: = 1			CB 377				8	2.10
A3M:@4L			ED 6F				18	2.4.8
A3M:@4R			ED 67				18	2.4.8

Instruction	Machine code			Clock cycles				Reference
	6800	8080/8085	Z80	6800	8080	8085	Z80	
A:#	43	2F	2F	2	4	4	4	
A:#12	88 12	EE 12	EE 12	2	7	7	7	
A:#A		AF	AF		4	4	4	
A:#B		A8	A8		4	4	4	
A:#C		A9	A9		4	4	4	
A:#D		AA	AA		4	4	4	
A:#E		AB	AB		4	4	4	
A:#H		AC	AC		4	4	4	
A:#L		AD	AD		4	4	4	
A:#M		AE	AE		7	7	7	
A:#M1234	B8 12 34			4				
A:#M12X	A8 12		DD AE 12	5			19	
A:#M12Y			FD AE 12				19	
A:#MZ12	98 12			3				2.4.6
A:&12	84 12	E6 12	E6 12	2	7	7	7	
A:&A		A7	A7		4	4	4	
A:&B		A0	A0		4	4	4	
A:&C		A1	A1		4	4	4	
A:&D		A2	A2		4	4	4	
A:&E		A3	A3		4	4	4	
A:&H		A4	A4		4	4	4	
A:&L		A5	A5		4	4	4	
A:&M		A6	A6		7	7	7	
A:&M1234	B4 12 34			4				
A:&M12X	A4 12		DD A6 12	5			19	
A:&M12Y			FD A6 12				19	
A:&MZ12	94 12			3				
A:*2	48		CB 27	2			8	2.4.8
A:++12	89 12	CE 12	CE 12	2	7	7	7	
A:++A		8F	8F		4	4	4	
A:++B		88	88		4	4	4	
A:++C		89	89		4	4	4	
A:++D		8A	8A		4	4	4	
A:++E		8B	8B		4	4	4	
A:++H		8C	8C		4	4	4	2.4.3.2
A:++L		8D	8D		4	4	4	
A:++M		8E	8E		7	7	7	
A:++M1234	B9 12 34			4				
A:++M12X	A9 12		DD 8E 12	5			19	
A:++M12Y			FD 8E 12				19	
A:++MZ12	99 12			3				

Instruction	Machine code			Clock cycles				Reference
	6800	8080/8085	Z80	68 00	80 80	80 85	Z 80	
A:+1	4C	3C	3C	2	5	4	4	2.4.9
A:+12	8B 12	C6 12	C6 12	2	7	7	7	↑
A:+A		87	87		4	4	4	
A:+B	1B	80	80	2	4	4	4	
A:+C		81	81		4	4	4	
A:+D		82	82		4	4	4	
A:+E		83	83		4	4	4	
A:+H		84	84		4	4	4	2.4.3.1
A:+L		85	85		4	4	4	
A:+M		86	86		7	7	7	
A:+M1234	BB 12 34			4				
A:+M12X	AB 12		DD 86 12	5			19	
A:+M12Y			FD 86 12				19	
A:+MZ12	9B 12			3				↓
A:−	40		ED 44	2			8	2.4.4
A:−−12	82 12	DE 12	DE 12	2	7	7	7	↑
A:−−A		9F	9F		4	4	4	
A:−−B		98	98		4	4	4	
A:−−C		99	99		4	4	4	
A:−−D		9A	9A		4	4	4	2.4.5.2
A:−−E		9B	9B		4	4	4	
A:−−H		9C	9C		4	4	4	
A:−−L		9D	9D		4	4	4	
A:−−M		9E	9E		7	7	7	↓
A:−−M1234	B2 12 34			4				↑
A:−−M12X	A2 12		DD 9E 12	5			19	2.4.5.2
A:−−M12Y			FD 9E 12				19	
A:−−MZ12	92 12			3				↓
A:−1	4A	3D	3D	2	5	4	4	2.4.9
A:−12	80 12	D6 12	D6 12	2	7	7	7	2.4.5.1
A:−>	44		CB 3F	2			8	2.4.8
A:−A		97	97		4	4	4	↑
A:−B	10	90	90	2	4	4	4	
A:−C		91	91		4	4	4	
A:−D		92	92		4	4	4	
A:−E		93	93		4	4	4	
A:−H		94	94		4	4	4	2.4.5.1
A:−L		95	95		4	4	4	
A:−M		96	96		7	7	7	
A:−M1234	B0 12 34			4				
A:−M12X	A0 12		DD 96 12	5			19	↓

Instruction	Machine code			Clock cycles				Reference
	6800	8080/8085	Z80	68 00	80 80	80 85	Z 80	
A:−M12Y			FD 96 12				19	2.4.5.1
A:−MZ12	90 12			3				2.4.5.1
A:/2	47		CB 2F	2			8	2.4.8
A:=0	4F			2				↑
A:=12	86 12	3E 12	3E 12	2	7	7	7	
A:=A		7F	7F		5	4	4	
A:=B	17	78	78	2	5	4	4	2.3.3
A:=C	07	79	79	2	5	4	4	
A:=D		7A	7A		5	4	4	
A:=E		7B	7B		5	4	4	↓
A:=G12		DB 12	DB 12		10	10	11	2.8
A:=G[C]			ED 78				12	2.8
A:=H		7C	7C		5	4	4	2.3.3
A:=IM	20					4		2.9
A:=L		7D	7D		5	4	4	↑
A:=M		7E	7E		7	7	7	
A:=M1234	B6 12 34	3A 34 12	3A 34 12	4	13	13	13	
A:=M12X	A6 12		DD 7E 12	5			19	2.3.3
A:=M12Y			FD 7E 12				19	
A:=MZ12	96 12			3				
A:=M[BC]		0A	0A		7	7	7	
A:=M[DE]		1A	1A		7	7	7	↓
A:=Q			ED 57				9	2.9
A:=R			ED 5F				9	2.10
A:=S	32			4				2.5
A:@L		07	07		4	4	4	2.4.8
A:@R		0F	0F		4	4	4	2.4.8
A:U12	8A 12	F6 12	F6 12	2	7	7	7	↑
A:UA		B7	B7		4	4	4	
A:UB		B0	B0		4	4	4	
A:UC		B1	B1		4	4	4	
A:UD		B2	B2		4	4	4	
A:UE		B3	B3		4	4	4	
A:UH		B4	B4		4	4	4	2.4.6
A:UL		B5	B5		4	4	4	
A:UM		B6	B6		7	7	7	
A:UM1234	BA 12 34			4				
A:UM12X	AA 12		DD B6 12	5			19	
A:UM12Y			FD B6 12				19	
A:UMZ12	9A 12			3				↓
AF:=:XX			08				4	2.10

Instruction	Machine code			Clock cycles				Reference
	6800	8080/8085	Z80	68 00	80 80	80 85	Z 80	
AF: = ST		F1	F1		10	10	10	2.5
AK:@L	49	17	17	2	4	4	4	2.4.8
AK:@R	46	1F	1F	2	4	4	4	2.4.8
B	5D			2				↑
B&12	C5 12			2				
B&M1234	F5 12 34			4				
B&M12X	E5 12			5				
B&MZ12	D5 12			3				2.4.7
B−12	C1 12			2				
B−M1234	F1 12 34			4				
B−M12X	E1 12			5				
B−MZ12	D1 12			3				↓
B.7: = 0			CB 270				8	2.10
B.7: = 1			CB 370				8	2.10
B:#	53			2				2.4.4
B:#12	C8 12			2				↑
B:#M1234	F8 12 34			4				
B:#M12X	E8 12			5				
B:#MZ12	D8 12			3				2.4.6
B:&12	C4 12			2				
B:&M1234	F4 12 34			4				
B:&M12X	E4 12			5				
B:&MZ12	D4 12			3				↓
B:*2	58		CB 20	2			8	2.4.8
B:++12	C9 12			2				↑
B:++M1234	F9 12 34			4				2.4.3.2
B:++M12X	E9 12			5				
B:++MZ12	D9 12			3				↓
B:+1	5C	04	04	2	5	4	4	2.4.9
B:+12	CB 12			2				2.4.3.1
B:+M1234	FB 12 34			4				↑
B:+M12X	EB 12			5				2.4.3.1
B:+MZ12	DB 12			3				↓
B:−	50			2				2.4.4
B:−−12	C2 12			2				↑
B:−−M1234	F2 12 34			4				2.4.5.2
B:−−M12X	E2 12			5				
B:−−MZ12	D2 12			3				↓
B:−1	5A	05	05	2	5	4	4	2.4.9
B:−1,JNZ+12			10 12				$^{8}/_{13}$	2.10
B:−12	C0 12			2				2.4.5.1

Instruction	Machine code			Clock cycles				Reference
	6800	8080/8085	Z80	68 00	80 80	80 85	Z 80	
B:−M1234	F0 12 34			4				↑
B:−M12X	E0 12			5				2.4.5.1
B:−MZ12	D0 12			3				↓
B:−>	54		CB 38	2			8	2.4.8
B:/2	57		CB 28	2			8	2.4.8
B:=0	5F			2				↑
B:=12	C6 12	06 12	06 12	2	7	7	7	
B:=A	16	47	47	2	5	4	4	
B:=B		40	40		5	4	4	2.3
B:=C		41	41		5	4	4	
B:=D		42	42		5	4	4	
B:=E		43	43		5	4	4	
B:=G[C]			ED 40				12	2.8
B:=H		44	44		5	4	4	↑
B:=L		45	45		5	4	4	
B:=M		46	46		7	7	7	2.3
B:=M1234	F6 12 34			4				
B:=M12X	E6 12		DD 46 12	5			19	↓
B:=M12Y			FD 46 12				19	2.3
B:=MZ12	D6 12			3				2.3
B:=S	33			4				2.5
B:@L			CB 00				8	2.4.8
B:@R			CB 08				8	2.4.8
B:U12	CA 12			2				↑
B:UM1234	FA 12 34			4				2.4.6
B:UM12X	EA 12			5				
B:UMZ12	DA 12			3				↓
BC:+1		03	03		5	6	6	2.4.9
BC:−1		0B	0B		5	6	6	2.4.9
BC:=1234		01 34 12	01 34 12		10	10	10	2.3
BC:=MM1234			ED 4B 34 12				20	2.3
BC:=ST		C1	C1		10	10	10	2.5
BK:@L	59		CB 10	2			8	2.4.8
BK:@R	56		CB 18	2			8	2.4.8
BL:=:XX			D9				4	2.10
C.7:=0			CB 271				8	2.10
C.7:=1			CB 371				8	2.10
C:*2			CB 21				8	2.4.8
C:+1		0C	0C		5	4	4	2.4.9
C:−1		0D	0D		5	4	4	2.4.9
C:−>			CB 39				8	2.4.8

Instruction	Machine code			Clock cycles				Reference
	6800	8080/8085	Z80	6800	8080	8085	Z80	
C:/2			CB 29				8	2.4.8
C: = 12		0E 12	0E 12		7	7	7	↑
C: = A	06	4F	4F	2	5	4	4	
C: = B		48	48		5	4	4	2.3
C: = C		49	49		5	4	4	
C: = D		4A	4A		5	4	4	
C: = E		4B	4B		5	4	4	2.3
C: = G[C]			ED 48				12	2.8
C: = H		4C	4C		5	4	4	↑
C: = L		4D	4D		5	4	4	
C: = M		4E	4E		7	7	7	2.3
C: = M12X			DD 4E 12				19	
C: = M12Y			FD 4E 12				19	↓
C:@L			CB 01				8	2.4.8
C:@R			CB 09				8	2.4.8
CBD			ED B8				*	2.10
CBU			ED B0				*	2.10
CK:@L			CB 11				8	2.4.8
CK:@R			CB 19				8	2.4.8
CSD			ED A8				16	2.10
CSU			ED A0				16	2.10
D.7: = 0			CB 272				8	2.10
D.7: = 1			CB 372				8	2.10
D:*2			CB 22				8	2.4.8
D: + 1		14	14		5	4	4	2.4.9
D: − 1		15	15		5	4	4	2.4.9
D: − >			CB 3A				8	2.4.8
D:/2			CB 2A				8	2.4.8
D: = 12		16 12	16 12		7	7	7	↑
D: = A		57	57		5	4	4	
D: = B		50	50		5	4	4	2.3
D: = C		51	51		5	4	4	
D: = D		52	52		5	4	4	
D: = E		53	53		5	4	4	↓
D: = G[C]			ED 50				12	2.8
D: = H		54	54		5	4	4	↑
D: = L		55	55		5	4	4	
D: = M		56	56		7	7	7	2.3
D: = M12X			DD 56 12				19	
D: = M12Y			FD 56 12				19	↓
D:@L			CB 02				8	2.4.8

Instruction	Machine code			Clock cycles				Reference
	6800	8080/8085	Z80	68 00	80 80	80 85	Z 80	
D:@R			CB 0A	·			8	2.4.8
DE:+1		13	13		5	6	6	2.4.9
DE:−1		1B	1B		5	6	6	2.4.9
DE:=1234		11 34 12	11 34 12		10	10	10	2.3
DE:=MM1234			ED 5B 34 12				20	2.3
DE:=ST		D1	D1		10	10	10	2.5
DEC	19	27	27	2	4	4	4	2.4.9
DK:@L			CB 12				8	2.4.8
DK:@R			CB 1A				8	2.4.8
E.7:=0			CB 273				8	2.10
E.7:=1			CB 373				8	2.10
E:*2			CB 23				8	2.4.8
E:+1		1C	1C		5	4	4	2.4.9
E:−1		1D	1D		5	4	4	2.4.9
E:−>			CB 3B				8	2.4.8
E:/2			CB 2B				8	2.4.8
E:=12		1E 12	1E 12		7	7	7	↑
E:=A		5F	5F		5	4	4	│
E:=B		58	58		5	4	4	2.3
E:=C		59	59		5	4	4	│
E:=D		5A	5A		5	4	4	│
E:=E		5B	5B		5	4	4	↓
E:=G[C]			ED 58				12	2.8
E:=H		5C	5C		5	4	4	↑
E:=L		5D	5D		5	4	4	│
E:=M		5E	5E		7	7	7	2.3
E:=M12X			DD 5E 12				19	│
E:=M12Y			FD 5E 12				19	↓
E:@L			CB 03				8	↑
E:@R			CB 0B				8	2.4.8
EK:@L			CB 13				8	│
EK:@R			CB 1B				8	↓
G12:=A		D3 12	D3 12		10	10	11	↑
G[C]:=A			ED 79				12	│
G[C]:=B			ED 41				12	│
G[C]:=C			ED 49				12	2.8
G[C]:=D			ED 51				12	│
G[C]:=E			ED 59				12	│
G[C]:=H			ED 61				12	│
G[C]:=L			ED 69				12	↓
H.7:=0			CB 274				8	2.10

Instruction	Machine code			Clock cycles				Reference
	6800	8080/8085	Z80	68 00	80 80	80 85	Z 80	
H.7: = 1	·		CB 374				8	2.10
H:*2			CB 24				8	2.4.8
H:+1		24	24		5	4	4	2.4.9
H:−1		25	25		5	4	4	2.4.9
H:−>			CB 3C				8	2.4.8
H:/2			CB 2C				8	2.4.8
H: = 12		26 12	26 12		7	7	7	↑
H: = A		67	67		5	4	4	│
H: = B		60	60		5	4	4	2.3
H: = C		61	61		5	4	4	│
H: = D		62	62		5	4	4	│
H: = E		63	63		5	4	4	2.3
H: = G[C]			ED 60				12	2.8
H: = H		64	64		5	4	4	↑
H: = L		65	65		5	4	4	│
H: = M		66	66		7	7	7	2.3
H: = M12X			DD 66 12				19	│
H: = M12Y			FD 66 12				19	↓
H:@L			CB 04				8	2.4.8
H:@R			CB 0C				8	2.4.8
HALT		76	76		7	5	4	2.9
HK:@L			CB 14				8	2.4.8
HK:@R			CB 1C				8	2.4.8
HL:+ +BC			ED 4A				15	↑
HL:+ +DE			ED 5A				15	2.4.3.2
HL:+ +HL			ED 6A				15	│
HL:+ +SP			ED 7A				15	↓
HL:+1		23	23		5	6	6	2.4.9
HL:+BC		09	09		10	10	11	↑
HL:+DE		19	19		10	10	11	2.4.3.2
HL:+HL		29	29		10	10	11	│
HL:+SP		39	39		10	10	11	↓
HL:− −BC			ED 42				15	↑
HL:− −DE			ED 52				15	2.4.5.2
HL:− −HL			ED 62				15	│
HL:− −SP			ED 72				15	↓
HL:−1		2B	2B		5	6	6	2.4.9
HL: = :DE		EB	EB		4	4	4	2.3.4
HL: = :ST		E3	E3		18	16	19	2.3.4,2.5
HL: = 1234		21 34 12	21 34 12		10	10	10	2.3
HL: = MM1234		2A 34 12	2A 34 12		16	16	16	2.3

Instruction	Machine code			Clock cycles				Reference
	6800	8080/8085	Z80	6800	8080	8085	Z80	
HL: = ST		E1	E1		10	10	10	2.5
I: = 0	0E	F3	F3	2	4	4	4	2.9
I: = 1	0F	FB	FB	2	4	4	4	2.9
IBD			ED BA				*	2.10
IBU			ED B2				*	2.10
IM: = 0			ED 46				8	↑
IM: = 1			ED 56				8	2.9
IM: = 2			ED 5E				8	|
IM: = A		30				4		↓
ISD			ED AA				16	2.10
ISU			ED A2				16	2.10
IX − 1234	8C 12 34			3				↑
IX − MM1234	BC 12 34			5				2.4.7
IX − MM12X	AC 12			6				|
IX − MMZ12	9C 12			4				↓
IX: + 1	08		DD 23	4			10	2.4.9
IX: + BC			DD 09				15	↑
IX: + DE			DD 19				15	2.4.3.2
IX: + IX			DD 29				15	|
IX: + SP			DD 39				15	↓
IX: − 1	09		DD 2B	4			10	2.4.9
IX: = :ST			DD E3				23	2.3.4, 2.5
IX: = 1234	CE 12 34		DD 21 34 12	3			14	↑
IX: = MM1234	FE 12 34		DD 2A 34 12	5			20	2.3
IX: = MM12X	EE 12			6				|
IX: = MMZ12	DE 12			4				↓
IX: = SP + 1	30			4				2.3, 2.5
IX: = ST			DD E1				14	2.5
IY: + 1			FD 23				10	2.4.9
IY: + BC			FD 09				15	↑
IY: + DE			FD 19				15	2.4.3.2
IY: + IY			FD 29				15	|
IY: + SP			FD 39				15	↓
IY: − 1			FD 2B				10	2.4.9
IY: = :ST			FD E3				23	2.3.4, 2.5
IY: = 1234			FD 21 34 12				14	2.3
IY: = MM1234			FD 2A 34 12				20	2.3
IY: = ST			FD E1				14	2.5
J + 12	20 12		18 12	4			12	↑
J1234	7E 12 34	C3 34 12	C3 34 12	3	10	10	10	2.6
J12X	6E 12			4				↓

Instruction	Machine code			Clock cycles				Reference
	6800	8080/8085	Z80	68 00	80 80	80 85	Z 80	
JK+12	25 12		38 12	4			$7/12$	
JK1234		DA 34 12	DA 34 12		10	$7/10$	10	
JKZ+12	23 12			4				
JN+12	2B 12			4				
JN1234		FA 34 12	FA 34 12		10	$7/10$	10	
JNK+12	24 12		30 12	4			$7/12$	
JNK1234		D2 34 12	D2 34 12		10	$7/10$	10	
JNKZ+12	22 12			4				
JNN+12	2A 12			4				2.6
JNN1234		F2 34 12	F2 34 12		10	$7/10$	10	
JNP1234		E2 34 12	E2 34 12		10	$7/10$	10	
JNV+12	28 12			4				
JNY+12	2C 12			4				
JNYZ+12	2E 12			4				
JNZ+12	26 12		20 12	4			$7/12$	
JNZ1234		C2 34 12	C2 34 12		10	$7/10$	10	
JP1234		EA 34 12	EA 34 12		10	$7/10$	10	
JS+12	8D 12			8				
JS1234	BD 12 34	CD 34 12	CD 34 12	9	17	18	17	
JS12X	AD 12			8				
JSK1234		DC 34 12	DC 34 12		$11/17$	$9/18$	$10/17$	
JSN1234		FC 34 12	FC 34 12		$11/17$	$9/18$	$10/17$	
JSNK1234		D4 34 12	D4 34 12		$11/17$	$9/18$	$10/17$	
JSNN1234		F4 34 12	F4 34 12		$11/17$	$9/18$	$10/17$	2.7
JSNP1234		E4 34 12	E4 34 12		$11/17$	$9/18$	$10/17$	
JSNZ1234		C4 34 12	C4 34 12		$11/17$	$9/18$	$10/17$	
JSP1234		EC 34 12	EC 34 12		$11/17$	$9/18$	$10/17$	
JSS7		377	377		11	12	11	
JSZ1234		CC 34 12	CC 34 12		$11/17$	$9/18$	$10/17$	
JV+12	29 12			4				
JY+12	2D 12			4				
JYZ+12	2F 12			4				
JZ+12	27 12		28 12	4			$7/12$	2.6
JZ1234		CA 34 12	CA 34 12		10	$7/10$	10	
J[HL]		E9	E9		5	6	4	
J[IX]			DD E9				8	
J[IY]			FD E9				8	
K:#		3F	3F		4	4	4	
K:=0	0C			2				2.3.7
K:=1	0D	37	37	2	4	4	4	
L.7:=0			CB 275				8	2.10

Instruction	Machine code			Clock cycles				Reference
	6800	8080/8085	Z80	68 00	80 80	80 85	Z 80	
L.7: = 1			CB 375				8	2.10
L:*2			CB 25				8	2.4.8
L:+1		2C	2C		5	4	4	2.4.9
L:−1		2D	2D		5	4	4	2.4.9
L:− >			CB 3D				8	2.4.8
L:/2			CB 2D				8	2.4.8
L: = 12		2E 12	2E 12		7	7	7	↑
L: = A		6F	6F		5	4	4	│
L: = B		68	68		5	4	4	2.3
L: = C		69	69		5	4	4	│
L: = D		6A	6A		5	4	4	│
L: = E		6B	6B		5	4	4	↓
L: = G[C]			ED 68				12	2.8
L: = H		6C	6C		5	4	4	↑
L: = L		6D	6D		5	4	4	│
L: = M		6E	6E		7	7	7	2.3
L: = M12X			DD 6E 12				19	│
L: = M12Y			FD 6E 12				19	↓
L:@L			CB 05				8	↑
L:@R			CB 0D				8	2.4.8
LK:@L			CB 15				8	│
LK:@R			CB 1D				8	↓
M1234	7D 12 34			6				2.4.7
M1234:#	73 12 34			6				2.4.4
M1234:*2	78 12 34			6				2.4.8
M1234:+1	7C 12 34			6				2.4.9
M1234:−	70 12 34			6				2.4.4
M1234:−1	7A 12 34			6				2.4.9
M1234:− >	74 12 34			6				2.4.8
M1234:/2	77 12 34			6				2.4.8
M1234: = 0	7F 12 34			6				↑
M1234: = A	B7 12 34	32 34 12	32 34 12	5	10	10	13	2.3
M1234: = B	F7 12 34			5				↓
M1234K:@L	79 12 34			6				2.4.8
M1234K:@R	76 12 34			6				2.4.8
M12X	6D 12			7				2.4.7
M12X.7: = 0			DD CB 12 276				23	2.10
M12X.7: = 1			DD CB 12 376				23	2.10
M12X:#	63 12			7				2.4.4
M12X:*2	68 12		DD CB 12 26	7			23	2.4.8
M12X:+1	6C 12		DD 34 12	7			23	2.4.9

Instruction	Machine code			Clock cycles				Reference
	6800	8080/8085	Z80	6800	8080	8085	Z80	
M12X:−	60 12			7				2.4.4
M12X:−1	6A 12		DD 35 12	7			23	2.4.9
M12X:−>	64 12		DD CB 12 3E	7			23	2.4.8
M12X:/2	67 12		DD CB 12 2E	7			23	2.4.8
M12X:=0	6F 12			7				↑
M12X:=34			DD 36 12 34				19	
M12X:=A	A7 12		DD 77 12	6			19	
M12X:=B	E7 12		DD 70 12	6			19	
M12X:=C			DD 71 12				19	2.3
M12X:=D			DD 72 12				19	
M12X:=E			DD 73 12				19	
M12X:=H			DD 74 12				19	
M12X:=L			DD 75 12				19	↓
M12X:@L			DD CB 12 06				23	↑
M12X:@R			DD CB 12 0E				23	2.4.8
M12XK:@L	69 12		DD CB 12 16	7			23	
M12XK:@R	66 12		DD CB 12 1E	7			23	↓
M12Y.7:=0			FD CB 12 276				23	2.10
M12Y.7:=1			FD CB 12 376				23	2.10
M12Y:*2			FD CB 12 26				23	2.4.8
M12Y:+1			FD 34 12				23	2.4.9
M12Y:−1			FD 35 12				23	2.4.9
M12Y:−>			FD CB 12 3E				23	2.4.8
M12Y:/2			FD CB 12 2E				23	2.4.8
M12Y:=34			FD 36 12 34				19	↑
M12Y:=A			FD 77 12				19	
M12Y:=B			FD 70 12				19	
M12Y:=C			FD 71 12				19	2.3
M12Y:=D			FD 72 12				19	
M12Y:=E			FD 73 12				19	
M12Y:=H			FD 74 12				19	
M12Y:=L			FD 75 12				19	↓
M12Y:@L			FD CB 12 06				23	↑
M12Y:@R			FD CB 12 0E				23	2.4.8
M12YK:@L			FD CB 12 16				23	
M12YK:@R			FD CB 12 1E				23	↓
M.7:=0			CB 276				15	2.10
M.7:=1			CB 376				15	2.10
M:*2			CB 26				15	2.10
M:+1		34	34		10	10	11	2.4.9
M:−1		35	35		10	10	11	2.4.9

Instruction	Machine code			Clock cycles				Reference
	6800	8080/8085	Z80	6800	8080	8085	Z80	
M:−>			CB 3E				15	2.4.8
M:/2			CB 2E				15	2.4.8
M:=12		36 12	36 12		7	7	10	↑
M:=A		77	77		7	7	7	
M:=B		70	70		7	7	7	
M:=C		71	71		7	7	7	2.3
M:=D		72	72		7	7	7	
M:=E		73	73		7	7	7	
M:=H		74	74		7	7	7	
M:=L		75	75		7	7	7	↓
M:@L			CB 06				15	↑
M:@R			CB 0E				15	2.4.8
MK:@L			CB 16				15	
MK:@R			CB 1E				15	↓
MM1234:=BC			ED 43 34 12				20	
MM1234:=DE			ED 53 34 12				20	
MM1234:=HL		22 34 12	22 34 12		16	16	16	
MM1234:=IX	FF 12 34		DD 22 34 12	6			20	
MM1234:=IY			FD 22 34 12				20	
MM1234:=SP	BF 12 34		ED 73 34 12	6			20	
MM12X:=IX	EF 12			7				
MM12X:=SP	AF 12			7				
MMZ12:=IX	DF 12			5				2.3
MMZ12:=SP	9F 12			5				
MZ12:=A	97 12			4				
MZ12:=B	D7 12			4				
M[BC]:=A		02	02		7	7	7	
M[DE]:=A		12	12		7	7	7	↓
NULL	01	00	00	2	4	4	4	
OBD			ED BB				*	↑
OBU			ED B3				*	2.10
OSD			ED AB				16	
OSU			ED A3				16	↓
Q:=A			ED 47				9	2.9
R:=A			ED 4F				9	2.10
RET	39	C9	C9	5	10	10	10	2.7
RI	3B		ED 4D	10			14	2.9
RK		D8	D8		5/11	6/12	5/11	2.7
RN		F8	F8		3/11	6/12	5/11	2.7
RNK		D0	D0		5/11	6/12	5/11	2.7
RNMI			ED 45				14	2.9

Instruction	Machine code			Clock cycles				Reference
	6800	8080/8085	Z80	68 00	80 80	80 85	Z 80	
RNN		F0	F0		$^5/_{11}$	$^6/_{12}$	$^5/_{11}$	↑
RNP		E0	E0		$^5/_{11}$	$^6/_{12}$	$^5/_{11}$	
RNZ		C0	C0		$^5/_{11}$	$^6/_{12}$	$^5/_{11}$	2.7
RP		E8	E8		$^5/_{11}$	$^6/_{12}$	$^5/_{11}$	
RZ		C8	C8		$^5/_{11}$	$^6/_{12}$	$^5/_{11}$	↓
S: = A	36			4				2.5
S: = B	37			4				2.5
SBD			ED B9				*	2.10
SBU			ED B1				*	2.10
SI	3F			12				2.7
SP: + 1	31	33	33	4	5	6	6	2.4.9
SP: − 1	34	3B	3B	4	5	6	6	2.4.9
SP: = 1234	8E 12 34	31 34 12	31 34 12	3	10	10	10	↑
SP: = HL		F9	F9		5	6	6	
SP: = IX			DD F9				10	
SP: = IX − 1	35			4				2.3, 2.5
SP: = IY			FD F9				10	
SP: = MM1234	BE 12 34		ED 7B 34 12	5			20	
SP: = MM12X	AE 12			6				
SP: = MMZ12	9E 12			4				↓
SSD			ED A9				16	2.10
SSU			ED A1				16	2.10
ST: = AF		F5	F5		11	12	11	↑
ST: = BC		C5	C5		11	12	11	
ST: = DE		D5	D5		11	12	11	2.5
ST: = HL		E5	E5		11	12	11	
ST: = IX			DD E5				15	↓
ST: = IY			FD E5				15	2.5
V: = 0	0A			2				2.3.7
V: = 1	0B			2				2.3.7
WI	3E			9				2.9
Z: = #A.7			CB 177				8	↑
Z: = #B.7			CB 170				8	
Z: = #C.7			CB 171				8	
Z: = #D.7			CB 172				8	
Z: = #E.7			CB 173				8	2.10
Z: = #H.7			CB 174				8	
Z: = #L.7			CB 175				8	
Z: = #M.7			CB 176				12	
Z: = #M12X.7			DD CB 12 176				20	
Z: = #M12Y.7			FD CB 12 176				20	↓

4

Programming: arithmetical operations

4.1 MINIMUM USABLE SYSTEM AND SOFTWARE

Programming is practical work which does not end until the program can be seen to be functioning correctly with actual data on an actual machine. The testing and correcting ('debugging') of programs is an integral part of the programmer's task. It is essential that the reader should have access to a suitable microprocessor system.

A system to be used by a beginner should have, if possible, a reasonable console device, preferably with an ASCII (4.2 below) keyboard and display (printer or VDU), although some beginners have done remarkably well with a 16-key calculator keyboard and a couple of 7-segment digital display devices. A RAM of 256 bytes is a minimum useful working store; a (small) PROM with a rudimentary monitor will save a great deal of trouble and is almost a necessity.

It is not a good idea to start work on a large system with expensive software. The microprocessor user will inevitably need to get much nearer to the hardware than users of large machines do, and it is as well to become familiar with the machine and the machine code at the beginning. This approach will enable the new user to appreciate, and to criticize, the software which may become available at a later stage, and which, if it is good, will enable him to work more efficiently, but which, if it is bad, can involve him in needless difficulty and expense.

For the first few programming exercises we assume only the following.

(i) RAM is available at addresses 1000 to 10FF (256 bytes).
(ii) The PROM (or perhaps a ROM) contains a simple *monitor program* which will be entered (that is, the execution of which will begin) on application of the system's RESET signal. This program should have at least:

(a) the ability to read a sequence of bytes (entered as pairs of hexadecimal digits) and store them in consecutive locations of the RAM;
(b) the ability to read and jump to any *address* (4 hex. digits), so that, for example, the execution of a program in RAM can be initiated;
(c) the ability to display the contents of the processor's registers;

(d)   the ability to display the contents of a store location, and to change those contents (if the location is in RAM).

(iii)   The PROM holds two basic subroutines (provided for the monitor, but available to other programs):

(a)   'input one character'—for reading a character from the keyboard and leaving its 'ASCII value' (Section 4.2 below) in register A;

(b)   'output one character'—for displaying a character whose ASCII value has been given in register A (see Section 2.8).

(iv)   The console device can read and display ASCII-coded characters.

If the available system differs from the outline specification in matters of detail, the examples below may need to be modified. For example, the RAM may be at some other address than 1000, and the input–output subroutines may use registers other than A. Lack of an ASCII-coded console will slow down the loading of programs as well as input of data and output of results, but for these problems it should still be practicable.

In order to present complete solutions here it is necessary to invent some details of the input–output subroutines. 'Input one character' is in PROM at address 0231; it reads into register A and uses no other registers. 'Output one character' is in PROM at address 0312; it outputs from register A and uses no other registers.

In the examples a call of 'input one character' will be written as 'A: = inchar' and a call of 'output one character' as 'outchar (A)'.

There is a point that should be noted particularly by programmers with experience of core stores. Although programs for microprocessor systems are originally written for, and developed in, RAM, it is likely that in their final form they will occupy PROM. Since PROM is a 'read-only' storage medium, there is no possibility of 'modifying' instructions in the way this is often done when they are in core. 'Working space' has to be in RAM; therefore the examples will be so arranged that locations needed for temporary storage are separate from those used for holding instructions.

4.2   ASCII CODE

The ASCII (American Standard Code for Information Interchange) seven-bit code is given in Table 4.1. When an ASCII character is given as an eight-bit value, two conventions for the additional bit are in common use:

(i)   the most significant bit is a zero;
(ii)   the most significant bit is a parity bit.

An existing console device may operate in either convention. We shall assume that our subroutines are designed to communicate with the console device in its proper convention, but that they respectively produce in A and require in A a character byte with a zero in the most significant bit position.

The examples require only the symbols 20 to 5F (letters, digits, other printing characters) and 0A (line feed), 0D (carriage return), and 1B (escape).

Table 4.1 ASCII Seven-bit Code

	0 0000	1 0001	2 0010	3 0011	4 0100	5 0101	6 0110	7 0111	8 1000	9 1001	A 1010	B 1011	C 1100	D 1101	E 1110	F 1111
0 ·000	NUL	SOH	STX	ETX	EOT	ENQ	ACK	BEL	BS	HT	LF	VT	FF	CR	SO	SI
1 ·001	DLE	DC1	DC2	DC3	DC4	NAK	SYN	ETB	CAN	EM	SUB	ESC	FS	GS	RS	VS
2 ·010	Spce	!	"	#	$	%	&	'	(	)	*	+	,	-	.	/
3 ·011	0	1	2	3	4	5	6	7	8	9	:	;	∨	=	∧	?
4 ·100	@	A	B	C	D	E	F	G	H	I	J	K	L	M	N	O
5 ·101	P	Q	R	S	T	U	V	W	X	Y	Z	[	\	]	←	↓
6 ·110	`	a	b	c	d	e	f	g	h	i	j	k	l	m	n	o
7 ·111	p	q	r	s	t	u	v	w	x	y	z	{	|	}	~	DEL

4.3   READING DECIMAL DIGITS

The execution of 'A: = inchar' is not complete until a key on the keyboard has been operated. If the '5' key is pressed, the result in A will be hex 35 (00110101). To convert this to the binary value of 5 (00000101) we need to subtract hex 30 (00110000). Thus,

    A: = inchar
    A: − 30

will give a binary value in the range 00000000 to 00001001 if the key operated is one of those marked '0' to '9'. But if some other key is pressed, A will show some meaningless value. So it will be good practice to check that the value delivered by the subroutine when the program expects a decimal digit is in the range 30 to 39. If it is, all well and good; if it is not, the program will have to jump to a 'failure routine'—perhaps to print (display) a question mark and then make a second attempt at reading.

The following sequence of instructions will read, check and convert a decimal digit:

    A: = inchar
    A − 30
    JN(to failure routine)
    A − 3A
    JNN(to failure routine)
    A: − 30

It will be used as the core of a program for the first example.

Example 1. Write a program, beginning at 1000, to read a sequence of decimal digits and store their binary values in consecutive locations beginning at 1080. The program is to end when a character other than a digit is read, leaving the ASCII value of this character in register A.

First, notice that at the 'failure' exits from the 'read, check and convert' sequence, A still contains the ASCII value of the newly read character—so there is no difficulty about the last part. To store numbers 'in consecutive locations' we need indexed addressing, or indirect addressing with a counting register. The index or count must

6800	8080, 8085, Z80
IX: = 1080	HL: = 1080
→A: = inchar	→A: = inchar
A − 30	A − 30
─JN	─JN
A − 3A	A − 3A
─JNN	─JNN
A: − 30	A: − 30
M00X: = A	M: = A (that is, M[HL]: = A)
IX: + 1	HL: + 1
─J	─J
→(continue)	→(continue)

be initialized at the starting address value, 1080. After reading, checking and converting each digit, we must store it and advance the index or counting register before reading the next character.

From this point on, programs for the 6800 begin to differ from those for 8080, 8085 and Z80. The 6800 has IX, the index register; the others have HL, which is an addressing register with an 'increment' instruction.

In the illustration on page 114, arrows are used to indicate where the jump instructions are to lead. An alternative convention is illustrated below. Here *labels* are placed on the left of instructions which are the dynamic successors of jump instructions, and in each of the jump instructions a reference to a label is written instead of the 'absolute' address of the destination. The form of the labels and of the references is as accepted by the *assembler* which is given and described in Chapter 8. For the present labels will be regarded as markers of instructions whose locations in store have not yet been determined. With one or two exceptions, in later examples the label convention

6800	8080, 8085, Z80	Comments
IX:=1080	HL:=1080	set starting address
01:A:=inchar	01:A:=inchar	read ASCII character
A−30	A−30	jump to exit
JN(L02)	JN(L02)	if not a digit
A−3A	A−3A	
JNN(L02)	JNN(L02)	
A:−30	A:−30	convert from ASCII to binary
M00X:=A	M:=A	store at set address
IX:+1	HL:+1	increment address
J(L01)	J(L01)	jump back for next character
02:	02:	

will be used and arrows will be omitted. Programmers, it has been observed, fall into two classes: those who regard the use of arrows in this kind of illustration as helpful, and those who regard it as contemptible. Readers who find themselves in the former class will find it easier to draw in their arrows than those in the latter class would to erase them.

Returning to the example, the next job is to put the program into machine code (hexadecimal) using the tables of Chapter 3. We need to know the starting address (entry point) of the input subroutine. For the 6800, with its relative jumps, we need to count bytes between instructions; for the other machines, with their direct (absolute) jumps, we need to know where each instruction will be stored. The result of all this in either case is shown in Figure 4.1.

The trickiest point in the 6800 program is working out the value to go into 1014. The instruction in 1013,1014 is a backward jump, so the number required is negative. The 'normal' continuation would be to 1015, but we want 1003—back 12 (hex!—eighteen in decimal) bytes. Table 2.1 gives −18 (decimal) equivalent to EE (hex). That is one way, but in practice the 6800 programmer will probably become quite proficient at counting forwards and backwards in hexadecimal.

```
G2800
1000   21   HL:=1080;
1003   CD   JS0231;
1006   FE   A-30;
1008   FA   JN1017;
100B   FE   A-3A;
100D   F2   JNN1017;
1010   D6   A:=-30;
1012   77   M:=A;
1013   23   HL:+1;
1014   C3   J1003;
1017   00   NULL;

MONITOR
>D1000,1017
1000  21 80 10 CD 31 02 FE 30 FA 17 10 FE 3A F2 17 10
1010  D6 30 77 23 C3 03 10 00
>
```

8080 version

```
>1000,1016
1000   CE   IX:=1080;
1003   BD   JS0231;
1006   81   A-30;
1008   23   JN+0B;
100A   81   A-3A;
100C   3A   JNN+07;
100E   80   A:=-30;
1010   A7   M00X:=A;
1012   08   IX:+1;
1013   20   J+EE;
1015   01   NULL;

MONITOR
>D1000,1015
1000  CE 10 80 BD 02 31 81 30 23 0B 81 3A 3A 07 80 30
1010  A7 00 08 20 EE 01
>
```

6800 version

Fig. 4.1

```
G2800
1000   CD   JS0231;
1003   FE   A-30;
1005   F8   RN;
1006   FE   A-3A;
1008   F0   RNN;
1009   D6   A:=-30;
100B   77   M:=A;
100C   23   HL:+1;
100D   C3   J1000;

MONITOR
>D1000,100F
1000  CD 31 02 FE 30 F8 FE 3A F0 D6 30 77 23 C3 00 10
>
```

8080 version

```
>1000,1013
1000   BD   JS0231;
1003   81   A-30;
1005   2B   JN+0B;
1007   81   A-3A;
1009   2A   JNN+07;
100B   80   A:=-30;
100D   A7   M00X:=A;
100F   08   IX:+1;
1010   20   J+EE;
1012   39   RET;

MONITOR
>D1000,1012
1000  BD 02 31 81 30 2B 0E 81 3A 2A 07 80 30 A7 00 08
1010  20 EE 39
>
```

6800 version

Fig. 4.2

The 8080–8085–Z80 program is straightforward—but the 'wrong order' of the two bytes of a double-length value (in 1001,1002; 1004,1005 etc.) must not be overlooked.

Before putting this program into the RAM for testing (and it is a good idea to test it before writing any more, as it is our first program), we should terminate it by making it hand over to the monitor. Exactly how this is to be done depends on the monitor; it may require an unconditional jump or subroutine call, or (on the 6800) a so-called 'software interrupt'. Many 8080 beginners write a HALT. The trouble with this, as they discover fairly quickly, is that to the naked eye the HALT and an endlessly repeated loop are indistinguishable. Entering the monitor gives a positive indication that the end of the program has been reached (somehow), and puts the machine into the right state to deal with a monitor command.

The testing procedure might begin as follows.

(i)   Type in the program, using the monitor.

(ii)   Use the monitor to start the execution of the program at 1000. The execution should halt at the first call of 'A: = inchar' at 1003.

(iii)   Type in some decimal digits followed by some other character. If all has gone well, the monitor should have been re-entered and be ready to

(iv)   display register A and locations 1080 onwards.

If the expected behaviour does not occur, or if the right results are not obtained, the problem is to find out why, and put matters right.

Question: If the value for 1014 is mistyped as EF (6800) or that for 1015 is mistyped as 04 (8080,8085,Z80), what will happen when the program is run?

If the program of Example 1 is turned into a *subroutine* it will be possible to call it as required in a further program. As a subroutine it will be more useful if the initialization of the addressing register is left to be done separately for each call. The starting address for each call will therefore be passed into the subroutine as a *parameter*.

Subroutines to replace the programs of Figure 4.1 are given in Figure 4.2. Note that the jump instructions of the 6800 subroutine are the same as those of the program even though they now lead to different locations; the jump addresses are *relative*. The conditional jumps of the 8080–8085–Z80 program have been replaced by *conditional return* instructions (which do not exist on the 6800).

Exercises

1.   Write a subroutine to read a sequence of letters and store them in consecutive locations beginning at the location whose address is given as a parameter. The subroutine is to end when a character other than a letter is read, leaving that character in register A.

2.   A message consists of a mixed sequence of letters and digits ending with a point (ASCII 2E). Using the subroutines now available, write a program to read a message and store all its letters in consecutive locations from M1080 onwards and all its digits in M10C0 onwards.

3.   Write a continuation to the program of exercise 2, using the 'output one character' subroutine (entry point 0312), to print out the string of letters stored in M1080 onwards.

4.4   DECIMAL INTEGERS—INPUT AND OUTPUT

The subroutine below will read, check and convert to binary, one decimal digit from the keyboard; if a non-digit key is pressed, it will print a question mark (ASCII 3F) and allow a further key operation.

```
01:A: = inchar
   A − 30
   JN(L02)
   A − 3A
   JNN(L02)
   A: − 30
   RET
02:A: = 3F
   outchar(A)
   J(L01)
```

We can write a call of this subroutine as 'A: = decdig'. Now consider the following subroutine. The central column shows an interpretation of each instruction. Clearly,

6800	Comment	8080, 8085, Z80
A: = decdig	1:A: = t	A: = decdig
A:∗2	2:A: = 2t	A: + A
B: = A	3:B: = 2t	B: = A
A:∗2	4:A: = 4t	A: + A
A:∗2	5:A: = 8t	A: + A
A: + B	6:A: = 10t	A: + B
B: = A	7:B: = 10t	B: = A
A: = decdig	8:A: = u	A: = decdig
A: + B	9:A: = 10t + u	A: + B
RET		RET

since there are two calls of 'A: = decdig', the subroutine reads two decimal digits— say t, u respectively. Instructions 2 to 6 *multiply* t by ten using B as a temporary store for $2t$. (This is probably the *quickest* way of multiplying by 10 when the result is known to be of single length, and this may be a consideration in other contexts. Here speed is of no consequence, since there is a lot of spare time between read operations.) Register B then holds $10t$ while u is read, and the final result is $10t + u$ in A. In other words, this subroutine reads a two-digit decimal integer and delivers its binary value in A. For example, if it reads '93' it will leave '01011101' (hex 5D) in A.

The subroutine will deal with any unsigned two-digit integer, that is, with any decimal integer in the range 00 to 99. But the full signed single-length range is −128 to +127, and this includes numbers expressed with or without sign and by 1, 2 or 3 significant digits. An 8080 subroutine to read any of these numbers is given in Chapter 8 (locations 0E74 to 0EB9). It should be studied carefully with attention to the following points.

(i)   The sign, + or −, may be given or omitted (+ assumed).
(ii)   The subroutine can terminate only when the character after the number's last digit is read. This symbol will not be a digit, but reading it must not cause a failure, and it must be left in a register for possible later examination. (The subroutine 'in–out' at 0020 delivers a copy of its result in each of A and C.)
(iii) There must be a check that the number does not go out of range. Even a 3-digit number beginning with 1 can be too big.

A subroutine which meets this specification should be part of the basic software of any system for serious use, as should a further subroutine (Chapter 8, locations 0EBA to 0F16) for reading double-length signed decimal integers, whose range is −32,768 to +32,767.

Returning to the series of exercises, consider the converse problem—that of displaying the decimal value (00 to 99) of a binary integer in this range. We have to divide by ten and then the two digits to be printed are respectively the quotient and remainder. Speed of division is not critical in this context, so the simple approach of repeatedly subtracting ten is adequate.

B:=00	Set tens digit to zero.
01:A−0A	Exit when A is less than ten (hex 0A); A is then the units
JN(L02)	digit.
A:−0A	Subtract ten from the 'units'
B:+1	Add one to the 'tens'
J(L01)	Repeat test.
02:B−0A	Failure if resultant tens digit is greater than nine.
JNN(failure)	
(continue)	Tens digit in B, units digit in A.

6800		8080, 8085, Z80
A		A−00
JN+1B	(to L01)	JN(failure)
B:=A		B:=00
A:=0		02:A−0A
02:B−0A		JN(L01)
JN+05	(to L03)	A:−0A
B:−0A		B:+1
A:+1		J(L02)
J+F7	(to L02)	01:C:=A
03:A−0A		A:=B
JNN+0C	(to L01)	A−0A
A:+30		JNN(failure)
outchar(A)		A:+30
B:+30		outchar(A)
A:=B		A:=C
outchar(A)		A:+30
RET		outchar(A)
01:J(failure)		RET

Fig. 4.3

```
>1000,1044
1000   BD   JS0231;
1003   81   A-30;
1005   2B   JN+07;
1007   81   A-3A;
1009   2A   JNN+03;
100B   80   A:-30;
100D   39   RET;
100E   86   A:=3F;
1010   BD   JS0312;
1013   20   J+EB;
1015   BD   JS1000;
1018   48   A:*2;
1019   16   B:=A;
101A   48   A:*2;
101B   48   A:*2;
101C   1B   A:+B;
101D   16   B:=A;
101E   BD   JS1000;
1021   1B   A:+B;
1022   39   RET;
1023   4D   A;
1024   2B   JN+1B;
1026   16   B:=A;
1027   4F   A:=0;
1028   C1   B-0A;
102A   2B   JN+05;
102C   C0   B:-0A;
102E   4C   A:+1;
102F   20   J+F7;
1031   81   A-0A;
1033   2A   JNN+0C;
1035   8B   A:+30;
1037   BD   JS0312;
103A   CB   B:+30;
103C   17   A:=B;
103D   BD   JS0312;
1040   39   RET;
1041   7E   J9999;
```

```
MONITOR
>D1000,1043
BD 02 31 81 30 2B 07 81 3A 2A 03 80 30 39 86 3F
BD 03 12 20 EB BD 10 00 48 16 48 48 1B 16 BD 10
00 1B 39 4D 2B 1B 16 4F C1 0A 2B 05 C0 0A 4C 20
F7 81 0A 2A 0C 8B 30 BD 03 12 CB 30 17 BD 03 12
39 7E 99 99
>
```

Fig. 4.4

```
       G2800
       1000   CD    JS0231;
       1003   FE    A-30;
       1005   FA    JN1010;
       1008   FE    A-3A;
       100A   F2    JNN1010;
       100D   D6    A:-30;
       100F   C9    RET;
       1010   3E    A:=3F;
       1012   CD    JS0312;
       1015   C3    J1000;
       1018   CD    JS1000;
       101B   87    A:+A;
       101C   47    B:=A;
       101D   87    A:+A;
       101E   87    A:+A;
       101F   80    A:+B;
       1020   47    B:=A;
       1021   CD    JS1000;
       1024   80    A:+B;
       1025   C9    RET;
       1026   FE    A-00;
       1028   FA    JN00B4;
       102B   06    B:=00;
       102D   FE    A-0A;
       102F   FA    JN1038;
       1032   D6    A:-0A;
       1034   04    B:+1;
       1035   C3    J102D;
       1038   4F    C:=A;
       1039   78    A:=B;
       103A   FE    A-0A;
       103C   F2    JNN00B4;
       103F   C6    A:+30;
       1041   CD    JS0312;
       1044   79    A:=C;
       1045   C6    A:+30;
       1047   CD    JS0312;
       104A   C9    RET;

       MONITOR
       >D1000,104A
       1000  CD 31 02 FE 30 FA 10 10 FE 3A F2 10 10 D6 30 C9
       1010  3E 3F CD 12 03 C3 00 10 CD 00 10 87 47 87 87 80
       1020  47 CD 00 10 80 C9 FE 00 FA B4 00 06 00 FE 0A FA
       1030  38 10 D6 0A 04 C3 2D 10 4F 78 FE 0A F2 B4 00 C6
       1040  30 CD 12 03 79 C6 30 CD 12 03 C9
       >
```

Fig. 4.5

The different internal arrangements of the 6800 and of the 8080, 8085 and Z80 call for different treatments of this idea when it is incorporated into a printing subroutine (Figure 4.3).

For the 6800 version, note that A and B have been interchanged, so that the tens digit, which is to be printed first, is produced in A; the units digit can remain in B while the tens digit is being printed. Note also that the failure exits have been made to lead first to an unconditional jump before going to the failure routine itself. This has been done in the example because it is very often necessary in practice. The range of the relative jump is only 127 bytes forward and 128 bytes back; the unconditional jump (operation code hex 7E) can go to any address, and the failure routine may well be more than 127 or 128 bytes away.

For the 8080–8085–Z80 version, an additional register C has been used as a temporary store because there is only one single-length accumulator with the required facilities (register A).

Fully coded versions of the two-digit read and print subroutines are given in Figures 4.4 and 4.5. Entry points are:

A: = decdig	1000 in both versions
Read	1015 for 6800; 1018 for 8080 version
Print	1023 for 6800; 1026 for 8080 version.

The print subroutines are complete except for one point—the provision of the address for the failure routine. In the 'A: = decdig' subroutine (that at 1000) 'failure' means only that a typing error has occurred. It is a simple matter to call attention to this by printing a question mark, and to allow a further attempt at typing a digit correctly. The read routine calls 'A: = decdig' twice, and a failure in either call is dealt with adequately in the same way.

A failure in the print routine is rather different, for it means that the value given to the subroutine in A is one with which the subroutine cannot cope. The 'easy' way out is to go to a failure routine in the monitor, if there is one. A good monitor will be able to lead back eventually to the beginning of the program, or even to the point in the program where the reading of data for the computation of the offending value is begun. In doing so it will have overcome a problem which exists in these subroutines and which must not be ignored.

In both versions of the print subroutine the failure exit is a jump out of the subroutine. If this jump takes place, the *return address* of the abandoned subroutine call is still on the stack. Indeed there may be other return addresses immediately 'underneath' it if the print subroutine has been called by another subroutine, which in turn has been called by another . . . What should happen to these depends on what is to be done after the failure report (error message) has been printed, or, more precisely, how the program is to be resumed. If the program has to restart right at the beginning, then the return addresses must be removed, perhaps by re-initializing the stack pointer. If we know, however, that there is one return address on the stack, the pair of instructions 'SP:+1; SP:+1' will remove it, and the program can be resumed at any suitable point that is not inside a subroutine.

Many programmers would regard the use of a 'failure exit' from a subroutine as poor practice to be avoided at all costs. On detecting an error condition during the execution of a subroutine they would cause it to print an error report (if appropriate) and then return normally, but with some value which will be recognized as implying that an error condition has occurred. Clearly, the calling program or subroutine must test for this value (often one bit—a software 'flag') and provide alternative continuations.

The following program will read two integers and add them. If the result is within range, it will be printed. If it is not, two question marks will be printed. In either event the program will then repeat, so that any number of cases can be processed. A new output line is given for each case.

6800	8080, 8085, Z80
01:A:=0A	01:A:=0A
outchar(A)	outchar(A)
A:=0D	A:=0D
outchar(A)	outchar(A)
JS1015	JS1018
S:=A	D:=A
JS1015	JS1018
B:=S	A:+D
A:+B	JS1026
JS1023	J(L01)
J(L01)	(failure):SP:+1
(failure):SP:+1	SP:+1
SP:+1	A:=3F
A:=3F	outchar(A)
outchar(A)	outchar(A)
outchar(A) ·	J(L01)
J(L01)	

Writing a program this way, as an endless loop (it is 'non-terminating'), will be deplored by many programming theorists. Their problem is that there is no place for the RESET signal in their theory! The RESET signal enables this program to be painlessly abandoned at any stage. Incidentally, it may be remarked in this context that a monitor program is almost certainly itself a non-terminating program. In both versions of the program, the first number has to be held in a temporary store while the second is being read. For the 8080–8085–Z80 version, register D can be used; but on the 6800 no spare register is available and so the stack is used (S: = A; ...; B: = S). When the program is translated into machine code and put into the RAM together with the subroutines, the addresses at the failure exits from the print subroutine will be the location of the instruction labelled '(failure)'.

Exercises

In each program, a new line should be given to each case; two successive numbers printed on the same line should be separated by a space.

1. Write a program to read pairs of numbers a, b and to print for each pair the sum $x = a + b$ and the difference $y = a - b$.

2.　Write a program to read sets of three numbers a, b, c and to print for each set the sums $x = b+c$, $y = c+a$, $z = a+b$ in that order.

3.　Using the division technique already used in the print subroutine, write a program to read pairs of numbers a, b and to print for each pair their quotient q and the remainder r. (*Note:* $a = b \times q + r$ and $0 \leq r < b$. Unless $b = 0$, both q and r are necessarily within range. See 4.5.5.)

Full-range single-length and double-length integer output subroutines are given in Chapter 8; they occupy together 0DCA to 0E73 and their entry points are 0E68 (output single-length signed integer from A) and 0DCA (output double-length signed integer from HL).

4.5　BINARY ARITHMETIC—INTEGERS

The foregoing sections have been concerned with reading integral values into single-length and double-length registers, and with printing out computed integral values from such registers. The *external form* of the values is decimal and the *internal form* is binary. Arithmetic on binary integers is the concern of this and the following sections.

The addition and subtraction of unsigned and signed binary integers have been discussed in sections 2.4.3 and 2.4.5.

4.5.1　Change of length of a number

To convert a single-length *unsigned* integer to double length it is necessary only to supply an upper byte of eight zero bits. In the conversion of a double-length *unsigned* integer to single-length, the upper byte must be checked to ensure that it is zero before it is removed.

To convert a single-length *signed* integer to double length we must form an upper byte of eight copies of the sign bit (the m.s.b. of the given value). It may be

6800	8080, 8085, Z80
(single-length value in A)	(single-length value in A)
B:=A	L:=A
A:=0	H:=00
B	A−H
JNN+01	RNN
A:−1	H:−1
RET	RET
(double-length value in AB)	(double-length value in HL)

worthwhile to have a subroutine for this. To convert a double-length *signed* integer to single length we must first check that the upper byte is eight copies of the m.s.b. of the lower byte. Again, a subroutine may be found worthwhile.

6800	8080, 8085, Z80
(double-length value in AB)	(double-length value in HL)
B	A:=L
JNN+01	A:&L
A:+1	JNN(L01)
JNZ+02	H:+1
A:=B	01:A:=H
RET	A:&H
J(failure)	JNZ(failure)
	A:=L
	RET
(single-length value in A)	(single-length value in A)

Extending the length of a multiple-length integer is simply providing an extra byte of eight zero bits (the unsigned case) or of eight copies of the original sign bit (the signed case). Conversely, the length of a multiple-length integer can be reduced by one byte if the most significant byte is eight zero bits (the unsigned case) or eight copies of the most significant bit of the next most significant byte (the signed case).

4.5.2 Comparisons

The 'test' and 'compare' instructions were introduced and discussed in Section 2.4.7.

The comparison of two multiple-length integers (of equal length!) can, clearly, be achieved by examining the result of multiple-length subtraction. But if there is a case for having the 'compare' operation which does not require space for the result of the subtraction, there is a stronger case for avoiding the need to store a multiple-length difference.

Suppose a, b are two n-length integers whose bytes are $a_{n-1}, a_{n-2}, \ldots, a_0$ and $b_{n-1}, b_{n-2}, \ldots, b_0$ respectively so that

$$a = \sum_{i=0}^{n-1} a_i 2^{8i} \text{ and } b = \sum_{i=0}^{n-1} b_i 2^{8i}.$$

If $a_{n-1} < b_{n-1}$ then $a < b$; if $a_{n-1} > b_{n-1}$ then $a > b$.

In each of these cases only the most significant bytes need to be compared. If, however, $a_{n-1} = b_{n-1}$ the next bytes a_{n-2}, b_{n-2}, must be compared; if these two are different, the comparison is complete—but if they are equal the next bytes must be compared, down to a_0, b_0 if necessary. Equality of a, b is determined only when all corresponding pairs of bytes have been found equal.

The comparison process may be expressed thus:

```
    i:=n-1
01:a_i-b_i
    RNZ
    i:-1
    JNN(L01)
    RET
```

If, at exit, $i < 0$, then $a = b$ (all pairs of bytes equal).

Otherwise,

(i)   if a, b are *unsigned*, or if a, b are *signed* and $i < n-1$, then if $K = 1$ we have $a < b$ and if $K = 0$ we have $a > b$;

(ii) if a, b are *signed* and $i = n-1$, the comparison is that of the two *signed* single-length integers a_{n-1}, b_{n-1}—see 2.4.7.

As a particularly simple case of this process, the following subroutine for the 8080, 8085 or Z80 will, given a, b as unsigned integers in HL, DE respectively, give $Z = 1$ if $a = b$; $Z = 0$, $K = 1$ if $a < b$; $Z = 0$, $K = 0$ if $a > b$. Unavoidably, it uses register A.

A: = H; A − D; RNZ; A: = L; A − E; RET;

4.5.3 Single-length multiplication

The product $a \times b$ of two eight-bit integers a, b has 16 bits. Although some micro-processors have instructions for multiplication, none of 6800, 8080, 8085, Z80 does. One way of generating products (and indeed higher functions) is to use external hardware. There are available, for example, multiplication ICs. Such a device can be built into the system so as to occupy four addresses. If a and b are 'written' to two of these, then the product can be obtained by 'reading' the other pair. The alternative is to have a subroutine.[1]

The usual multiplication procedure is like the 'long multiplication' of school arithmetic. As an example, $5 \times 7 = 35$ in decimal.

In binary:
```
                00000101
          ×     00000111
                --------
                00000101
               00000101.
              00000101..
             00000000...
            00000000....
           00000000.....
          00000000......
         00000000.......
                --------
         0000000000100011
                --------
```

---

[1]Integrated circuits for further arithmetic operations, compatible with microprocessor systems, are now widely available. Some of these are capable of effecting a complete range of floating-point operations (cf. Section 4.7) and evaluating several trigonometrical and other functions (cf. Section 6.3). The incorporation of such a device into a system may involve techniques such as those mentioned in Section 5.7; each type will require special consideration. The programming of operations outside the specification of those in the device may or may not be helped by the existence of the device.

It is in fact simple: the rule is to add the multiplicand (00000101) into the partially formed result for each '1' in the multiplier (00000111) at the position of that bit. More precisely, for $i = 0(1)7$, if $b_i = 1$ then we add $a \times 2^i$ into the developing result.

The following is a single-length multiplication subroutine in which the product is formed in AB (6800) or HL (8080,8085,Z80). This product is the unsigned double-length product of two unsigned single-length integers.

6800	8080, 8085, Z80
(*a*, *b* assumed in RAM)	(*a* in register C, *b* in E)
A:=0	HL:=0000
B:=0	A:=C
IX:=0008	D:=H
02:A:*2	B:=08
B:*2	02:HL:+HL
A:++00	A:@L
M(a):*2	JNK(L01)
JNK(L01)	HL:+DE
B:+M(b)	01:B:−1
A:++00	JNZ(L02)
01:IX:−1	RET
JNZ(L02)	(result $a \times b$ in HL)
RET	
(result $a \times b$ in AB)	

This subroutine will not, however, produce the expected result in all cases if one or other of the factors is *signed*. This is because a sign-bit has a special interpretation; in the subroutine as given all eight bits of each factor have been treated alike. To find out how the generated product can be *corrected* for the signs of the factors we return to the definition of the value of a signed integer (2.4.2). We have

$$a = -2^7 a_7 + \sum_{i=0}^{6} a_i 2^i$$

and

$$b = -2^7 b_7 + \sum_{i=0}^{6} b_i 2^i.$$

The product generated by the subroutine is

$$P = \sum_{i=0}^{7} a_i 2^i \times \sum_{i=0}^{7} b_i 2^i$$

$$= (a_7 2^8 + a) \times (b_7 2^8 + b)$$

$$= a \times b + 2^8 (a_7 \times b + b_7 \times a).$$

(The term in 2^{16} is lost since the product has 16 bits only.) Therefore the *sign correction* to be *added* to P to give the signed product is $-2^8 (a_7 \times b + b_7 \times a)$. In other words,

(i)   if *a* is negative, we must subtract *b* from the upper half of the generated product;
(ii)   if *b* is negative, we must subtract *a* from the upper half of the generated product.

Clearly, if a and b are both negative, both sign corrections must be applied.

As will be seen below, in the multiplication of multiple-length signed numbers it is necessary to be able to multiply together (i) two unsigned numbers, (ii) a signed number and an unsigned number, and (iii) two signed numbers. So it is helpful to have each of the sign corrections available as a subroutine.

6800	8080, 8085, Z80
(product for correction in AB)	(product for correction in HL)
M(a)	A:=C
JNN(L01)	A−00
A:−M(b)	RNN
01:RET	A:=H
(product corrected for sign of a)	A:−E
	H:=A
(product for correction in AB)	RET
M(b)	(product corrected for sign of a in C)
JNN(L02)	(product for correction in HL)
A:−M(a)	A:=E
02:RET	A−00
	RNN
(product corrected for sign of b)	A:=H
	A:−C
	H:=A
	RET
	(product corrected for sign of b in E)

Multiplication of two signed single-length integers to give a signed double-length product is now:

     unsigned multiplication
     sign correction for a
     sign correction for b
     return

The subroutines of this section are part of the software given in Chapter 8. They occupy locations 0F18 to 0F43.

4.5.4 Multiple-length multiplication

Consider the multiplication of two triple-length integers

$$a = 2^{16}a_2 + 2^8a_1 + a_0, \; b = 2^{16}b_2 + 2^8b_1 + b_0.$$

We have

$$a \times b = 2^{32}a_2b_2 + 2^{24}(a_2b_1 + a_1b_2) + 2^{16}(a_2b_0 + a_1b_1 + a_0b_2)$$

$$+ 2^8(a_1b_0 + a_0b_1) + a_0b_0.$$

The result $a \times b$ requires six bytes. The formation of the product from the double-length partial products can be represented by the arrangement, familiar to some

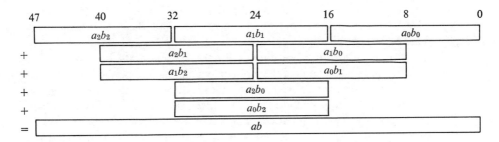

readers, known as the 'Wallace tree'. If a and b are *unsigned* integers, this scheme generates their unsigned product. If they are *signed* integers, the signed product can be produced by (i) subtracting b from the upper half if a is negative and (ii) subtracting a from the upper half if b is negative. Thus, continuing the diagram, there are two possible approaches to the programming of the sign corrections. One is to proceed as indicated in the diagrams, first forming the unsigned product and then correcting for each of the two signs. The other is to note that four of the partial products (a_1b_1,

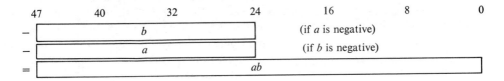

a_1b_0, a_0b_1, a_0b_0) are of unsigned numbers, four others (a_2b_1, a_2b_0, a_1b_2, a_0b_2) are each of a signed number and an unsigned number, while the ninth (a_2b_2) is of two signed numbers. 'Incremental' sign corrections can be made when each of the five last partial products is formed. But it must not be overlooked that in the first four of these five there may be a carry-bit to be taken into the higher bytes of the product.

The 8080, 8085 and Z80 have several registers and double-length addition instructions which can be used to good effect in double-length and triple-length multiplication. This is illustrated by the further multiplication subroutines given in Chapter 8. The subroutine at 2400 gives in DEHL the 32-bit product of the 16-bit unsigned integers given in BC and DE. It uses the method of 4.5.3 but with 16-bit addition at each step. The subroutine at 2420 uses that at 2400 to give the signed product of signed integers; unlike that at 0F3A it prepares the sign correction in its result registers *before* beginning the unsigned multiplication. This makes the single sign-correction version at 2556 and that at 2562 possible for only a few additional bytes of instructions. At 250A is a subroutine for generating in BCDEHL the 48-bit signed product of the two 24-bit signed integers given in BHL and CDE. The method is to partition each factor into a signed 8-bit 'head' and an unsigned 16 bit 'tail'. Then the effect of the Wallace tree with incremental sign correction is achieved by accumulating in order the product of the tails (subroutine at 2400), the product of the head of one factor with the tail of the other (subroutine at 2556), the product of the heads (subroutine at 0F3A), and the product of the other head and tail (subroutine at 2562). In order to avoid the use of explicit RAM addresses the stack pointer is used to address these partial products in the formation of the result. This misuse of the stack would not have been necessary had there been other stack pointers (cf. 2.5, 2.7).

These subroutines were made for the 8080 and 8085; no doubt the additional registers and instructions of the Z80 will enable them to be shortened for that machine.

All the subroutines referred to above are based on conventional long multiplication. Another approach to *signed* multiplication is to use 'Booth's algorithm'. This procedure uses systematically a trick which is commonly used in mental arithmetic. In multiplying, for instance, 77 by 99 we should first multiply by 100, to obtain 7700, and then subtract 77×1 to obtain the result 7623. This, for the particular case, is considerably shorter than multiplying out in full. The algorithm looks at the multiplier as a sequence of bits beginning with the least significant. As long as this sequence is of zeroes it does nothing. When the sequence changes to ones, it does a subtraction for the first one and nothing for subsequent ones. When the sequence changes to zeroes, it does an addition for the first zero and nothing for subsequent zeroes. So in multiplying 5 (00000101) by 7 (00000111) the algorithm would see 7 as a sequence of three ones followed by five zeroes. For the first one it would subtract 5×2^0 giving the partial result -5 (11111011). For the second and third ones it would do nothing. The next bit (d_3) is a zero so it would add 5×2^3 (00101000) giving the complete result 00100011 (35). Thus instead of the three additions of the conventional method (there being three ones in the multiplier) we have one subtraction and one addition (there being two sequence changes in the multiplier).

If, however, we interchange the factors and multiply 7 by 5 using Booth's algorithm we require two additions and two subtractions ($0 - 7 \times 2^0 + 7 \times 2^1 - 7 \times 2^2 + 7 \times 2^3 = 35$), whereas the conventional method requires only two additions (there being two ones in the multiplier). In multiplying two *n*-bit numbers to produce a 2*n*-bit product, each method requires a program loop to be executed *n* times. If the multiplier has *m* ones, the conventional method will add during *m* of these *n* steps. The conventional method may also require the one or two subtractions for the sign correction; Booth's algorithm gives the signed product directly. Against this, the conventional method requires marginally fewer instructions.

4.5.5 Single-length division

Division of an integer *a* by another integer *b* is an operation which produces two integer values—the *quotient q* and the *remainder r*.

If *a*, *b* are *unsigned* integers, then *q*, *r* are defined by the following relations:

$$a = q \times b + r, \ 0 \leq r < b$$

Division is *undefined* if the divisor, *b*, is zero.
If *a*, *b* are unsigned *single-length* integers and $b \neq 0$, then *q*, *r* are both unsigned single-length integers.

The definition suggests a simple algorithm for computing q and r.

$$q:=0$$
$$r:=a$$
$$01:r-b$$
$$\text{RN}$$
$$r:-b$$
$$q:+1$$
$$\text{J(L01)}$$

This is in fact the method that was used for dividing by ten in Section 4.4. It was remarked there that it was a slow method; in the context of a decimal output subroutine that was unimportant. In other contexts, however, it can be unreasonably slow—for the worst case ($a = 255$, $b = 1$) the loop is executed 255 times.

A faster method is based on 'long division'. First, the divisor b is shifted *up* (that is, to the left) until one more shift would make it bigger than the dividend a. If the shift is s places, we now have $2^s b$, and $2^s b \leq a < 2^{s+1} b$. Subtracting the shifted divisor from the dividend, we obtain $a - 2^s b$ instead of the dividend, and we have one bit q_s of the quotient q. The divisor is now shifted down until it becomes less than the residual dividend. Subtraction can then take place and another bit of the quotient is obtained. The 'shift down and subtract' stops when the divisor has been shifted back to its original position. This process is of course much more complicated than that given above but it is in most cases much faster. In symbols:

$$p:=1$$
$$s:=1$$
$$01:b-a$$
$$\text{JNN(L02)}$$
$$p:+1$$
$$s:+1$$
$$b:*2$$
$$\text{JNN(L01)}$$
$$bK:@R$$
$$p:-1$$
$$02:q:=0$$
$$03:q:*2$$
$$a-b$$
$$\text{JN(L04)}$$
$$a:-b$$
$$q:+1$$
$$04:a:*2$$
$$p:-1$$
$$\text{JNZ(L03)}$$
$$\text{RET}$$

(The instructions $b:*2$ through $p:-1$ are bracketed and marked $\divideontimes$.)

At the return the quotient is q and the remainder is $r - a \times 2^{-s}$. Here s records the maximum value reached by the position counter p. The instructions marked $\divideontimes$ are provided to prevent the divisor from encroaching on the sign bit ($bK:@R$ must reverse the effect of $b: *2$). The instructions $s: = 1$, $s: +1$ can be omitted if the remainder is not wanted.

If a and b are *signed* integers, q and r are defined by:

$$a = q \times b + r$$

if $b > 0$ then $0 \leq r < b$

if $b < 0$ then $b < r \leq 0$.

The simple, slow algorithm splits into four cases with this definition:

<table>
<tr><td>(i)</td><td>$a \geq 0, b > 0$</td><td>(ii)</td><td>$a < 0, b > 0$</td></tr>
<tr><td></td><td>$q: = 0$</td><td></td><td>$q: = 0$</td></tr>
<tr><td></td><td>$r: = a$</td><td></td><td>$r: = a$</td></tr>
<tr><td></td><td>$01: r - b$</td><td></td><td>$02: r - b$</td></tr>
<tr><td></td><td>RN</td><td></td><td>RN</td></tr>
<tr><td></td><td>$r: -b$</td><td></td><td>$r: +b$</td></tr>
<tr><td></td><td>$q: +1$</td><td></td><td>$q: -1$</td></tr>
<tr><td></td><td>J(L01)</td><td></td><td>J(L02)</td></tr>
<tr><td>(iii)</td><td>$a \geq 0, b < 0$</td><td>(iv)</td><td>$a < 0, b < 0$</td></tr>
<tr><td></td><td>$q: = 0$</td><td></td><td>$q: = 0$</td></tr>
<tr><td></td><td>$r: = a$</td><td></td><td>$r: = a$</td></tr>
<tr><td></td><td>$03: b - r$</td><td></td><td>$04: b - r$</td></tr>
<tr><td></td><td>RN</td><td></td><td>RN</td></tr>
<tr><td></td><td>$r: +b$</td><td></td><td>$r: -b$</td></tr>
<tr><td></td><td>$q: -1$</td><td></td><td>$q: +1$</td></tr>
<tr><td></td><td>J(L03)</td><td></td><td>J(L04)</td></tr>
</table>

The faster procedure can also be split in the same way. But for many, if not most, applications it is not necessary to take such a pedantic view of the remainder, and it is enough to divide $|a|$ by $|b|$ giving $|q|$. If the signs of a, b are different then $q = -|q|$.

4.5.5.1   Multiple-length quotient of single-length numbers

If, in the long division procedure of the last section, the first instruction $p: = 1$ is replaced by $p: +1$, and the procedure is entered with a positive integral value of p, p_0, say, then the value of q at exit is

$$q = \frac{a}{b} \times 2^{p_0}$$

But this is not simply the original q shifted up p_0 places. The p_0 right-most bits are significant figures—the division carried out is actually $a \times 2^{p_0}$ divided by b. Of course, since a/b is single-length, this new q requires $8 + p_0$ bits. If p_0 is limited to the range $0 \leq p_0 \leq 8$, any quotient is within double-length range.

Let us see how p_0 can be used in a particular case. Suppose $a = 27$ (decimal) and $b = 10$ (decimal) $(a/b = 2.7$, mathematically)

If $p_0 = 0$ we obtain $q = \dfrac{27 \times 2^0}{10} = 2$

$p_0 = 1$ $\qquad q = \dfrac{27 \times 2^1}{10} = 5$ $\qquad (2 \times 2.5)$ $\qquad (2\frac{1}{2})$

$p_0 = 2$ $\qquad q = \dfrac{27 \times 2^2}{10} = 10$ $\qquad (4 \times 2.5)$ $\qquad (2\frac{2}{4})$

$p_0 = 4$ $\qquad q = \dfrac{27 \times 2^4}{10} = 43$ $\qquad (16 \times 2.6875)$ $\qquad (2\frac{11}{16})$

$p_0 = 8$ $\qquad q = \dfrac{27 \times 2^8}{10} = 691$ $\qquad (256 \times 2.6992)$ $\qquad (2\frac{179}{256})$

The larger the value of p_0, the better idea we have of the fractional part of the true quotient of a and b. The case $p_0 = 8$ is of particular interest. In the example, the result for this case is the integer 691 (decimal). If we look at the two bytes of the result separately, the value in the upper byte is 2 (the integral part of $27/10$) and the value in the lower byte is 179 (decimal), representing the fractional part $^{179}/_{256}$ of our approximation to 2.7.

This is the first time we have come across a possible representation of non-integral numbers. This and other possible representations will be considered in detail at a later stage. Clearly longer quotients than double-length can be generated by increasing the range of p_0.

A subroutine for unsigned division of single-length integers for the 8080/8085/ Z80 is given in Chapter 8; its entry point is at 0F50. Its p_0 is limited to 8, and so its result is double-length. A signed version is also given; its entry is at 0F76.

4.5.6 Division of multiple-length integers

For division of double-length integers, the same procedures as in the foregoing section are possible, provided each *step* is programmed for the appropriate number length. It is not feasible to build up the quotient in terms of divisions of single-length integers.

Double-length counterparts of the 8080/8085/Z80 subroutines mentioned at the end of the last section are given in Chapter 8; their entries are at 0F9B and 0FCD respectively.

For division of longer quantities, another approach is possibly better. This is to find the reciprocal of the divisor and multiply the dividend by this. Reciprocals will be considered when we deal with non-integral quantities.

4.6   BINARY ARITHMETIC OF NON-INTEGRAL QUANTITIES

4.6.1 'Fixed-point' representation of non-integral quantities

The number 2.75 has an *integral part*, 2, and a *fractional part*, 0.75. We can say that it stands for $2 + {}^{75}/_{100}$, or 275×10^{-2}, both expressions containing only integers. We say that 2.75 has two *decimal places*, and three *significant figures*.

The same ideas can be taken over into the binary representation of non-integral quantities. The binary number 10.11 has an *integral part* 10(2) and a fractional part 0.11 $({}^3/_4)$. We can say that it stands for $10 + {}^{011}/_{100}$, or ${}^{1011}/_{0100}$, both expressions containing only (binary) integers. We say that 10.11 has two *binary places* and four *significant bits*.

Now a byte, or word, in a microprocessor system accommodates 8 bits and nothing else. There is no way of placing a *binary point* between two of its bits. But the programmer can imagine that there is a binary point somewhere in the byte, and he can program his arithmetic as if there is a binary point.

So the number $2^3/_4$ (10.11) can be represented by the byte 00001011 on the understanding that there should be a binary point between d_1 and d_2, or that the byte has two binary places.

Another number, $3^7/_8$ (11.111) can be represented by the byte 00011111, with an imaginary point between d_2 and d_3, or three binary places.

4.6.2 Multiplication

If we *multiply* these two bytes (using a subroutine for signed or unsigned multiplication) we will obtain the 16-bit product,

$$0000000101010101$$

which, regarded as an integer, has the (decimal) value 341. But the two bytes of which this is the product had 2 and 3 binary places respectively. Therefore this product has five $(2+3)$ binary places, and represents

$$1010.10101 \ (10^{21}/_{32})$$

which, since $2^3/_4 \times 3^7/_8 = 10^{21}/_{32}$, is correct.

If one number, x, is stored with m binary places, and another number y is stored with n binary places, when they are multiplied their product xy will have $m+n$ binary places. To justify this, we look at the representation another way. The number x is actually represented in the machine by the *integer* $x \times 2^m$, and y by the *integer* $y \times 2^n$; integer multiplication gives the product $xy \times 2^{(m+n)}$, which represents xy to $m+n$ binary places.

In the example, $2^3/_4$ is represented by $2^3/_4 \times 2^2 = 11$ (00001011) and $3^7/_8$ by $3^7/_8 \times 2^3 = 31$ (00011111); $11 \times 31 = 341 = 10^{21}/_{32} \times 2^5$.

4.6.3 Addition and subtraction

For *addition* there is a slight complication. Consider our two numbers in decimal form, 2.75 and 3.875. Before we add these we must (mentally at least) align the decimal points, thus:

$$2.75$$
$$3.875$$
$$\overline{}$$
$$6.625 \quad (6^5/8).$$

In a similar way, the binary points have to be aligned before binary addition can be effected:

$$10.11$$
$$11.111$$
$$\overline{}$$
$$110.101 \quad (6^5/8).$$

In other words, each has to be expressed to the same number of binary places (b.p.).

Before the addition, one of them has 2 b.p., the other 3. If we shift the 3 b.p. number down (to the right) one place, making both of them 2 b.p., we shall lose the l.s.b. of that number—which of course we should prefer not to do. So we shift the 2 b.p. number *up* (to the left) one place, making both of them 3 b.p. Then we can apply integer addition thus:

$$00001011 \;(2 \text{ b.p.}) \qquad \begin{array}{ll} 00010110 & (3 \text{ b.p.}) \\ + \; 00011111 & (3 \text{ b.p.}) \\ \hline 00110101 & (3 \text{ b.p.}) \end{array}$$

Both numbers added were 3 b.p.; the sum therefore has 3 b.p. So the result represents

$$110.101 \quad (6^5/8)$$

which is correct.

Thus, if one number, x, is held with m b.p., and another number y, is held with n b.p., then:

(i)   if $m = n$, direct addition will give the sum $x+y$ to $m \; (= n)$ binary places;

(ii)   if $m > n$, then y must be shifted *up* $(m-n)$ places; addition will then give the sum $x+y$ to m binary places;

(iii) if $m < n$, then x must be shifted *up* $(n-m)$ places; addition will then give the sum $x+y$ to n binary places.

In case (i), x is represented by $x \times 2^m$ and y by $y \times 2^m$, since $m = n$. Adding these, we obtain $x \times 2^m + y \times 2^m = (x+y) \times 2^m$, that is $x+y$ to m b.p.

In case (ii), x is represented by $x \times 2^m$, before the shift y is represented by $y \times 2^n$; after the shift y is represented by $y \times 2^n \times 2^{m-n} = y \times 2^m$. Adding $x \times 2^m$ and $y \times 2^m$ we obtain $(x+y) \, 2^m$ as before.

In case (iii), before the shift x is represented by $x \times 2^m$; after the shift x is represented by $x \times 2^m \times 2^{n-m} = x \times 2^n$; y is represented by $y \times 2^n$. Addition of $x \times 2^n$ and $y \times 2^n$ gives $(x+y) \times 2^n$, that is $x+y$ to n b.p.

Subtraction is exactly analogous to addition.

There is, however, a difficulty which should not be overlooked. In shifting any number up, there is a danger of it going out of range. In signed arithmetic, the most significant bit (the left-most 1 of a positive number or the left-most 0 of a negative number) must not be allowed to reach the sign bit position.

In many cases the programmer knows that the numbers arising during the computation are such that this can never happen, but in most cases he will not have this certainty. In general, therefore, before each shift left a check should be made. If the check shows that the shift up cannot be done correctly, the only possibility of allowing addition or subtraction is to shift the other number *down*.

As we have seen, shifting down means losing information; if it has to be done, it should be done so as to lose as little information as possible—cf. 4.6.4, on rounding.

The addition or subtraction itself can produce a result out of range. (Addition will do this if the numbers have the same sign and are near the limit of the range; subtraction will do it if they have opposite signs and are near the limit.) But this is not catastrophic, as the overflowed result can be shifted down (carefully!), giving a result within range and with one less binary place than expected in the usual way.

4.6.4 Division

Division is like multiplication, in that it can be done without preparation by shifting. Division of x (m b.p.) by y (n b.p.) gives x/y to $(m-n)$ b.p. However, if m and n are equal or nearly so the result may have too few binary places to give the degree of precision wanted. Hence the idea of 'p_0' as discussed in 4.5.5.1.

A division subroutine with this 'p_0' facility will give the quotient x/y to $(m-n+p_0)$ binary places.

Taking $x = 2.75$ with 2 b.p.

and $y = 3.875$ with 3 b.p., as before,

with $p_0 = 0$ (or no p_0 facility), the quotient would be zero, to -1 b.p.,[2] which is a rather poor representation of 0.7097.

However, with $p_0 = 8$, the quotient would be the *integral part* of

$$\frac{(2.75 \times 2^2) \times 2^8}{(3.875 \times 2^3)} = 90$$

This is 0000000001011010 in binary. The number of binary places is $2-3+8 = 7$. So the interpretation of the quotient is 0.1011010 which is $90/128 = 0.703125$, a somewhat better approximation to 0.7097.

This example shows how the division subroutine might be modified to give better results in this type of application. It would be even better to use the *remainder* to *round* the quotient

$$\frac{(2.75 \times 2^2) \times 2^8}{3.875 \times 2^3} = \frac{2816}{31} = 90 \text{ remainder } 26.$$

---

[2] A negative number of binary places means that the imagined point is to the right of the lower end of the existent bits.

As 26 is more than half of the divisor 31 we could use this fact to *round up* the quotient to 91. So the improved result is

$$0000000001011011, \text{ with 7 b.p.}$$

i.e. 0.1011011
which is $91/128 = 0.7109$—closer still to 0.7097.

The reader might verify that with $p_0 = 16$ and rounded division the result is, to 15 b.p., $^{23255}/_{32768} = 0.7097$ (actually, the binary result is within 0.01 per cent of the true result).

4.7   'FLOATING-POINT' BINARY NUMBERS

The application of the ideas of Section 4.6 in a program is largely a matter of managing the various shifts that are necessary to keep the required degree of precision (number of binary places) and at the same time to keep the numbers within range. In order to do this the programmer must not only know the range of values and precision of each input quantity and the range and required precision of each result, but he must also work out in advance of programming the range and precision of every intermediate quantity arising during the execution of the program.

In many small jobs this work is fairly straightforward, and worth the trouble. The resultant program can be made both compact and efficient. But in jobs of any size and complexity it becomes complicated, time-consuming and tedious. Worst of all, it can and does lead to errors in programming, particularly to subtle errors which can be extremely difficult to track down and correct.

The answer, of course, is to make the machine do the work. Instead of having an imaginary binary point whose position has to be taken into account in writing the instructions which operate on the value in store, we can associate with each value in store an integer, occupying a further byte, whose value represents the position of the binary point. The techniques of Section 4.6 are based on the assumption that every value occurring in a particular location or register and operated on by a particular instruction will be held to the *same* number of binary places. In other words, each such value is a value of a *fixed-point variable*. In the scheme to be described here, every value is held with an associated integral value defining the position of its binary point, and such values are operated on by subroutines which make use of these associated values. We call values represented in this way *floating-point values*.

The idea is already very familiar in the so-called 'scientific notation' for decimal numbers using 'mantissa' and 'exponent'. The exponent is an integral power of ten by which the mantissa is multiplied to give the intended value. Thus, 3×10^{10} is written instead of 30000000000; and 1.727×10^{-7} is written instead of 0.0000001727. This notation has the advantage, where values span a wide range, of avoiding the writing of large numbers of leading and trailing zeroes. In these circumstances it is compact, less prone to transcription errors, and easy to read. It is customary to write these 'decimal floating-point' numbers with a mantissa in the range 1 to 10 (or -10 to -1) and in tabulation to use a constant number of significant figures in the mantissa.

4.7.1   Representation and conventions

There are several different conventions for the representation of floating-point binary numbers in computers, but they are all based on the same considerations.

A value x is represented by a pair of values a, b such that $x = a \times 2^b$. The mantissa a is *normalized* so that its most significant figure (the left-most 1 if it is positive or the left-most 0 if it is negative) is always in the same bit position near the 'left-hand end' of the space it occupies, and the exponent b, always an integer, takes account of this. From this point there are so many major and minor variations that a 'general' floating-point system cannot be described. The description below is therefore that of a particular scheme which has been implemented for the 8080 and 8085.

Four bytes are used for each floating-point number, three for the mantissa a and one for the exponent b.

The mantissa is held as a signed triple-length fixed-point binary number to 22 binary places. Except for the case $a = 0$, the most significant bit of its value is in the d_{21} position. Because of the convention of the 8080 of storing the *upper* half of a double-length value at the location of the *higher* address of a pair, the exponent occupies the highest address of the four locations and the mantissa the lower three.

As an example the value 'ten' is represented thus:

Address of byte: $n+3$	$n+2$	$n+1$	n
7 6 5 4 3 2 1 0	7 6 5 4 3 2 1 0	7 6 5 4 3 2 1 0	7 6 5 4 3 2 1 0
0 0 0 0 0 1 0 0	0 0 1 0 1 0 0 0	0 0 0 0 0 0 0 0	0 0 0 0 0 0 0 0
	23 22 21 20 19 18 17 16	15 8	7 0

                           Binary point displaced by value of exponent
Binary point of mantissa (22 b.p.)

| ←   EXPONENT   → | ←   MANTISSA   → |

Here $a = {}^5/_8$ and $b = 4$ ($10 = {}^5/_8 \times 2^4$). In general, then, we have:

for $x = 0$; $a = 0$, $b = 0$

for $x > 0$; $^1/_2 \leq a < 1,$ $-128 \leq b \leq +127$

for $x < 0$; $-1 \leq a < -^1/_2,$ $-128 \leq b \leq +127$

With this scheme, therefore, we can represent any value x, where

$$x = 0$$

or

$$2^{-129} < \left| x \right| < 2^{+127};$$

that is

$$1.47 \times 10^{-39} < |x| < 1.70 \times 10^{+38}$$

to a precision of one part in 2^{22} (better than 6 significant decimal figures).

Variations

A longer or shorter *mantissa* will affect the precision, not the range. A 32-bit mantissa corresponds to about 9 significant figures, and a 16-bit mantissa to about 4. A 16-bit *exponent* increases the range from about $10^{\pm38}$ to about $10^{\pm9864}$; that is from a quite useful, though possibly occasionally inadequate, range to an enormous, unnecessarily wide, range. As a compromise, some large machines use a hexadecimal exponent, so that a mantissa a and exponent b represent not $a \times 2^b$ but $a \times 16^b$. This extends the range to about $10^{\pm154}$, which is adequate in nearly all reasonable circumstances. However, this variation has a very unpleasant side effect. Since the exponent can only change by 1 when the mantissa is multiplied or divided by 16, it is possible that the most significant figure of the mantissa is not in the 'usual' place but 1, 2, or 3 places to its right. In the last case the number of significant bits is reduced by 3; or, in decimal terms, there is one less significant figure. In a system with a 24-bit mantissa this reduction from 6 to 5 decimals can be a severe disadvantage.

An extra significant bit in the mantissa can be obtained by allowing its most significant figure to be next to the sign bit. Then there is the possibility of overflow on addition or subtraction (see below)—this is not difficult to handle on machines with overflow flags. It may well be worth the trouble.

The table overleaf gives the floating-point representations of a selection of values. The dotted line gives the position of the binary point if we regard the exponent as defining this position.

4.7.2 Normalization

The conversion of an *integer* (single-, double- or triple-length) to floating-point form is fairly straightforward. The integer is converted to triple-length if necessary, for the mantissa, and the exponent is put equal to 22 (decimal). At this stage we have an unnormalized floating-point number, which must be *normalized*. This consists in shifting the mantissa, so that its most significant figure is in the correct position, and adjusting the exponent accordingly. The procedure is as follows.

(i)   If the mantissa is zero, the exponent is made zero.

(ii) If the most significant bits of the mantissa are 01 ... or 10 ... , the mantissa must be shifted down one place and 1 must be *added* to the exponent. The shift down should be *rounded*; this is done by adding 1 to the l.s.b. position of the mantissa before shifting.[3]

(iii) If the most significant bits of the mantissa are 000 ... , or 111 ... , the mantissa must be shifted *up* until the m.s.b.'s are 001 ... or 110 ... . The number of places shifted must be *subtracted* from the exponent.

[3]If there is any possibility of the addition of this '1' producing overflow—specifically, if the integer being converted is $(2^{22}-1)$—provision should be made to avoid this rounding.

Decimal value	Hex value Exp. Mantissa			
	D	E	H	L
1	01	20	00	00
10	04	28	00	00
100	07	32	00	00
1000	0A	3E	80	00
100000	0E	27	10	00
1000000	11	30	D4	00
10000000	14	3D	09	00
10^7	18	26	25	A0
10^8	1B	2F	AF	08
10^{16}	36	23	86	F2
10^{32}	6B	27	71	6B
0·1	FD	33	33	33
0·01	FA	28	F5	C3
0·001	F7	20	C4	9C
0·0001	F3	34	6D	C6
10^{-5}	F0	29	F1	6B
10^{-6}	ED	21	8D	EF
10^{-7}	E9	35	AF	E5
10^{-8}	E6	2A	E6	3C
10^{-16}	CB	39	A5	65
10^{-32}	96	33	EC	48
$\pi = 3.14159$	02	32	43	F7
$1/\pi = 0.31831$	FF	28	BE	61
$\pi/180 = 0.017453$	FB	23	BE	8D
$180/\pi = 57.2958$	06	39	4B	B8
$\log_{10}\pi = 0.49715$	FF	3F	A2	9B
$\ln \pi = 1.14473$	01	24	A1	A1
$e = 2.71828$	02	2B	7E	15
$\log_{10}e = 0.43429$	FF	37	96	F6
$\log_e e = 1.4427$	01	2E	2A	8F
$\gamma = 0.57722$	00	24	F1	1A
$\sqrt{2} = 1.41421$	01	2D	41	3D
$\ln 2 = 0.69315$	00	2C	5C	86
$\ln 10 = 2.30259$	02	24	D7	63

The Binary value columns give the Exponent (bits 7 6 5 4 3 2 1 0) and the Mantissa (bits 23 22 21 20 19 18 17 16 15 14 13 12 11 10 9 8 7 6 5 4 3 2 1 0) corresponding to the hex values above.

Remarks:

The binary point is to the right of mantissa bits .

The binary point is to the left of mantissa bits.

The conversion of a *fixed-point number* to floating-point form is the same, except that the number of binary places must be *subtracted* from the exponent at the end.

In the 8080/8085 implementation given in Chapter 8, (ii) is done by the subroutine at 25CB, and (i) and (iii) by that at 25A3. In both cases the exponent is in B and the mantissa in AHL. The downward shift of AHL (2568–2576) is a rather difficult process to follow. On the 6800 and Z80 this could be done more simply.

4.7.3 Auxiliary routines

Before looking at the subroutines for adding, subtracting, multiplying, and dividing floating-point numbers, we should consider some operations on triple-length numbers which these subroutines will have to be able to perform. Most of these operations will themselves need to be written as subroutines.

4.7.3.1 Shifting triple-length numbers

Arithmetic shifts of triple-length numbers have already been mentioned in regard to normalization. In the 8080/8085 implementation,

(i)   at 2568 is a subroutine for a *truncated* shift down of AHL (truncated because the l.s.b. is lost);

(ii)   at 2577 is a subroutine for a *rounded* shift down of AHL (as described in 4.7.2, a 1 is added in the least significant position before shifting);

(iii)   at 2583 is a subroutine for a *truncated* shift down of AHL by the number of places equal to the integer given in B;

(iv)   at 258B is a subroutine for a rounded shift down of AHL by the number of places equal to the integer given in B ($2^B \times d_0$ is added to AHL before the shift to effect the rounding).

4.7.3.2 Adding triple-length numbers (same number of b.p.)
AHL:+CDE is simply HL:+DE
$$A:++C$$

4.7.3.3 Subtracting triple-length numbers (same number of b.p.)
AHL:−CDE would be simply A:&A (to clear K)
$$HL:--DE$$
$$A:--C$$

on the Z80, but on the 8080 and 8085 more instructions are needed, and a subroutine (at 25D8) of 12 bytes is necessary.

4.7.3.4 Multiplying triple-length numbers

BCDEHL: = BHL × CDE (signed) is effected by the subroutine at 250A. This in turn makes use of the subroutine for double-length multiplication at 2400 and that for single-length multiplication at 0F3A. In studying 250A, the reader should note how the stack is used as a temporary store.

Reduction of the 48-bit product to triple-length (24 bits) is effected by the subroutine at 25E4. The routine assumes that the two factors were 22 b.p. each, so the 48-bit product has 44 b.p. This is shifted up 2 places (giving 46 b.p.) and then the least significant 24 bits are removed leaving a triple-length number with 22 ($= 46 - 24$) b.p. In this last step, however, if the m.s.b. of the removed twenty-four is a 1, a 1 is added to the remaining part in its l.s.b. position for rounding.

The result of applying these two subroutines in order is the 22 b.p. product of two 22 b.p. numbers.

4.7.3.5   Dividing triple-length numbers

A triple-length division subroutine making use of single- and double-length division is not a practical proposition. A direct triple-length division subroutine is a more reasonable possibility, but perhaps not the best. Since we have multiplication, why not form the quotient x/y by multiplying x by the *reciprocal* of y? A reciprocal subroutine is simpler than general division because, although the method is similar, since the dividend is essentially a '1' followed by a sequence of zeroes, we can avoid the necessity of reserving registers for it. Even so, it is rather a tricky business, and the stack, for once, does not provide an easy form of temporary storage.

The reciprocal subroutine at 267A finds the reciprocal of an unsigned (positive) floating-point number whose exponent is given in D and mantissa in EHL. So, if it is applied to $x = a \times 2^b$ its result is $(-b-s)$ in D and $2^s/a$ to 22 b.p. in EHL, where s is the shift required to give a normalized mantissa.

The subroutine at 26D9 finds the reciprocal of a signed floating-point number by using the unsigned routine to give the reciprocal of the modulus and changing sign if necessary afterwards.

4.7.4   The floating-point subroutines—general

The internal registers of the 8080, 8085 and Z80 are sufficient to allow a reasonably convenient way of handling numbers of 4 bytes in length. In the floating-point 'package' described here, the four registers DEHL are made to behave like a floating-point accumulator, D holding the exponent and EHL the mantissa (the most significant byte is in E, the least significant in L). The double-length register BC is used as an addressing register.

It is possible to describe the effects of the floating-point subroutines in the same notational system as has been developed for the machine instructions. For the set of locations occupied by a floating-point number in store, say M1234, M1235, M1236, M1237, we can write MMMM1234, or, more briefly, M⁴1234. The exponent will be in M1237, the most significant byte of the mantissa in M1236, the middle byte in M1235, and the least significant byte in M1234. (Here the 'block-address' is 1234).

The subroutines of the 'package' include:

'Store':   M⁴[BC]: = DEHL
                Stores a copy of the f.p. (floating-point) number held in the f.p. accumulator in the locations whose block-address is given in BC (entry 2608).

'Fetch':   DEHL: = M⁴[BC]

The converse of 'store' (entry 2619).

'Multiply':   DEHL: × M⁴[BC]

The number in the f.p. accumulator is multiplied by the number at the locations whose block-address is given in BC and the product is left in the f.p. accumulator. The value in BC is left unchanged (entry 264B).

'Reciprocal': DEHL:/

The number in the f.p. accumulator is replaced by its reciprocal (entry 26D9).

'Divide':   DEHL:/M⁴[BC]

The number in the f.p. accumulator is divided by the number given by the address in BC and the quotient is left in the f.p. accumulator. The value in BC is left unchanged (entry 26EC).

'Change sign of accumulator': DEHL:—

The sign of the number in the f.p. accumulator is reversed (entry 265B).

'Change sign of stored number': M⁴[DE]:—

The sign of the number whose address is given in DE (not BC—this subroutine is used by 'subtract', see below) is reversed (entry 266A).

'Add':   DEHL: = M⁴[HL] + M⁴[DE]

The sum of the numbers whose addresses are given in HL and DE is left in the f.p. accumulator (entry 26F7). (This specification is admittedly awkward. DEHL: + M⁴[BC] would have been more consistent and easier to use, but it was decided on chiefly to avoid awkward stack manipulations.)

'Subtract': DEHL: = M⁴[HL] − M⁴[DE]

The difference of the numbers whose addresses are given in HL and DE is left in the f.p. accumulator (entry 2731).

The *fetch* and *store* subroutines are very simple, using BC as an index register. In both cases the stack is used to preserve AF through the subroutine call (this is known as making the subroutine *transparent* to AF).

The *multiplication* begins, with the aid of the stack, by getting the two mantissae in BHL and CDE respectively, and the sum of the exponents in A. The sum of the exponents is then stacked while the product of the mantissae is formed in AHL. Then the sum of the exponents is unstacked into B, and BAHL is normalized. Finally, BA is copied into DE and we have the floating-point product in DEHL.

The *reciprocal* subroutine is described briefly in 4.7.3.5.

The *division* begins by stacking DEHL, the dividend. Then it fetches the divisor and replaces it by its reciprocal in DEHL. It then jumps to the fourth instruction of the multiplication routine—and thus continues by multiplying the dividend by the reciprocal of the divisor.

The *addition* subroutine is rather more complicated. (Experienced programmers will no doubt see evidence of corrections in the version given here.) The first part examines the most significant bytes of the two mantissae. If either is zero, the result of the addition is simply the other number. If neither is zero, the addition must be carried out (26FE onwards). First the difference of the exponents is formed (in B) and the mantissa to be shifted down is put into AHL (a normalized number cannot be shifted up). Then the shift (if by a non-zero number of places) is applied, using a conditional subroutine call. Then the addition of the mantissae takes place, the appropriate exponent is placed in B and the full normalization procedure is applied, and the subroutine ends with the result in DEHL.

The subroutine for *subtraction* begins by changing the sign of the number being subtracted *in situ*. Then the addition subroutine is called (so $a+b$ is implemented by $a+(-b)$), and finally the sign that was changed is restored.

4.7.5   Floating-point input and output

The function of a floating-point read subroutine is to accept a value typed on the console keyboard in some form of decimal floating-point notation and to leave this value in the machine in normalized floating-point binary. Conversely, a floating-point print or display subroutine should, given a normalized floating-point binary value, output this value in an acceptable decimal floating-point form.

It is usual for the mantissa of a decimal f.p. number to be normalized so as to lie in the range -10 to -1 (if negative) or $+1$ to $+10$ (if positive), or zero. The number of significant figures in the mantissa should be no more than is justified by the computation (for an output value) or by the quality of source information (for an input value). The exponent is simply a one- or two-digit signed decimal integer.

4.7.5.1.   Floating-point output

The subroutine at 2B80 prints a signed mantissa to six significant figures and a signed one- or two-digit exponent, the two parts being separated by the letter E; the value to be printed is expected as a normalized f.p. binary number in DEHL.

For example, the value 0.0000610351 is displayed as

$$+6.10351E-5.$$

The action of the subroutine is as follows. First the sign of the mantissa is printed; if the number is negative its sign is reversed in the f.p. accumulator DEHL. Then if the mantissa is zero the second stage is bypassed (2B91 to 2BDE). A non-zero number is then compared with the f.p. constant representing ten, the upper end of the range for printing a decimal mantissa. If it is greater than or equal to 10, it is divided by 10 and 1 is added to the decimal exponent. The comparison is repeated and division by 10 carried out until the residual number is less than 10. This last phase will have had no effect on a number originally less than 10. Now the comparison is with the lower end of the range, 1; if the number is less than 1 it is repeatedly multiplied by 10 until a number greater than or equal to 1 results. Thus at this stage we have a mantissa p, held as a f.p. binary number in the range 1 to 10, and an exponent, q, held as a binary integer such that the number to be printed $x = p \times 10^q$. The mantissa is then printed. The f.p. binary number which represents it is reduced to fixed-point form, quadruple length in DEHL to 24 b.p. Register D then contains the integral part of the mantissa. A 'decimal round-off' quantity, $1/2 \times 10^{-5}$ (hex 00.000054) is added at this stage. The value of D is then printed. Then a 'print fraction' subroutine (07E6) is called which prints the decimal point followed by five decimal places. Each of these is found by multiplying the residual quantity by 10 (as in Section 4.4) and taking the integral part. Finally 'E' and the value of the decimal exponent are printed, the latter having been held on the stack during the printing of the mantissa.

This subroutine can cause a teletype to 'hiccup'. If it is given a number with a very large (positive or negative) exponent, the repeated division or multiplication can take longer than the full-speed interval (1/10 or 1/30 s) between two successive printing characters. This will be noticed as a pause between the sign and first digit of the mantissa. (Floating-point division or multiplication takes up to $4^1/_2$ ms). In use, occasionally a mantissa 10.00000 will be printed rather than 1.00000. This is due to a 'last-minute' carry out of the normal range. The value printed, though 'non-standard', is nevertheless correct.

Improvements to this subroutine, such as avoiding the 'hiccup', anticipating the 'last-minute' carry and printing a number of significant figures specified by a parameter, will unfortunately make it even longer.

The user is warned not to believe figures in the printed mantissa which are not justified by the data and the computation which produced the results.

4.7.5.2 Floating-point input

The subroutine at 2745 reads a number from the keyboard and delivers its value as a floating-point binary number in DEHL. Although the number must be presented as mantissa followed by exponent, each part may be typed in standard or non-standard form. For example, '1' may be typed in any of the following ways:

$$1E0$$
$$+1.00000E+00$$
$$+0.001E+3$$
$$1000E-3$$

Thus the first character read can be a sign or a digit. If it is a sign, a marker is set; if it is a digit the marker is set as for the $+$ sign and the digit character is held. Thereafter an integral value is built up in AHL. If a point '.' is encountered at any stage (including at the first character position) the number of digits occurring after it is counted. The integral value is converted to floating-point and stacked. The exponent is then read, using the ordinary 'read single-length integer' subroutine, and the count of digits in the mantissa after the decimal point is subtracted from its value. This gives the power of ten by which the floating-point integral value is to be multiplied. Values of 10^1, 10^2, 10^4, 10^8, 10^{16}, 10^{32} are stored with the subroutine. The bits of the exponents are examined one by one and the floating point number multiplied or divided by a power of ten accordingly. This is a compact and quick way of multiplying or dividing by an arbitrary power of ten—see 27AD onwards.

4.7.6 Simple programming with floating-point subroutines

If the floating-point subroutines are available, programming of simple problems is reduced to writing little more than a succession of subroutine calls.

Example. Write a program for converting Fahrenheit temperatures to Centigrade (Celsius). The formula is $C = (F - 32) \times 5/9$. First, we type in the *constants*, 32, 5, 9. The machine then returns to a new line. We type in a Fahrenheit temperature and the machine responds by printing the corresponding Centigrade value. It returns for a new line, and so it is prepared to read and convert further temperatures.

JS2745 BC: = 1300 JS2608	The operator types '32E0'—machine reads this value and stores it in M^41300.
JS2745 BC: = 1304 JS2608	The same with '5E0' and M^41304.
JS2745 BC: = 1308 JS2608	The same with '9E0' and M^41308.
01:JS0200	'Carriage return line feed'—see Chapter 8.
JS2745 BC: = 130C JS2608	The operator types in a Fahrenheit value which is stored at M^4130C.
HL: = 130C DE: = 1300 JS2731	The machine forms $F - 32$ in DEHL.
BC: = 1304 JS264B	The machine forms $(F - 32) \times 5$ in DEHL.
BC: = 1308 JS26EC	The machine forms $(F - 32) \times 5/9 = C$ in DEHL.
JS2B80 J(L01)	The machine prints the C value. (Unconditional jump to repeat)

The accompanying illustration shows how this program was introduced into the computer and used. Details of use of the monitor, assembler and disassembler are in 6.1.

```
        GOCOO                                       The assembler is entered.
        JS2745;              CD  45  27
        BC:=1300;            01  00  13
        JS2608;              CD  08  26
        JS2745;              CD  45  27
        BC:=1304;            01  04  13
        JS2608;              CD  08  26
        JS2745;              CD  45  27
        BC:=1308;            01  08  13             As each instruction is typed in by the
        JS2608;              CD  08  26               operator, the machine responds with
        01:JS0200;           CD  00  02               the hex code.
        JS2745;              CD  45  27
        BC:=130C;            01  0C  13
        JS2608;              CD  08  26
        HL:=130C;            21  0C  13
        DE:=1300;            11  00  13
        JS2731;              CD  31  27
        BC:=1304;            01  04  13
        JS264B;              CD  4B  26
        BC:=1308;            01  08  13
        JS26EC;              CD  EC  26
        JS2B80;              CD  80  2B
        J(L01);              C3  1B  10
        FINISH;                                      End of input text.
        MONITOR
        >S1010 C2-  11-                              Indication of length of program.

        >M1180,11C1,1000                             Program copied to run-time location.
        >X
        NZHPK  A      BC     DE     HL     SP    PC
        01110  10    2020   0010   10C0   17F2  OCEF
                            1042   1000              Preparation for disassembler.

        >G2800                                       The disassembler is entered.
        1000    CD    JS2745;
        1003    01    BC:=1300;
        1006    CD    JS2608;
        1009    CD    JS2745;
        100C    01    BC:=1304;
        100F    CD    JS2608;
        1012    CD    JS2745;
        1015    01    BC:=1308;                      Disassembler  output—note  absolute
        1018    CD    JS2608;                          address in place of label at 103F.
        101B    CD    JS0200;
        101E    CD    JS2745;
        1021    01    BC:=130C;
        1024    CD    JS2608;
        1027    21    HL:=130C;
        102A    11    DE:=1300;
        102D    CD    JS2731;
        1030    01    BC:=1304;
        1033    CD    JS264B;
        1036    01    BC:=1308;
        1039    CD    JS26EC;
        103C    CD    JS2B80;
        103F    C3    J101B;

        MONITOR
        >
```

```
D1000,1041                                    hex dump
1000 CD 45 27 01 00 13 CD 08 26 CD 45 27 01 04 13 CD
1010 08 26 CD 45 27 01 08 13 CD 08 26 CL 00 02 CD 45
1020 27 01 0C 13 CD 08 26 21 0C 13 11 00 13 CD 31 27
1030 01 04 13 CD 4F 26 01 08 13 CD EC 26 CL 80 2B C3
1040 1B 10
>G1000                                        The program is entered.
32E0 5E0 9E0                                  The constants are typed in.
32E0 +0·00000E0
212E0 +1·00000E2
984E-1 +3·68888E1                             After each Fahrenheit value is typed in,
-4E1 -4·00000E1                                  the machine responds with the cor-
98·4E0 +3·68888E1                                responding Centigrade value and
-40E0 -4·00000E1                                 moves to a new line.
-459·67E0 -2·73150E2
68E0 +2·00000E1
50E0 +1·00000E1

MONITOR                                       Reset to monitor.
>
```

Exercises

1. Write the converse program for converting Centigrade to Fahrenheit.
2. Write a program for combining electrical resistances in parallel ($1/R = 1/R_1 + 1/R_2$). The program will, for each case, read in R1 and R2, and print R.).

4.7.7 Condition flags and floating-point numbers

Immediately after the exit from a subroutine which has computed a new floating-point number in DEHL, the values of the condition flags do not necessarily give any useful information about this number. However, flags can be set quite simply.

The sequence of instructions

$$A := E$$
$$A : \& A$$

will set the flag Z if DEHL is zero, and it will set the flag N if DEHL is negative. (The most significant byte of the mantissa is all that needs to be examined as we have a normalized value.)

However, the reader must be reminded that floating-point arithmetic, unlike integer arithmetic, is inherently inexact, and the fact that a computed value is exactly zero is usually meaningless. In most cases the information wanted is whether a computed value is *sufficiently small*, or, in other words, is zero within some given tolerance. More precisely, we accept a value x as zero within an absolute error E if $|x| < E$.

So, if x is in DEHL:

```
     A := E
     A :& A
     JNN(L01)              Store |x| at M⁴ (a)
     JS265B
01:BC := a
     JS2608
     HL := a
```

with "Store $|x|$ at M^4 (a)" to the right of the JNN(L01)/JS265B lines.

> DE: $= b$ Form $|x|$ $-$ E (E assumed at M^4 (b))
> JS2731
> A: $=$ E
> A:&A
> JNN x is 'non-zero'
> (x is 'zero')

Clearly, floating-point arithmetic should never be used for *counting*, which is essentially concerned with exact integral values.

4.8   BINARY-CODED-DECIMAL ARITHMETIC

BCD arithmetic was introduced in the description of 'decimal adjustment' (2.4.9). It depends on the interpretation of a byte as a pair of decimal digits. An unsigned decimal integer in the range 0 to 99 can be held in one byte as a pair of 'nibbles' each representing a decimal digit. It follows that an unsigned decimal integer in the range 0 to 9,999 can be held in a pair of bytes. These ranges are considerably narrower than the ranges of unsigned binary numbers (0 to 255 single-length, 0 to 65,535 double-length).

Input–output of unsigned BCD integers is clearly very simple: subroutines such as those given at the end of 4.4 can be used directly, the only necessary modification being the replacement of 'A: = one hex' by 'A: = decdig' in the input subroutines.

However, even with the assistance of the 'decimal adjustment' instruction, arithmetic on BCD numbers tends to be rather cumbersome. This will become clear as elementary routines are developed. In practice the uses of BCD arithmetic are very limited. Users of calculators who have discovered that calculator ICs use BCD arithmetic may well be surprised by this assertion. But there is no contradiction. A calculator is usually required to display every number which arises in the course of its operation. Each number entered is displayed; the result of each calculating step, and of each internal transfer, is also displayed. So the simplicity of BCD input–output is important for calculators. In a microprocessor system it is likely that a result to be displayed or printed will have been generated from a long sequence of operations. The complication of the decimal-to-binary and binary-to-decimal conversions on input and output is more than justified by the comparative simplicity of the binary arithmetic. Occasionally, when a small amount of rather simple calculation is required, it may be convenient to use BCD arithmetic in the microprocessor in conjunction with the simple BCD input–output subroutines.

In the following, a decimal integer of $2n$ decimal digits is regarded as held in n bytes of store. The digits are denoted by $a_{2n-1}, a_{2n-2}, \ldots, a_1, a_0$, and the bytes hold $a_{2n-1} a_{2n-2}, a_{2n-3} a_{2n-4}, \ldots, a_1, a_0$ respectively. The most significant digit (coefficient of 10^{2n-1}) is a_{2n-1} and the least significant digit (units digit) is a_0.

4.8.1   Addition of unsigned integers

4.8.1.1   Single-length

If $a = a_1a_0$ and $b = b_1b_0$, then each can be held in a single byte. Their sum $c = a+b$ is in the range 0 to 198 (decimal) and is represented by $c = c_2c_1c_0$ where c_1c_0 will appear in the accumulator and c_2 (0 or 1) will appear in the carry flag. We can write, for all four microprocessors,

$$A := a_1a_0$$
$$A : + b_1b_0$$
$$\text{DEC}$$
$$(c_2)c_1c_0 := (K)A.$$

The notation in the last line means that A contains the units and tens digits of the result while the carry flag K contains the hundreds digit. If $K = 0$, the result c is within single-length range.

4.8.1.2   Double-length

Here the carry digit generated in the addition of the two lower pairs of digits must be taken into account when adding the upper pairs of digits:

$$A := a_1a_0$$
$$A : + b_1b_0$$
$$\text{DEC}$$
$$\left. \begin{array}{l} c_1c_0 := A \\ A := a_3a_2 \end{array} \right\} \begin{array}{l} \text{These instructions do not} \\ \text{affect the carry flag.} \end{array}$$
$$A : + + b_3b_2$$
$$\text{DEC}$$
$$(c_4)c_3c_2 := (K)A$$

4.8.1.3   Multiple-length

The 8080, 8085 and Z80 have addressing registers which can be used where the long integers are held in blocks of consecutive locations. We suppose $a = a_{2n-1}\,a_{2n-2}\ldots a_1a_0$ to be held in locations p to $p+n-1$ inclusive, so that a_1a_0 are at location p, a_3a_2 at $p+1$, $\ldots a_{2n-1}\,a_{2n-2}$ at $p+n-1$. (This is consistent with addressing practice on these machines.) Similarly, suppose b, of the same length, to be held in q to $q+n-1$, and the result c to be required in r to $r+n-1$.

The addition is best done by a subroutine which requires the base addresses p, q, r of a, b, c in the addressing registers and the addition length n in a counting register. Writing a call of the subroutine as 'long BCD add', we have in the program

$$DE := p$$
$$HL := q$$
$$BC := r$$
$$A := n$$
long BCD add

and the subroutine itself can be:

A:&A	(or any other suitable instruction which clears K)
ST: = AF	(save byte counter)
01:A: = M[DE]	(fetch next byte of a)
A:+ +M	(add in, with carry, next byte of b)
DEC	(decimally adjust this partial result)
M[BC]: = A	(store next byte of result)
DE:+1	
HL:+1	(increment addressing registers)
BC:+1	
HL: = :ST	
H:−1	(count down)
HL: = :ST	
JNZ(L01)	(repeat until n steps done)
HL: = ST	(clear stack)
RET	(K holds the coefficient of 10^{2n} of the result—the lower digits have been stored.)

(For the three count-down instructions: None of these instructions affects the carry flag.)

The awkward treatment of the counting in this example, and the subsequent loss of the address in HL, is due to the fact that 'AF: = ST' would destroy the carry bit needed in the 'add with carry'. It is not possible to unstack A alone. Instead of 'HL: = ST' it may be preferable to have 'SP:−1; SP:−1'.

If the result is known to be within $2n$-digit range, K can be ignored at exit from the subroutine, but if there is any doubt the program should continue by examining K and taking action appropriate to its value.

Because the 6800 is not so well endowed with addressing registers as are the others, the 6800 version of this subroutine is very much more complicated. In writing it we should be far more concerned with managing the addressing than with the arithmetic; the problems will be discussed in the chapter on non-numerical operations (Chapter 5).

4.8.2 Signed BCD integers

Before considering subtraction, it is necessary to decide how negative integers can be represented in BCD.

Analogy with binary arithmetic suggests a 'tens complement' arrangement where, instead of representing an unsigned integer in the range 00 to 99, a byte represents a signed integer in the range −50 to +49. It is possible to develop a consistent scheme for addition and subtraction on this basis, but it becomes very cumbersome indeed for multiplication. Another idea is to have an additional bit (which will have to be accommodated in a nibble or byte of its own) to indicate a 'borrow' of 100. Thus, writing the value of the borrow bit in parentheses,

+23   would be represented as   (0)23 $(0 \times 100 + 23)$
−23   would be represented as   (1)77 $(−1 \times 100 + 77)$

Use of a borrow bit and one byte allows the representation of any signed integer in the range −100 to +99.

The *sum* of two such numbers is in the range -200 to $+198$, and their *difference* is in the range -199 to $+199$.

Addition of signed integers represented in this way is the same as of unsigned integers as far as the byte digits are concerned, but special treatment is required for the borrow bits. A carry bit 1 arising from the adjusted byte addition represents $+100$; each borrow bit 1 represents -100. We can make a table. Overflow can

Borrow bits	Carry bit	Result
0,0	0	Positive and within range
0,0	1	Positive and out of range
0,1 or 1,0	0	Negative and within range
0,1 or 1,0	1	Positive and within range
1,1	0	Negative and out of range
1,1	1	Negative and within range

occur if the operands have the same sign, and in this case it is indicated by carry from the byte addition.

Negation of a signed integer x is possible unless $x = -100$, in which case $-x$ is out of range.

Suppose $-99 \leq x \leq +99$. For the positive part of the range, where $+1 \leq x \leq +99$, x is represented by a *zero* borrow bit and the BCD value x.

The value $-x$ will be represented by a *one* borrow bit and the BCD value $100-x$ ($+1 \leq 100-x \leq +99$).

For the negative part of the range, where $-99 \leq x \leq -1$, x is represented by a *one* borrow bit and the BCD value $100+x$.

The value $-x$ will be represented by a *zero* borrow bit and the BCD value $-x$ ($-x = 100 - (100+x)$ and $+1 \leq -x \leq +99$).

So in both of these cases the value can be *negated* by inverting the borrow bit and forming the 100-complement of the BCD part of the value. The sequence

$$A: = 99$$
$$A: -x$$
$$A: +01$$
$$DEC$$

forms the required complement. This is so because the subtraction gives $99-x$ directly in BCD without need of adjustment, and the adjustment applied after the addition of 01 will operate correctly.

Now we must consider the value $x = 0$. This will have a borrow bit of 0, and two zero BCD digits. Negating the borrow bit will make it 1, and the complementing sequence will give $K = 1$ and $A = 00$. Interpreting $K = 1$ as $+100$, and the borrow bit as -100, it is clear that these two cancel each other, and we are left with the original representation for $-x = 0$.

In the odd case $x = -100$, the original value has a borrow bit of 1 and two zero BCD digits. Negating the borrow bit will make it 0, and the complementing sequence will give $K = 1$ and $A = 00$. The result is out of range; we have the value

0 given by the borrow bit and BCD digits, and the carry flag indicates a value out of range (and stands for the carry $+100$).

Subtraction of signed BCD values can now be carried out by negation followed by addition $(a-b \equiv a+(-b))$.

This will involve the sequence

```
A:=99
A:-b
A:+01
DEC
A:+a
DEC
```

on the 6800, 8080 and 8085. On the Z80, however, since decimal adjustment is also effective after subtraction, this sequence can be reduced to

```
A:=a
A:-b
DEC
```

Extension of these procedures for multiple-length values follows the same pattern as that for addition. The instruction 'A:$-b$' in either case is replaced by 'A:$--b$' for byte pairs after the first.

4.8.3 BCD multiplication

Consider the subroutine:

```
      A:=00
01:B:-1
      RN
      A:+c
      DEC
      J(L01)
```

If, on entry, $00 \leq (B,C) \leq 09$, then at exit $00 \leq A \leq 81$ and A is the *product* of the BCD *digits* originally in B and C.

Consider now:

```
      HL:=0000
02:B:-1
      RN
      A:=L
      A:+C
      DEC
      L:=A
      A:=H
      Λ:| | 00
      DEC
      H:=A
      J(L02)
```

If, on entry $00 \leq B \leq 09$ and $00 \leq C \leq 99$ (two BCD digits), then at exit $0000 \leq HL \leq 0891$, and HL is the *product* of the BCD digit given in B and the unsigned two-digit BCD integer given in C.

This second subroutine can be applied to form the product of two unsigned two-digit BCD integers given in B,C.

Writing HL $:= B_0 \times C$ (BCD) for a call to this subroutine, the following subroutine will produce in HL the BCD product (four digits) of the two unsigned two-digit BCD integers given in B, C.

```
D: = B
A: = B
A:&F0
A:@R
A:@R
A:@R
A:@R
B: = A
HL: = B₀ × C (BCD)
HL:+HL
HL:+HL
HL:+HL
HL:+HL
A: = D
HL: = :DE
A:&0F
B: = A
HL: = B₀ × C (BCD)
A: = E
A:+L
DEC
L: = A
A: = D
A:+ +H
DEC
H: = A
RET
```

A call of this subroutine might be written as HL:$=B \times C$ (BCD).

Clearly, it can be used to build up products of longer BCD integers, by the method suggested in 4.5.4.

For *signed* multiplication the same subroutine can be used; the sign corrections required are (cf. 4.5.3) similar to those required in binary multiplication. If either factor is negative, the *other* is to be *subtracted* from the upper half of the product.

The unsigned BCD multiplication subroutine above requires 50 bytes and is capable of multiplying two integers each in the range 0 to 99, to give a product between 0 and 9801.

By contrast, the unsigned binary multiplication subroutine, $DEHL := BC \times DE$, at 2400 in Chapter 8, has 32 bytes only and is capable of multiplying two integers in the range 0 to 65,535 to generate a product between 0 and 4,294,836,225.

Any reader who remains unconvinced that BCD arithmetic is cumbersome should write a BCD multiplication subroutine to match the range of this binary multiplication subroutine.

4.8.4 BCD fractions

As in the case of fixed-point binary working (4.6), a decimal point position can be taken into account in BCD arithmetic. In addition and subtraction, the imagined decimal point must be aligned before the operation can take place. Where the numbers of decimal places are equal, no preparation is necessary. Where the numbers of decimal places differ by an even number, the preparation will be in ensuring that properly corresponding pairs of bytes are addressed in each step. Where the numbers of decimal places differ by an odd number, however, one is faced with the awkward task of shifting one of the BCD numbers through 4 bit positions to the left. This is, perhaps, tolerable on the Z80 with its 'nibble shift' instructions, but it is very tedious on the others.

Note: Computations with sums of money are best regarded not as dealing with numbers of pounds (dollars, *schillings*, etc.) held to two decimal places, but as dealing with *integral* numbers of new pence (cents, *gröschen*, etc.). BCD arithmetic is then tolerable in simple 'debit and credit' accounting. As soon as multiplication in the form of 'percentage calculations' (interest, sales tax, VAT, discount) becomes involved, however, there can be no doubt that binary arithmetic will be found to be much more powerful and convenient than BCD. Truncation or rounding to an integral value are operations whose effect is independent of the number base. Rounding to d decimal places of a binary quantity held to p binary places can be approximated by adding $\frac{1}{2} \, 10^{-d} \, 2^p$ to it.

5

Programming: non-numerical operations

5.1   NON-NUMERICAL QUANTITIES

We have already, in the chapters on instructions and on arithmetical operations, encountered many instances of quantities which are not thought of primarily as numbers, and many instances of operations which are not thought of in arithmetical terms. Examples of the former are instructions, addresses, states of flags, ASCII representations of characters. Examples of the latter are conversion between codes, preparation of addresses for entry to a subroutine, and (Exercise 2 of 4.3) the distinction between coded representations of digits and letters.

The 'assembler' and 'disassembler' which form a considerable part of the software given in Chapter 8 are concerned with 'translation' between one 'language' and another, between the notation introduced with the hope of easing human understanding and the strings of bits required by the microprocessor. These programs, though they make use of many arithmetic instructions, are only incidentally concerned with arithmetic and numbers. Their computation is the repeated determination of what string of bits (symbols) in one 'language' corresponds to what string of symbols (bits) in the other.

The distinction between 'numerical' and 'non-numerical' computation should not be over-emphasized or misunderstood. It exists only in the minds of programmers and users; in the machine there are only bits. Strings of bits which find their way into the instruction register are instructions; the other sets of bits in the system mean only what they are intended to mean. The popular notion that 'data processing' or 'information processing' is in some way a higher activity for programmers or electrons than mere 'number crunching' is false.

5.2   COPYING 'BLOCKS' OF INFORMATION

The Z80 'block copy' instructions, introduced in 2.10, enable one to copy blocks of information (that is, sets of bytes occupying consecutively addressed locations) from one part of the store to another part of the store (which must, of course, be in RAM). Their effect (+ for ED B0, − for ED B8) was written as:

repeat M[DE: ± 1]:= M[HL: ± 1], BC: −1 **until** BC: = 0000;

If such an operation is required on any of the other processors it has to be programmed. Even on the Z80 itself it is worth-while knowing how to program it in terms of simpler instructions if any variation of its operation is required.

On the 8080 and 8085 the same registers can be made available. A direct 'translation' in the form of a subroutine is:

```
(ST: = AF)
01:A: = M
   HL: ± 1
   M[DE]: = A
   DE: ± 1
   BC: −1        ⎫
   A: = B        ⎬
   A:UC          ⎭
   JNZ(L01)
(AF: = ST)
RET
```

Here the first point to notice is that no direct store-to-store copying instruction is available and register A must be used as a 'stepping stone'. The stack operations are written in as optional instructions to make the subroutine 'transparent' to A (that is, to make it appear as if the subroutine does not use A). The 'increment' and 'decrement' instructions do not affect any condition flags, and so the rather ugly trick of the three bracketed instructions is used to test whether the counter has been reduced to zero. (A will be cleared if neither of B, C contains a 'one').

The use of the double-length register for the counter is only necessary if block lengths are likely to exceed 256 bytes. If they will not exceed this amount, a single-length counter is sufficient, and the three bracketed instructions can be replaced simply by B: −1.

It is rather more difficult to translate this into 6800 instructions, for the 6800 has only one addressing register, IX. There is, however, a restricted situation in which a fairly simple subroutine is possible. This is when the two 'starting addresses' are less than 256 bytes apart and there are no more than 256 bytes to be copied. We can then have something like:

```
(S: = A)
01:A: = M00X
   M(j)X: = A        (j) stands for a pair of hexadecimal digits
   IX: ± 1
   B: −1
   JNZ + F8          (to L01)
(A: = S)
RET
```

Here the first 'destination' address is assumed to have a value higher by j than that of the first 'source' address. If the opposite is the case, the 00 and (j) bytes have to be interchanged. In the former case IX is given the first source address before entry, in the latter case the first destination address. The subroutine is unsatisfactory in that in either case (j) has to be 'planted' in the subroutine body—a disreputable programming trick, older even than cores, which nowadays is possible only when the subroutine (or part of it) is held in RAM.

The full range of the Z80 specification requires considerably more elaboration. Since we have in effect three double-length counters in operation we need six bytes of RAM for working space. Before entering the subroutine, the first source address must be placed in MM(source), the first destination address in MM(destination), and the number of bytes to be copied in MM(count).

```
        (S: = A)
   01 :IX: = MM(source)
      A: = M00X
      IX: ± 1
      MM(source): = IX
      IX: = MM(destination)
      M00X: = A
      IX: ± 1
      MM(destination): = IX
      IX: = MM(count)
      IX: − 1
      MM(count): = IX
      JNZ + E4          (to L01)
      (A: = S)
      RET
```

Whether we use a Z80 'block copy' instruction, or one of these subroutines, there is an important point to be considered carefully.

If the source block and the destination block are disjoint (that is, have no location in common) there is no trouble. But if they overlap there may be a danger that locations in the area of overlap may be written into (used as destinations) before they have been copied (used as sources).

This is best seen in a diagram such as Figure 5.1. In case (i), if the copying proceeds by *incrementing*, the source information between (a) and (b) will be lost before it can be copied, but if it proceeds by *decrementing* the whole operation will be done correctly. In case (ii) incrementing will produce the correct result but decrementing will not.

A general rule for achieving correct results, whether there is overlap or not, is as follows. If the lowest source address is *higher* than the lowest destination address, use *incrementing*—go forward. If the lowest source address is *lower* than the lowest destination address, use *decrementing*—go backward. In the latter case the process starts with the *highest* source and destination addresses.

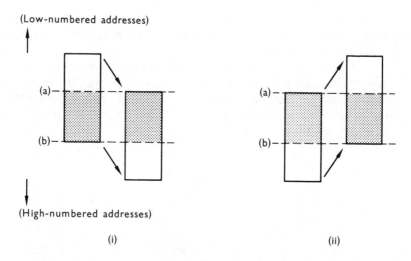

(Low-numbered addresses)

(High-numbered addresses)

(i)   (ii)

Fig. 5.1.

In *comparing* addresses it should be remembered that an address is an unsigned double-length integer. The 6800 operation written 'IX-q' can be used for testing the equality of addresses but not directly for other comparisons (2.4.7).

The monitor 'block copy' operation is described in Chapter 8; it occupies locations 0180 to 01E5.

5.3   SEARCHING A LIST

The Z80 has the 'block search' instructions ED B1 ($+$) and ED B9 ($-$) whose effects (2.10) are:

$$\textbf{repeat } A-M[HL:\pm 1], \ BC:-1 \textbf{ until } BC=0000 \ \lor Z;$$

An 8080–8085 subroutine with the same principal effect is:

```
    ST: = DE
    D: = A
01 :A − M
    HL: ± 1
    BC: − 1
    JZ(L02)
    A: = B
    A:UC
    A: = D
    JNZ(L01)
    K: − 1
02 :DE: = ST
    RET
```

At exit, Z = 0. If K = 0, an element whose value is equal to the value in A has been found, and its address is one less than the value in HL. If K = 1, no match has been found and BC = 0000.

A better subroutine, whose effect is, however, slightly different from that of the Z80 instructions, is (a) below. Here, if K = 0 at exit, HL contains the address of the matched element. The shorter version (b) can be used if there is no need to have the subroutine transparent to D, and version (c) can be used if the block length is never more than 256 bytes.

ST: = DE	D: = A	01:A − M
D: = A	01:A − M	RZ
01:A − M	RZ	HL: ± 1
JZ(L02)	HL: ± 1	B: −1
HL: ± 1	BC: −1	JNZ(L01)
BC: −1	A: = B	K: = 1
A: = B	A:UC	RET
A:UC	A: = D	
A: = D	JNZ(L01)	
JNZ(L01)	K: = 1	
K: = 1	RET	
02:DE: = ST		
RET		
(a)	(b)	(c)

Version (c) translates almost directly into 6800 instructions:

```
01:A − M00X
   JZ+05          (to L02)
   IX: ± 1
   B: −1
   JNZ+F8         (to L01)
   K: = 1
02:RET
```

For block lengths of more than 256 bytes the following is necessary:

```
   MM(address): = starting address
   MM(count): = block length
01:IX: = MM(address)
   A − M00X
   JZ+(to L02)
   IX: ± 1
   MM(address): = IX
   IX: = MM(count)
   IX: −1
   MM(count): = IX
   JNZ+(to L01)
   K: = 1
02:RET
```

However, it may be better to avoid this by partitioning the block into sections of 256 bytes or less.

A frequently required operation is to find the highest or lowest valued element in a block. For example, if the elements of a block are ASCII representations of letters, and these letters have to be arranged or printed in alphabetical order, a search for the lowest element will find the first letter of the new list, or the first letter to be printed. Again, the arrangement of numbers into descending numerical order will begin with a search for the highest element.

A procedure for finding the *lowest* element in a block can be expressed thus:

$m := m0;$
for $i := 1$ **to** n **do**
    if $a_i < m$ **then begin** $m := a_i; j := i$ **end**

Here $m0$ is any number which is *higher* than every element of the block; n is the number of elements in the block; and a_i is the ith element of the block. The procedure goes through the elements one by one; if an element is found to be less than the value in m its value replaces that value and its position is recorded in j. Thus at the end m contains the value of the lowest element and j gives its position.

Suppose the elements are ASCII representations of capital letters. These lie in the (hex) range 41 (A) to 5A (Z). The address of the first element will be in IX (6800) or HL (8080,8085,Z80) and the number of elements in B. The value of the result will

6800	8080, 8085, Z80
A:=5B	C:=5B
01:A−M00X	01:A:=M
JKZ+05 (to L02)	A−C
A:=M00X	JNK(L02)
MM(address):=IX	C:=A
02:IX:+1	D:=H
B:−1	E:=L
JNZ+F3 (to L01)	02:HL:+1
RET	B:−1 ⎫ Z80: one instruction
	JNZ(L01) ⎭
	RET

be in A (6800) or C (8080,8085,Z80) and the address of this lowest element in MM (address) or DE. Where the lowest value belongs to more than one element, the address at exit will be that of the first of these found—that with the lowest address. Changing 'JKZ' to 'JK' in the 6800 version will give that with the highest address.

If this is required (or tolerable) the following 8080–8085–Z80 subroutine is a byte shorter and avoids register C:

```
     A: = 5B
01:A − M
     JK(L02)
     A: = M
     D: = H
     E: = L
02:HL:+1
     B:−1
     JNZ(L01)
     RET              (result value in A, address in DE)
```

In this version, it should be noted that the initial value of m could equally well be 5A, that is exactly the highest possible value. (Then if every letter in the block is Z, at exit A will hold 5A (Z) and DE will hold the address of the last element of the block.)

A search for the *highest* value in a block will be similar, except that the initial value of m should be, depending on the variation used, *less than* or equal to the lowest possible value of an element.

In this example the carry flag K has been used as a discriminant because the values of the elements have been unsigned integers. If, in another example, the elements are signed numbers, then comparison of values and subsequent use of flags will have to take account of the points made in 2.4.7.

If the elements to be examined are not in consecutive locations, but are regularly spaced some small number of bytes apart, these subroutines can be simply modified by introducing further increment instructions (IX:+1 or HL:+1) immediately after the existing one.

If the elements are of multiple length, clearly a multiple-length initial value must be set and multiple-length comparison (see 4.5.2) must be carried out.

5.4   SORTING

Sorting is a considerable subject in its own right which has already filled several textbooks.[1] Here it is possible only to touch briefly on a few of the simplest and most useful methods.

If we have the subroutines of the last section, it will clearly be worth-while to make use of them, either directly or as a source of ideas.

A relatively straightforward problem is that of printing out in numerically descending order a set of numbers which have been stored consecutively as they have been computed. A procedure for this might be expressed as follows:

repeat (find highest member of set;
             print highest member;
             delete member just printed from set) **until** set is empty.

---

[1]Robert P. Rich, *Internal Sorting Methods Illustrated with PL/I Programs*. Englewood Cliffs NJ: Prentice–Hall Inc., 1972.

If the 'delete' step is omitted, the procedure will print the highest value of the set as given over and over again indefinitely. Exactly how deletion is to be effected will depend on (a) whether the list is required to be kept in store for further computation, and (b) the range of values of the elements.

If the list is *not* required after printing, deletion of an element may simply be its replacement by a value beyond the initial value of *m*. This will ensure that it will not be selected for printing again. If there is no available value beyond the initial value of *m*, one trick is to replace the printed element by a copy of the current last element of the block and to reduce the length of the block by one element.

If the list *is* required after printing, there are two main alternatives. If sufficient RAM is available, the list can be copied into free RAM and the printing done from the copy. The other possibility is to 'mark' (rather than 'delete') each element as it is printed, and to use a modified search routine which ignores marked elements. Marking is possible if there is an unused bit in the element which can be used to accommodate the mark; the marks may have to be removed after printing.

In all cases the single step has to be executed *n* times, each time printing the highest remaining value. Thus the whole procedure will have the form of a counting loop, counting down from *n*, which prepares for each step by giving the starting address and length of the block occupied by the (residual) list to the 'find highest' subroutine.

These techniques can be simply adapted if what is required is a sorted list in another part of RAM. The only modification is to replace the call of the printing subroutine by a sequence of instructions which will append the value concerned to a list as a new element.

But perhaps a more frequent requirement is to sort a list in its own space, that is without the use of any 'scratch-pad' working store. The sorting textbooks discuss several methods of varying speed, compactness, and elegance. The method discussed below is not the fastest, but it is certainly one of the simplest.

The algorithm is that of 'Shellsort', an ALGOL 60 procedure by J. Boothroyd based on work by D. A. Shell.[2] The essential text of the procedure is given below. (Readers unfamiliar with ALGOL 60 may skip this; but if they return to it after reading the remainder of this section it should not be too difficult to understand.)

procedure *Shellsort* (a, n); **value** n; **real array** a; **integer** n;
    comment the n elements of the array a are to be sorted into
        numerically ascending order;
    begin integer i, j, k, m; **real** w;
        $m := n$;
        for $m := m \div 2$ **while** $m \neq 0$ **do**
            begin $k := n - m$;
                for $j := 1$ **step** 1 **until** k **do**
                    begin for $i := j$ **step** $-m$ **until** 1 **do**
                        begin if $a_{i+m} \geq a_i$ **then go to** $L1$;

---

[2] J. Boothroyd, 'Algorithm 201'. *Communications ACM*, **6**, 445 (1963); D. A. Shell, 'A high-speed sorting procedure', *Communications ACM*, **2**, 30 (1959).

$$w := a_i; \; a_i := a_{i+m}; \; a_{i+m} := w$$
$$\textbf{end } i;$$
$$L1 : \textbf{end } j;$$
$$\textbf{end } m;$$
$$\textbf{end } Shellsort;$$

comment for descending order replace '$\geq$' by '$\leq$';

A 'literal' translation of the body of this procedure into the notation as so far developed and used in this book is the following.

	begin integer i,j,k,m; **real** w;
$m := n$	$m := n;$
$06 : m : /2$	**for** $m := m \div 2$
JZ(L05)	**while** $m \neq 0$
$k := n - m$	**do begin** $k := n - m;$
$j := 1$	**for** $j := 1$ **step** 1
$04 : k - j$	**until** k
JN(L03)	
$i := j$	**do begin for** $i := j$ **step** $-m$
$02 : i - 1$	**until** 1
JN(L01)	
$a_{i+m} - a_i$	**do begin if** $a_{i+m} \geq a_i$
JNN(L01)	**then go to** $L1;$
$a_{i+m} := : a_i$	$w := a_i; \; a_i := a_{i+m}; \; a_{i+m} := w$
$i : -m$	**end** $i;$
J(L02)	
$01 : j : +1$	$L1 : \textbf{end } j;$
J(L04)	
$03 : \text{NULL}$	**end** $m;$
J(L06)	
$05 : \text{RET}$	**end** $Shellsort$

This can be shortened into a more 'idiomatic' translation for eventual use in a microprocessor as follows.

step	
1	$m := n$
2	$06 : m : /2$
3	RZ
4	$k := n - m$
5	$j := 0$
6	$01 : j : +1$
7	$k - j$
8	JN(L06)

step

9	$i: = j$
10	$02 : i - 1$
11	JN(L01)
12*	$a_{i+m} - a_i$
13	JNN(L01)
14	$a_{i+m} : = : a_i$
15	$i : -m$
16	J(L02)

* (for descending order replace this by $a_i - a_{i+m}$)

Given n elements $a_1, \ldots, a_n$, this procedure sorts them into numerically ascending order so that on exit we have $a_1 \leq a_2 \leq a_3 \leq \ldots \leq a_n$. (With the indicated modification it sorts them into numerically descending order so that on exit $a_1 \geq a_2 \geq a_3 \geq \ldots \geq a_n$.)

The working of the procedure on some small lists of small integers is illustrated in Figure 5.2. The core of the process is the comparison of the values of a pair of elements; these elements are interchanged if they are the 'wrong way round'. In the first stage, the elements are chosen to be $n/2$ positions apart (where '/' stands for truncated integer division, so $10/2 = 5$, $5/2 = 2$, etc.), and all such pairs are examined. For the next stage this separation is halved ($m : /2$); it is now possible for a value to be moved in several steps of m positions from its place at the beginning of the stage towards the top of the list. This is done by comparing it with the elements at the ends of the steps and interchanging, until it meets an element with respect to which it is the 'right way round'. In the final stage, $m = 1$; after this stage the procedure terminates with the elements in the required order.

The reader may find it helpful to work through the steps of the procedure with pencil and paper on, say, the digits of a telephone number.

Before committing any of the procedure to machine code, it is necessary to consider the possible ranges of the variables. In the first version for the 8080/8085 ranges which will lead to the simplest possible subroutine will be assumed.

First, suppose the items to be sorted are unsigned single-length integers. Each occupies one byte, and so the whole list takes a block of RAM n bytes long. The value of n is necessarily positive; and it can be seen from steps 1 to 8 that m, k and j are also positive and none can exceed n in value. For steps 12 and 14, i must be in the range 1 to $n-m$—that is, positive and less than n—but there is a slight problem caused by step 15. This step may make i go negative. (If it does there will be a jump at step 11.) Thus taking i overall, it is a signed variable with a possible range of $-(n/2)$ to $+n$. If we treat i as signed and single-length, then n, m, k, j will be positive and in particular n should not be more than 128.

We can allocate m, n, k, j, i to the registers B, C, D, E, H. The awkward passages of the procedure are going to be steps 12 and 14, where addresses are to be calculated. Leaving these for the time being, there is no difficulty in turning the remainder of the procedure into machine code.

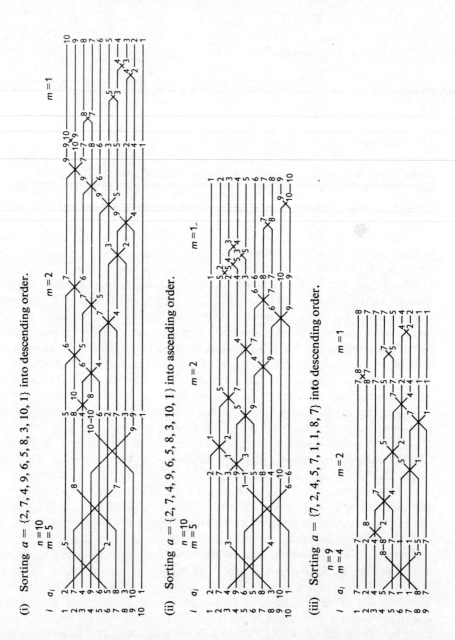

(i) Sorting $a = \{2, 7, 4, 9, 6, 5, 8, 3, 10, 1\}$ into descending order.

(ii) Sorting $a = \{2, 7, 4, 9, 6, 5, 8, 3, 10, 1\}$ into ascending order.

(iii) Sorting $a = \{7, 2, 4, 5, 7, 1, 1, 8, 7\}$ into descending order.

Fig. 5.2. Examples of application of 'Shell sort'

step

1	$m:=n$	B:$=$C;
2	06:m:/2	06:A:$=$B; A:&FE; A:@R; B:$=$A;
3	RZ	RZ;
4	$k:=n-m$	A:$=$C; A:$-$B; D:$=$A;
5	$j:=0$	E:$=$00;
6	01:j:$+1$	01:E:$+1$;
7	$k-j$	A:$=$D; A$-$E;
8	JN(L06)	JN(L06);
9	$i:=j$	H:$=$E;
10	02:$i-1$	02:H:-1;
11	JN(L01)	JN(L01); H:$+1$;
12	$a_{i+m}-a_i$	$a_{i+m}-a_i$;
13	JNN(L01)	JNK(L01);
14	$a_{i+m}:=:a_i$	$a_{i+m}:=:a_i$;
15	$i:-m$	A:$=$H; A:$-$B; H:$=$A;
16	J(L02)	J(L02);

Note that in the machine-code version of line 13 the flag K (carry) rather than N (negative) is used to give the result of comparison of two unsigned integers (cf. Section 2.4.7). The remaining section requires care. Perhaps the best plan on the 8080 is to use the stack to save information during the addressing operations. Suppose this has been done, and we have the address of a_1 in HL, i in A, and m in B. Then we may write:

12	HL:-1;	(notional) address of a_0
	C:$=$A;	i
	A:$=$B;	m
	B:$=$00;	
	HL:$+$BC;	address of a_i in HL
	D:$=$H;	
	E:$=$L;	address of a_i in DE
	C:$=$A;	m
	HL:$+$BC;	address of a_{i+m} in HL
	HL:$=$:DE;	interchange addresses (see text)
	A:$=$M[DE];	a_{i+m}
	A$-$M	$a_{i+m}-a_i$
13	JNK(L01);	
14	B:$=$A;	
	A:$=$M;	
	M[DE]:$=$A;	
	M:$=$B;	$a_{i+m}:=:a_i$

Finally, we have to fit this section into the previous part. A complication arising during this operation is that the base address (that of a_1) will be available in HL at entry to the subroutine, and will have to be preserved for use at each execution of the passage given immediately above. A possible result is given in Figure 5.3 as a completely coded subroutine with entry at 1000.

```
      G2800
1000    41    B:=C;
1001    78    A:=B;
1002    E6    A:&FE;
1004    0F    A:@R;
1005    47    B:=A;
1006    C8    RZ;
1007    79    A:=C;
1008    90    A:-B;
1009    57    D:=A;
100A    1E    E:=00;
100C    1C    E:+1;
100D    7A    A:=D;
100E    BB    A-E;
100F    FA    JN1001;
1012    E5    ST:=HL;
1013    63    H:=E;
1014    25    H:-1;
1015    FA    JN103F;
1018    24    H:+1;
1019    7C    A:=H;
101A    E3    HL:=:ST;
101B    E5    ST:=HL;
101C    D5    ST:=DE;
101D    C5    ST:=BC;
101E    2B    HL:-1;
101F    4F    C:=A;
1020    78    A:=B;
1021    06    B:=00;
1023    09    HL:+BC;
1024    54    D:=H;
1025    5D    E:=L;
1026    4F    C:=A;
1027    09    HL:+BC;
1028    EB    HL:=:DE;
1029    1A    A:=M[DE];
102A    BE    A-M;
102B    D2    JNK1032;
102E    47    B:=A;
102F    7E    A:=M;
1030    12    M[DE]:=A;
1031    70    M:=B;
1032    C1    BC:=ST;
1033    D1    DE:=ST;
1034    E1    HL:=ST;
1035    E3    HL:=:ST;
1036    D2    JNK103F;
1039    7C    A:=H;
103A    90    A:-B;
103B    67    H:=A;
103C    C3    J1014;
103F    E1    HL:=ST;
1040    C3    J100C;

MONITOR
>D1000,1042
1000 41 78 E6 FE 0F 47 C8 79 90 57 1E 00 1C 7A BB FA
1010 01 10 E5 63 25 FA 3F 10 24 7C E3 E5 D5 C5 2B 4F
1020 78 06 00 09 54 5D 4F 09 EB 1A BE D2 32 10 47 7E
1030 12 70 C1 D1 E1 E3 D2 3F 10 7C 90 67 C3 14 10 E1
1040 C3 0C 10
>
```

Fig. 5.3.

Given the value n in C and the address of a_1 in HL, this subroutine sorts the values of $a_1, \ldots, a_n$ into numerically ascending order. If the interchange instruction HL: = :DE is replaced by NULL, the modified subroutine will sort the values into numerically descending order.

There are many possible variations of this subroutine, some of which may be of interest as exercises for the reader. For example:

(i) Length of list. The subroutine can be made to deal with lists of up to 255 elements by adapting the conditional jumps at 100F and 1015. That at 100F can be simply replaced by 'jump if carry', but what of the other? Double-length working throughout will of course allow longer lists to be sorted.

(ii) Elements of other kinds:

(a)   If the elements are *signed* single-length integers, the difference $a_{i+m} - a_i$ may go out of single-length range and the comparison $A - M$ at 102A will then be inadequate—see Sections 2.4.7 and 4.5.2.

(b)   If the elements are *double-length*, then the calculation of addresses, the comparison of elements and the interchange operation all have to be modified.

(c)   An important case of *multiple-length* quantities which may need to be sorted is *names*, made up of varying numbers of letters, to be put into alphabetical order. It would be convenient to have a small block of, say, sixteen bytes reserved for each name. Then each name would be 'left justified' in its block—that is, the initial letter would go into the 'most significant byte' and unused bytes to the right, down to the 'least significant', would be 'padded out', each with a space (ASCII 20). Comparison of names stored in this way is then exactly the same as that of multiple-length unsigned integers. In practice each name is likely to be part of a *record* (Section 5.6), and it is the records which are to be sorted. If the records occupy equal blocks of store, the names will be spaced at equal intervals. This will enable the names to be addressed regularly; the comparison will concern the names only, but the interchange operation will have to affect a pair of complete records.

5.5   'PACKED' INFORMATION—QUANTITIES LESS THAN ONE BYTE IN LENGTH

In almost every application there will be quantities whose range of values is so restricted that they can be held in less than one byte each. A rather artificial example of this is the BCD digit of four bits, held two to a byte; it was discussed at length in Section 4.8. More natural examples are logical conditions, requiring only one bit each. The most important of these are held by condition flags, several of them together making a flag register. In addition, a particular program may be concerned with other conditions, or one-bit variables, and need them to be held as (parts of) ordinary bytes. At least two cases of this have been met already—the marker holding the sign of an input number while its digits are being read (Section 4.4), and the marker indicating that a particular item of a list undergoing some process has been dealt with (Section 5.3).

Suppose we have four quantities a, b, c, d of respectively 1, 2, 3, 2 bits. It may be worthwhile to 'pack' them all into one byte (the standard package) as follows:

7	6	5	4	3	2	1	0
a	b		c			d	

Packing and unpacking sequences will be something like the following:

A:$=a$	B:$=$A
$2\times$ A:$+$A ($2\times$ A:$*2$)	A:&03
A:$+b$	d:$=$A
$3\times$ A:$+$A	A:$=$B
A:$+c$	A:&1C
$2\times$ A:$+$A	$2\times$ A:@R ($2\times$ A:$->$)
A:$+d$	c:$=$A
	A:$=$B
	A:&60
	$3\times$ A:@L ($5\times$ A:$->$)
	b:$=$A
	A:$=$B
	A:&80
	A:@L ($2\times$ AK:@L)
	a:$=$A

The sequence on the left packs a, b, c, and d into one byte in register A; that on the right unpacks the byte given in A into its four components. The notation '$2\times$', '$3\times$', '$5\times$' to the left of an instruction indicates that that instruction should be written 2, 3 or 5 times. Instructions in brackets are alternatives with equivalent effects in the example.

In the *monitor* (Section 8.2.3), the X-branch has to unpack a copy of the flag register into its five one-bit values, and it has to be able to assemble five given bits into a byte for the flag register (024D–0263, 0312–031E; 0296–02AB, 031F–032C).

The *disassembler* (Section 8.4) treats each operation-code byte in the program on which it is operating as a packed byte. The 8080 code, as can be seen clearly in the Karnaugh map for it in Chapter 3, falls into the following main packets:

01......	inter-register transfers, r_1:$=r_2$ (but not 01110110)
10......	accumulator operations, Aopr
11...110	accumulator operations, AopJ
11...0.1	conditional jumps and returns
11...100	conditional calls
11..0.01	stack operations
11...111	special subroutine calls

00...0.1	double-length register operations
00...10.	single-length register operations
00...110	single-length register operations
00...010	fetch or store
00...111	shifts and miscellaneous
11..1.01	miscellaneous
11...011	miscellaneous
00...000	null or undefined

The disassembler recognizes the operation code '10010101' (95) as an accumulator operation by its two left-most bits. It then separates the 'operator field', the next three bits '010', meaning ':−', and the 'register field', the last three bits '101', meaning 'L'. Using a simple table look-up for each of these, it prints 'A' followed by ':−' followed by 'L' for the whole instruction 'A:−L' (8.8, 28A3 et seq).

Conversely, the *assembler* (8.3), given the form 'A:−L', has to pack elements corresponding to 'A'(accumulator operation), ':−'(subtraction), 'L'(register) together to form the object-program byte '10010101' (8.8, 04A6 et seq).

5.6   RECORDS AND FILES

Packed information frequently forms part of each of the *records* of a *file*. The idea of a file comes from bookkeeping, where it means a set of records in a common form, each concerned with a particular account. 'File' in computing now usually has the more general sense of a set of pieces of information, called 'records', each piece having the same 'structure'—that is, consisting of the same number of 'items' of information or 'fields' related to each other in a common way.

A simple file in this sense would be a picture for display by a visual display unit (v.d.u.), each point of which has a record consisting of a pair of coordinate values, perhaps one byte each. In a more complicated file, a record might be a set of instrument readings—for example, clock time, various temperatures, pressures, etc.— so that the file represents the history of a physical process.

The 'processing' of a file usually means carrying out the same operation on each of its records in sequence ('sequential processing') or on a selection of records in some computed order ('random access processing'). In the example of the picture, the translation, rotation or scaling of the picture would be achieved by applying a common transformation to the records. In the 'physical process' example, reports on interesting events can be made on the basis of records satisfying certain criteria.

In many existing microcomputer applications, file processing takes place, but is hardly recognized as such. If all the records are in RAM together at the same time—as in the sorting and searching examples of Sections 5.3 and 5.4—the fact that they form a file seems to be of little consequence. 'Serious' file processing concerns files held in secondary store (Section 1.3.1)—typically, sequential files on magnetic tape (cassette?) and random-access files on discs. These devices and the programming associated with them are outside the scope of this book.

5.7   SPECIAL PERIPHERAL DEVICES

Various interfaces between a microprocessor system and a console device were briefly discussed in Section 2.7. Many peripheral devices can be managed with a very much simpler interface. For example an *on/off switch* S to be controlled by the computer program need *logically* have no more than what is shown in Figure 5.4.

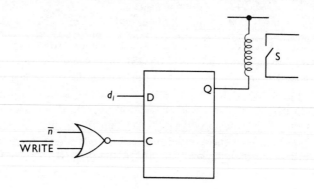

Fig. 5.4

Here the switch S is open while $Q = 1$ and closed while $Q = 0$. The value of Q is that of D when a pulse is received at C. A pulse will be received at C if a 'write' pulse from the microprocessor occurs while the address 'n' is decoded from the address bus. At the time Q will take the value of bit d_i of the data bus.

Thus $A := 00$ (or any other value with $d_i = 0$)

$M(n) := A$ (or '$G(n) := A$' if applicable)

will *close* the switch S,

and $A := FF$ (or any other value with $d_i = 1$)

$M(n) := A$ (or '$G(n) := A$' if applicable)

will *open* the switch S.

Instead of the relay containing S, the connection to Q might be some other device such as a logic circuit which can be activated by a *pulse* from Q. The sequence of instructions

$$\left.\begin{array}{l} A := 00 \\ M(n) := A \\ A := FF \\ M(n) := A \\ A := 00 \\ M(n) := A \end{array}\right\} \quad \text{(or variations suggested above)}$$

will generate a pulse at Q. The *width* of this pulse will be the time between corresponding phases of the fourth and sixth instructions, when the flip-flop is clocked. This is the same as the sum of the execution times of the last two instructions.

Execution times in terms of clock periods are given in the 'dictionary' at the end of Chapter 3. For this example, with near-maximum clock frequencies the pulse width will be between 5 and 7 µs. If such a pulse width is acceptable, this is all well and good. If a shorter width is required, it may be necessary to put a monostable with suitable timing components at Q. For longer pulses, a monostable may still be usable, but it is also possible to program a desired time by inserting time-killing instructions between the last two output instructions. A 'NULL' will take between 1 and 2 µs; other instructions take longer than this, but of course care must be exercised in their choice. Delays of up to 1 or $1\frac{1}{2}$ ms can be achieved by means of a simple counting loop:

```
     A: = some value
01:A:−1
   JNZ(L01)
```

Use of a double-length register will give a time range up to $\frac{1}{4}$ or $\frac{1}{3}$ s. Of course, in all cases precise timings depend on the actual clock frequency.

Warning: Programs containing time-critical passages may need to be adapted before being run on a new system. Although the 8080 and 8085 have substantially the same instruction set, their timings are different in many cases. Over the common part of the instruction set, the Z80 timings also differ from those of the 8080.

In practice, the interface in Figure 5.4 will not be made up of additional discrete logic components, but it will be found to be part of an existing output port. For example, the Intel 8212 contains eight copies of the circuit shown and may be used to control up to eight outputs of the type discussed. The parallel interface adaptors mentioned in Section 1.4.1 can also be used, for 16 or 24 output lines. In all cases the programming considerations are the same and the same techniques can be used for managing pulse widths.

For a one-bit input device, probably the simplest interface is that shown in Figure 5.5. An instruction such as 'A: = M(n)' will cause the three-state buffer to be enabled and the value of the input bit X to be read to bit i of register A. Again, the 8212 and the parallel interfaces can supply the hardware functions.

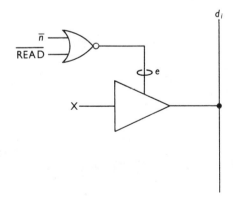

Fig. 5.5

Unfortunately, not all inputs can be treated so simply. If there are any restrictions on the validity of the signal at X inherent in the complete system, such as time periods when it is undefined, a more complicated interface will be required. That is outside the scope of this book.

The input–output techniques described above have proved adequate for the interface to the PROM programmer (Sections 8.1, 8.2.5). Figure 5.6 shows how it is connected to the 6820 for a 6800 system and to the 8255 for an 8080 system (see Section 1.4.1). The eight 'data' lines are used both as inputs and, at other times, as outputs in the manner described above. The 'program' pulse is carefully measured; the 'count' pulse can be of almost any width. The other outputs are simply levels. The one control input (counter overflow) can fortunately be simply read at any time.

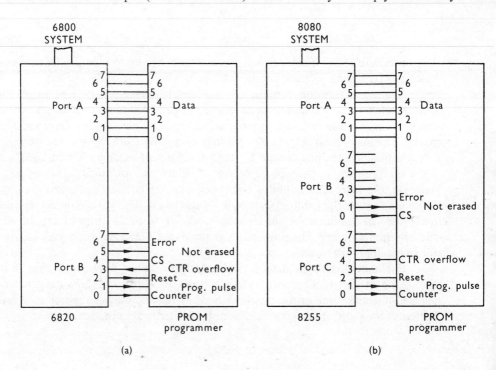

Fig. 5.6

6

Programming at higher levels

6.1 BASIC TOOLS FOR PROGRAMMING AT MACHINE-CODE LEVEL

In Section 4.1 the features of a rudimentary monitor program were described. With such a minitor it is possible to work through the examples and exercises of Chapters 4 and 5. It is also possible to go on to write and test substantial programs—but most programmers would find the task tedious, boring, repetitive and unreasonably slow. To overcome this, and if possible to make programming an agreeable activity, we need a good, reliable set of software 'tools', or programming aids which will enable the chores of programming to be passed on to the machine itself.

We have so far been working entirely at 'machine-code level'. That means that the solution to every problem has been found in terms of the instructions of a microprocessor's instruction set. Although, on paper, we have been able to use a fairly readable notation for these instructions, they have had to be expressed as pairs of hexadecimal digits for typing into the system. The only sense in which the work has not been altogether conducted at this level is that use has been made of the provision for subroutines; by building up a collection of useful subroutines we have made it possible to invoke any of a number of quite complex operations at any point in a program for the price of a single instruction.

There are three immediate ways in which the programmer's lot can be improved:

(i) the monitor can be extended to provide more and better facilities for the testing, correction and running of programs;
(ii) the subroutine collection can be put into PROMs, and arrangements put in hand for the development of the 'software library';
(iii) means whereby instructions in their written form can be typed in directly, to be converted to machine-code by the computer itself, can be provided.

A *monitor* whose facilities are described below (6.1.1) forms part of the software package of Chapter 8. It occupies 864 (decimal) bytes (0000–035F) with its subroutines; a technical description is given in 8.2. The *subroutines* which have been developed, described or referred to in Chapters 4 and 5 are listed below in 6.2 with the information required for their proper use. Technical descriptions will be found in 8.2.2, 8.2.4, 8.5 and 8.6 and their text with annotations is in 8.8. Clearly, the choice of subroutines to be held permanently in PROM, and of others to be held on secondary storage media such as cassettes, paper tape or the written page, is a matter for each user, or each group of users, to decide.

For (iii) what is needed is a program which will, among other things to be discussed later, read in any instruction in the form used by the programmer in writing, and generate the corresponding byte or bytes of machine code. The notation used in this book requires, for each microprocessor, about $1\frac{1}{2}$K bytes of 'transcription routines'. To be at all practical, a transcription program will be written to read a sequence of instructions, perhaps to print the machine-code version of each immediately after it is read, but certainly to store the sequence of machine-code bytes so that after the whole transcription operation there will be a program in store ready to run when required. To be really worth-while, this transcription program will provide further facilities which, fortunately, require little additional space or effort.

As we have seen in the examples, 'absolute' (explicit) addresses are often unknown at the time when a program is being written. The extent of a relative jump, in any case not easy to count, may be subject to change. So the *assembler* (if that is what it is to be called) will need to read labels and to be able to deal with references to labels. How this can be managed is shown in 8.3. At the same time means for establishing constants and defining working storage space can be implemented. The assembler for the 8080 given in Chapter 8 (technical description in 8.3, text in 8.8) provides these facilities in about $2\frac{1}{4}$K bytes. Users' instructions are given below, in 6.1.2.

A complementary program, a *disassembler*, will be found extremely useful. Such a program, requiring about 1K bytes (more for the Z80, less for the 8080) will take a (piece of) program held in the store and print out an 'assembly language' transcription. The 8080 disassembler given in Chapter 8 (technical description in 8.4, text in 8.8, 2800–2B7F) has been used to prepare the illustrations in this book. It is in practice used much more frequently than the assembler—it gives a readable and accurate document after a program has been modified or corrected. Users' instructions are in 6.1.3 below.

These programming aids and a PROM programmer with its software (6.1.4) will go a long way towards meeting the need expressed in the opening paragraph above. Even so, we shall still be working entirely at the level of machine code, for the assembler (and disassembler) maintain a one-to-one correspondence between written instructions and machine instructions. In 6.3 the question of programming at higher levels will be introduced.

6.1.1 Monitor

When the system is switched on, or reset, or when the monitor is called by another program, the message 'MONITOR' is printed or displayed, followed by the *cue-mark* '>' at the left-hand margin of the next line. The cue-mark is also printed at the completion of any of the operations D, I, M, S, X described below. It means that the monitor is ready to receive an instruction for immediate execution. Each monitor instruction is one letter (D, G, I, M, R, S, X) possibly followed by one or more addresses as specified below. An *address* must be typed as exactly four unseparated hexadecimal digits, and a *byte* as two unseparated hexadecimal digits. On detecting any false keyboard operation, the monitor will abandon the execution of its current instruction, print '?'. and then a cue-mark on a new line. In the following, actual numerical values are used as examples, and any such value may be replaced by any other of the same length. In all cases 'comma' (',') may be replaced by 'space'.

D—*'display'*. Typing in 'D1234,1269' will cause all information from the start address 1234 to the finish address 1269 inclusive to be printed in hexadecimal, thus:

```
D1234,1269
1234 B9  19  5B  08  00  1F  6B  04  3B  CB  24  99
1240 FE  2A  77  08  FB  48  DD  14  ED  09  FE  85  FF  4E  E5  02
1250 FF  A3  FB  42  E9  6C  7D  20  FF  92  FB  CF  F7  1A  FF  06
1260 FB  04  37  03  4E  03  05  02  FB  03
>
```

The display may be abandoned at any time while it is in progress by pressing 'escape', thus:

```
D1234,1269
1234 B9  19  5B  08  00  1F  6B  04  3B  CB  24  99
1240 FE  2A  77  08  FB  48  DD  14  ED  09  FE  85  FF  4E  E5  02
1250 FF  A3  FB  42  E9  6C  7D  20
>
```

G—*'go'*. Typing in 'G1234' causes the response 'newline' followed by a jump to 1234 with the flags and registers having the values they had when the monitor was last entered, subject to any changes by 'X', below. See also 'R'.

I—*'input'*. This is used for loading a succession of byte values into consecutive locations in RAM, beginning at a start address. Typing in 'I1234' causes the response 'new line'; the machine will now read any number of pairs of hex digits, assigning their values to consecutive locations. In typing, space, comma and return characters may be used freely to break up the layout of the bytes on the paper or screen, but the two digits of a byte may not be separated. Separators will not be stored. The operation is terminated by pressing the 'escape' key. All completed pairs of digits will have been stored. (Any input character other than a hex digit in place of the second digit of a pair will cause a failure response. The location to which the odd digit would have been assigned is unaffected. All completed bytes will have been stored.)

M—*'copy'*. Typing 'M1234,1269,1475' causes the block of information at locations 1234 to 1269 inclusive to be *copied* into locations 1475 to 14AA inclusive, which must of course be in RAM. For other values of the addresses, the destination block may partly overlie the source block, but it will on completion always hold a copy of the original source block—see 5.2. There will be a failure if the second address is lower than the first address.

Note: 'M' does *not* stand for 'move'. The source block may be partly over-written, but with this exception it remains where it was.

R—*'resume program'.* Typing 'R' causes the response 'newline'. The program from which the monitor was last called is then resumed where it left off—see 'break-points', below. More precisely, if a program has called the monitor by 'JSS1' (hex CF), and in the meantime only D, I, M, S or X instructions not affecting PC (see 'X' below) have been executed, then there will be a jump to the address immediately after that of the location holding the 'CF', with the saved flag and register values as possibly modified by 'X'.

S—*'substitute'.* This is used for examining and, if required, modifying the contents of individual locations in store, or of small groups of consecutive locations. Type 'S' followed by an address followed by a space or comma; the machine will respond by displaying the value held at that address, followed by a hyphen (minus sign '−'). Any new value can now be typed in, or the existing value can be left un-disturbed (no key operation). If a space or comma is now typed, the machine will display the value held at the next address, followed by a hyphen. Again, this value can be accepted or replaced. If 'return' is typed, the operation is concluded.

X—*'examine registers'.* Typing 'X' causes a display of the flag and register values to be printed as follows:

```
> X
NZHPK     A     BC     DE     HL     SP     PC
0 1 0 1 0     27    0D3E   F3 B2   00C3   17F2   00 21
```

If any flag-value is to be changed, type in a new set of five bits. The carriage will then move the remaining two spaces to align with 'A'. If no flag-value is to be changed, press the space bar once; the carriage will move to 'A'.

A new value for 'A' may now be typed in; a space will move the carriage to 'BC'. The remaining registers are treated as double-length; any may be changed by typing in a four-digit value at the proper position. The whole operation may be finished at any stage by typing 'return'.

Note: 'PC' shows the address to be used by a following 'R' instruction, if any; altering PC during an X-operation and following this by R has the same effect as a G to the same new address (PC value).

Although control can be returned to the monitor at any time by application of the RESET signal, and this is the only possibility for retrieving the situation when one's program has gone astray, it will be found to be good practice to end a program dynamically with 'JSS1' (hex CF). This gives a proper entry to the monitor preserving all flag and register values. In addition, it will be helpful to place *breakpoints* at judicious intervals in the program. For each breakpoint, place a 'JSS1' (CF) instruc-tion. During the execution of the program, at each breakpoint the monitor will be called and its facilities can be used to investigate matters and make any necessary corrections or alterations. Then 'R' can be used to resume the program. Removal of breakpoints is easily effected by replacing each 'CF' by '00' (NULL), using the 'S' instruction.

6.1.2 Assembler

The assembler requires the monitor and its subroutines in order to operate correctly. As given in Chapter 8 it is capable of generating an object program of up to 1646 (decimal) bytes in length.

Instructions must be presented in the forms listed for the 8080 in Chapter 3. In the instruction lists, '12' appears throughout as an example of a single-byte value. It may be replaced by any other value expressed as two hexadecimal digits. This value becomes the second (J) byte of the generated machine code instruction.

The value '1234' is given throughout the lists as an example of a double-length value which becomes the second and third (J and K) bytes of the generated machine-code instruction. (So, for example, 'J1234' gives rise to 'C3 34 12'.) Any such value may be replaced by any of a number of different forms defined below. In these forms 'h' stands for a hexadecimal digit which may be freely chosen at each occurrence. The forms are:

(i)   hhhh   (exactly) four hex digits (explicit form)

(ii)   (Lhh)   (label form)—note *two* hex digits—this will be translated by the assembler into the address of the label 'hh'—see below

(iii)   (Xh)   this will be translated into the starting address of the Xh block

(iv)   (Xh ± hh)   the address hh bytes above (+) or below (−) the starting address of the Xh block. *Note* that hh here is an *unsigned* integer, and so the range ± hh is ± 255 (decimal)

(v)   (I ± hh)   translated into the address hh bytes above or below that of the (statically) following instruction. Again, hh is *unsigned*.

Any instruction may be prefixed by a *label* of the form 'hh:'. In the implementation of Chapter 8 only the 64 (decimal) labels '00:' to '3F:' are provided for. In particular the first instruction of a subroutine should be labelled—so, for example, if a subroutine begins with '07:A: = B' it may be called by 'JS(L07)'.

'X-blocks', each of not more than 255 (decimal) bytes and not more than sixteen in number, may be declared at the head of the source program. For example, a program may begin:

> X0:20;
>
> X3:10;
>
> XE:80;
>
> 01:A: = 00;

In the corresponding object program, the starting address of the X0 block will be 1000 (the first RAM address); that of the X3 block will be 1020; that of the XE block will be 1030; and the label '01:' will have the address 10B0. The form of declaration is 'Xh:hh'—no X-declaration may come after the first instruction of the program. X-blocks are used (i) to reserve working-space in RAM, and (ii) to locate the first instruction of the object program at a particular address

Immediately after the last X-declaration (if any), or immediately after any unconditional jump (not subroutine jump) or unconditional return instruction, a block of constant values may be inserted. For this there is an 'assembler-directive' written 'VALUES' which would normally be labelled, thus:

> 02:VALUES;
> 'ASCII-STRING'

The assembler inserts the ASCII values of the characters between quotation marks into consecutive locations starting at the address of the label. Also:

> 03:VALUES;
> #01 23 45 67#

inserts the values represented by the pairs of hexadecimal digits. (Here there must be an even number of digits; space, line feed, return between pairs are ignored; the digits of a pair must not be separated.)

The assembler is entered by the monitor instruction 'G0C00'. X-declarations (if any), instructions and constant blocks may now be typed in. Each one must be terminated by ';' or 'return'. The machine will then print (display) a semicolon and up to three bytes of object code as appropriate, before returning to the beginning of a new line for the next. If the instruction as presented refers to a label which has not yet been placed, the machine prints 'FD' ('forward') as the third byte. Otherwise, the machine prints the final form of the second and third bytes, as described above. If an instruction is incorrectly typed, it may be cancelled by typing 'rub out' ('delete'); the machine will print '?' but will add no new bytes to the object program; a further attempt at typing the instruction can now be made. However, if the ';' or 'return' terminating the mis-typed instruction has been entered, the machine will generate three blank bytes (00 00 00) for the object code. It may also print '?'.

The end of the program (that is, the end of its text) must be indicated by the directive 'FINISH'. When this is recognized, the machine will fill in the 'FD' addresses and return to monitor control.

At this point the RAM contains the following information which can be displayed by means of the monitor instructions:

1180 onwards	instructions and constant values of the object program
1010–1011	address of location immediately after last byte of object program
1020–103D	starting addresses of blocks X1 to XF. X0 begins at 1000. MM $(1020+2h)$ has starting address of $X(h-1)$
103E–103F	address of first instruction of program for execution
1040–10BF	addresses of labels. At run-time, label hh will be at the location given by MM$(1040+2hh)$.

Prior to execution, the instructions and constants of the object program must be *copied* to the location specified in MM103E. This can be simply done by the monitor instruction 'M1180,x,y' where $x = $ MM1010-1 and $y = $ MM103E. (Note that $y = 1000$ if there are no X-blocks.)

In Section 4.7.6 there is a record of the assembly and execution of a simple program.

6.1.3 Disassembler

The disassembler is called by the monitor instruction 'G2800'. Its output is as given in 8.8 and in several illustrations. The start address and finish address for a call on the disassembler are the values given in HL and DE respectively, usually by a monitor 'X' instruction. More precisely, if at the call HL $= x$ and DE $= y$, the print-out will (if $x < y$) begin at location x and continue until the last instruction whose I-byte is at an address less than y has been printed. The disassembler ends by calling the monitor with 'JSS1' (CF).

The disassembler is not able to distinguish between instructions and other types of information. If it is allowed to operate on, for example, a block of numerical values, the result will be nonsense.

6.1.4 Programming and reading PROMs

The programs at 0360 and 03C0 can be used only if there is a particular type of PROM programmer interfaced as indicated in 5.7. This programmer is designed for the 2708/8708 1K PROM. If a blank PROM is installed in the programmer and the programming program is called by 'G0360', then the information in RAM locations 1000–13FF will be written into the PROM. The program checks for the erased condition of the PROM at the beginning, and at the end it reads the newly programmed PROM byte by byte to compare its contents with those of the source. In the event of a discrepancy a warning lamp is lit. A call of the PROM-reading program by 'G03C0' will cause the information in the PROM installed in the programmer to be copied into RAM locations 1000–13FF. (If there is no such PROM the RAM will be filled with one-bits.)

Taken in conjunction with the monitor facilities, these programs enable PROMs to be programmed and edited very conveniently. They are all that has been used for the software of this book.

The programs will, of course, have to be replaced if some other type of programmer or some other type of PROM is to be used.

6.2 SUBROUTINES

In order to use a subroutine we have to know what it does (its *result*, the registers and the subroutines if any that it *uses*), what information it needs in order to do it (*entry*), what information it leaves behind (*exit*), what happens if it is called with invalid data (*failure*), any special features (*notes*), as well as the address of its first instruction.

This information for the subroutines of Chapter 8 is given below in four sections: input (6.2.1), output (6.2.2), fixed-point arithmetic (6.2.3), and floating-point arithmetic (6.2.4). (There are several other subroutines in Chapter 8, but they were written for specific application and are unlikely to be of use in other contexts.)

6.2.1 Input

'A: = inchar' at 0038 (called by JSS7, hex FF)
> *Result:* ASCII character read from keyboard into A and C.
> *Exit:* ASCII value (no parity bit, 4.2) in A, C.
> *Uses:* A, C.

'In-out' at 0020 (called by JSS4, hex E7)
> *Result:* ASCII character read from keyboard and 'echoed' (see 6.2.2) to printer (screen).
> *Exit:* A, B, C all contain ASCII value of (last) character output.
> *Uses:* A, B, C; subroutines at 0010, 0038.

'In string (ESC)' at 03EC
> *Entry:* Destined address of first character of string in HL.
> *Result:* String of ASCII characters read, printed and written into store at given address onwards. Terminating symbol 'escape' (1B) ends operation and is stored.
> *Exit:* HL has location of 'escape' character.
> *Uses:* A, B, C, H, L, subroutines at 0018,0038.

'A: = in byte' at 0220
> *Result:* Reads pair of hex digits and combines them into 1 byte leaving resultant value in A.
> *Exit:* Result in A; hex value of first digit in D.
> *Uses:* A, B, C, D; subroutines at 0010, 0020, 0028, 0038, 01E6.
> *Failure* exit to monitor if either digit is not one of 0–9, A–F.
> *Late entries:* If the ASCII value of the first digit is already in A, the subroutine may be entered at 0221. If the hex (binary) value of the first digit is already in A, the subroutine may be entered at 0225.

'HL: = in address' at 01F7
> *Result:* Reads four hex digits and combines them into one double-length integer, in HL.
> *Exit:* Result in HL, second byte also in A.
> *Uses:* A, B, C, D, H, L; subroutines at 0010, 0020, 0028, 0038, 0220, 01E6.

'A: = in decimal integer' at 0E74
> *Result:* Reads signed decimal integer n ($-128 \leq n \leq +127$), optional sign and up to three digits, and leaves its binary value in A.
> *Exit:* Value of n in A; terminating character (ASCII) in C.
> *Failure* exit to monitor if integer out of range or incorrect character read.
> *Uses:* A, B, C, D, E; subroutines at 0020, 0028, 01E6.

'HL: = in decimal integer' at 0EBA
> *Result:* Reads signed decimal integer n ($-32768 \leq n \leq +32767$), optional sign and up to five digits, and converts to binary leaving value in HL.
> *Exits:* Value of n in HL; terminating character (ASCII) in C.
> *Failure* exit to monitor if integer out of range or incorrect character read.
> *Uses:* All registers; subroutines at 0020, 0028, 01E6.

'DEHL: = in f.p. number' at 2745 (floating-point read)

    Results: Reads decimal floating-point number from keyboard and converts this binary floating point (4.7.1), leaving value in DEHL.

    Exit: Value in DEHL; terminating character lost.

    Uses: all registers; subroutines at 0020, 0E74, 25A3, 264B, 26EC, 265B.

    Notes: (i)   Form of input: for mantissa, optional sign and sequence of digits with or without one decimal point; and for exponent, 'E' and optionally signed single-length integer terminated by a non-digit.

        (ii)   Limits of input value x: $2.9388E-38 \leq |x| \leq 3.4028E+38$. No more than 7 digits in mantissa—checks on validity of input are not exhaustive—*failure* exit to monitor if check finds error.

        (iii)   Constants: f.p. constants held as follows: 10 at 27DF, 100 at 27E3, 10^4 at 27E7, 10^8 at 27EB, 10^{16} at 27EF, 10^{32} at 27F3.

6.2.2 Output

'Out char (C)' at 0018 (called by JSS3, hex DF)

    Entry: ASCII value (4.2) in C.

    Result: Corresponding character printed (displayed).

    Exit: A, C both have given ASCII value.

    Uses: A, C.

'Echo' at 0010 (called by JSS2, hex D7)

    Entry: ASCII value in C.

    Result: Prints '$' for 1B ('escape'); prints 'return' followed by 'line feed' for 0D ('return'); prints character corresponding to given value otherwise.

    Exit: A, B, C all contain ASCII value of (last) character printed.

    Uses: A, B, C; subroutine at 0018.

'CRLF', 'newline' at 0200

    Result: Outputs 'return' followed by 'line feed'.

    Exit: A = B = C = 0A.

    Uses: A, B, C; subroutines at 0010, 0018.

'Out string (B)' at 005F

    Entry: String of ASCII values in consecutive store locations; the number of them in B; the address of the first in HL.

    Result: The string of corresponding characters printed.

    Exit: B = 00; HL increased by number of characters printed; ASCII value of last printed character in A, C.

    Uses: A, B, C, H, L; subroutine at 0018.

'Out string (ESC)' at 03F6

    Entry: String of ASCII values in consecutive store locations; the last must be '1B' Address of the first in HL.

    Result: The string of corresponding characters printed up to but excluding 'escape' (1B).

    Uses: A, B, C, H, L; subroutine at 0018.

'Out byte (A)' at 0204
>   *Entry:* Byte to be printed, in A.
>   *Result:* Prints value of A as two hexadecimal digits.
>   *Uses:* A, B, C; subroutines at 0018, 0030.

'Out decimal integer (A)' at 0E68
>   *Entry:* Signed binary integer in A.
>   *Result:* Prints value of integer, sign and up to three decimal digits, right-justified in field of six characters' width.
>   *Uses:* All registers; subroutines at 0018, 005F, 0DCA.

'Out decimal integer (HL)' at 0DCA
>   *Entry:* Double-length signed binary integer in HL.
>   *Result:* Prints value of integer, sign and up to five decimal digits, right-justified in field of six characters' width.
>   *Uses:* All registers; subroutines at 0018, 005F.

'Out decimal fraction (HL)' at 07E6
>   *Entry:* Fraction x, $0 \leq x < 1$, represented by unsigned integer $x \times 2^{16}$ in HL.
>   *Result:* Prints decimal point and first five decimal places of value of x.
>   *Exit:* $B = 00$.
>   *Uses:* All registers; subroutines at 0018, 0231, 0C1A, 0CF1.
>   *Late entry:* If the number n of required digits (where $1 \leq n \leq 16$) is already in B, the subroutine can be entered at 07E8.

'Out signed fraction (HL 15 b.p.)' at 24EB
>   *Entry:* Value x, $|x| < 1$, represented by signed integer $x \times 2^{15}$ in HL.
>   *Result:* Value of x printed as sign, '0.', and four decimal digits.
>   *Uses:* All registers; subroutines at 0018, 07EB, 0F93.
>   *Note:* Entry at 24E8 causes result to be preceded by a space.

'F.p. print (DEHL)' at 2B80 (floating-point print)
>   *Entry:* Floating-point value (4.7.1) of x in DEHL.
>   *Result:* Decimal floating-point value of x printed.
>   *Uses:* All registers; subroutines at 0020, 0E74, 25A3, 264B, 26EC, 265B.
>   *Notes:*   (i)   Form of output: for mantissa m, sign and five decimal places, value normalized so that $m = 0$ or $1 \leq |m| \leq 10$ (thus both 1.00000 and 10.00000 are possible); for exponent, 'E' followed by integer—no sign printed for positive value.
>   (ii)   The binary-to-decimal conversion may cause error of up to $\pm 4 \times 10^{-5}$ in printed value of mantissa.

6.2.3   Fixed-point arithmetic

'ASCII-Hex' at 0028 (called by JSS5, hex EF)
>   *Entry:* ASCII value (4.2) in A; value in 30 to 39 (for 0 to 9) or 41 to 46 (for A to F) expected—see 'Check hex' below.
>   *Result:* (If given value as expected) corresponding hex (binary) value in A (range 00 to 0F).
>   *Uses:* A.

'Hex-ASCII' at 0030 (called by JSS6, hex F7)
>   *Entry:* Value in range 00 to 0F in A (see 'Check hex' below).
>   *Result:* ASCII value of corresponding hex digit in A.
>   *Uses:* A.

'Check hex' at 01E6
>   *Entry:* Value to be checked, in A.
>   *Result:* Null if value in A is in range 00 to 0F.
>   *Failure* exit to monitor otherwise. Alters no registers.

'HL − DE' at (i) 0231, (ii) 0C1A
>   *Entry:* Unsigned double-length integers in HL, DE.
>   *Result:* Flags N, Z set according to the value of HL − DE.
>   *Exit:* HL, DE unchanged.
>   *Uses:* (i) A, B, C; (ii) A only.
>   *Note:* See 4.5.2.

'HL:-DE' at 0CF1
>   *Entry:* Double-length integers x, y in HL, DE respectively.
>   *Result:* Double-length value $(x-y)$ in HL.
>   *Exit:* Result in HL, y in DE.
>   *Uses:* A, HL, (DE).

'AHL:−CDE' at 25D8
>   *Entry:* Triple-length integers x in AHL, y in CDE.
>   *Result:* Triple-length value $(x-y)$ in AHL.
>   *Exit:* Result in AHL, y in CDE.
>   *Uses:* AHL, (CDE).

'HL:/2' at 24CF
>   *Entry:* Signed number in HL.
>   *Result:* This number rounded and shifted down one place, signed, in HL.
>   *Exit:* Result in HL.
>   *Uses:* A, HL, subroutine at 0FF1.

'AHL:/2' at 2568 and at 2577; 'AHL:/2^B' at 2583 and at 258B
>   See 4.7.3.1.

'HL: = C × E (unsigned)' at 0F20
>   *Entry:* Unsigned integers x in C, y in E.
>   *Result:* Unsigned value of $x \times y$ in HL.
>   *Exit:* Result in HL, B = D = 00, C = x, E = y.
>   *Uses:* A, B, (C), D, (E), H, L.

'HL: = C × E (signed)' at 0F3A
>   *Entry:* Signed integers x in C, y in E.
>   *Result:* Signed value of $x \times y$ in HL.
>   *Exit:* Result in HL, B = D = 00, C = x, E = y.
>   *Uses:* A, B, (C), D, (E), H, L; subroutines at 0F18, 0F20, 0F32.

‘DE: $= D \times E$ (unsigned)’ at 0F44
  Entry: Unsigned integers x in D, y in E.
  Result: Unsigned value of $x \times y$ in DE.
  Exit: Result in DE; other registers unchanged.
  Uses: D, E, subroutine at 0F20.

‘DEHL: $= BC \times DE$ (unsigned)’ at 2400
  Entry: 16-bit unsigned integers x in BC, y in DE.
  Result: 32-bit unsigned integer $x \times y$ in DEHL.
  Exit: Result in DEHL, x in BC.
  Uses: A, (BC), DE, HL.

‘DEHL: $= BC \times DE$ (signed)’ at 2420
  Entry: 16-bit signed integers x in BC, y in DE.
  Result: 32-bit signed integer $x \times y$ in DEHL.
  Exit: Result in DEHL.
  Uses: All registers; subroutine at 2400.

‘HL: $= BC \times DE$ (15 b.p.)’ at 2440
  Entry: x, 15 b.p., in BC; y, 15 b.p., in DE; $-1 \leq x,y < +1$.
  Result: $x \times y$, 15 b.p. in HL (except for $x = y = -1$).
  Exit: Result in HL.
  Uses: All registers; subroutines at 2400, 2420.

‘BCDEHL: $= BHL \times CDE$ (signed)’ at 250A
  Entry: 24-bit signed integers x in BHL, y in CDE.
  Result: 48-bit signed integer $x \times y$ in BCDEHL.
  Exit: Result in BCDEHL.
  Uses: All registers; subroutines at 0F3A, 2400, 2556, 2562.

‘HL: $= (B/D) \times 2^C$ (unsigned)’ at 0F50
  Entry: Unsigned integers y in B, x in D, p in C ($0 \leq p \leq 14$ decimal).
  Result: Unsigned value (see below) of $(y/x) \times 2^p$ in HL.
  Exit: Result in HL; C $= 00$.
  Failure exit to monitor if result out of range.
  Uses: A, B, C, D, H, L.
  Note: Special cases for p: for $p = 0$ result is double-length integer in HL; for $p = 8$ result is single-length integer in H; for $p = 14$ result has 14 b.p. in HL. Result is correct to truncation unless $(y > 63 \wedge y > x) \wedge ([y/2] \times 2 \neq y)$ in which case result is $[(y/2)/x] \times 2^{p+1}$.

‘HL: $= (B/D) \times 2^C$ (signed)’ at 0F76
  Entry: Signed integers y in B, x in D, p in C ($0 \leq p \leq 14$).
  Result: Signed value of $(y/x) \times 2^p$ in HL.
  Exit: Result in HL; C $= 00$.
  Failure exit to monitor if result out of range.
  Uses: All registers; subroutine at 0F50.
  Note: As for 0F50, but read $|x|$, $|y|$ for x,y.

'HL: = (BC/DE) × 2^A (unsigned)' at 0F9B

Entry: Unsigned double-length integers y in BC, x in DE; unsigned integer p in A ($0 \le p \le 14$).
Result: Unsigned value of $(y/x) \times 2^p$ in HL.
Exit: Result in HL.
Failure exit to monitor if result out of range.
Uses: All registers, subroutines at 0231, 0CF1.

'HL: = (BC/DE) × 2^A (signed)' at 0FCD

Entry: Signed double-length integers y in BC, x in DE; unsigned integer p in A ($0 \le p \le 14$).
Result: Signed value of $(y/x) \times 2^p$ in HL.
Exit: Result in HL.
Failure exit to monitor if result out of range.
Uses: All registers; subroutines at 0231, 0CF1, 0F9B.

'HL: = sqrt(BC) × 2^7' at 0BE0

Entry: Positive integer x in BC ($0 \le x \le 16383$).
Result: Positive value of $2^7 \times x$ in HL ($0 \le 2^7 x \le 16383$).
Exit: Result in HL, x in BC.
Uses: A, (BC), DE, HL; subroutines at 0231, 0CF1, 0F9B.
Note: See 6.3.

'HL: = sqrt(HL) × 2^8' at 0D6F

Entry: Positive integer x in HL ($0 \le x \le 16383$).
Result: Value of $2^8 \times y$ in HL, where $y = x$ and $0 \le 2^8 \times y \le 32767$.
Exit: Result in HL.
Failure exit to monitor if x out of range (negative).
Uses: A, HL; subroutines at 0231, 0BE0, 0C1A, 0CF1, 0F9B.
Note: At exit H has the integral part of y and L the fractional part of y.

'Polynomial (15 b.p.)' at 2452

Entry: Argument x, 15 b.p. in BC ($-1 \le x < +1$); order of polynomial n as integer in A; address of location of a_n in HL; coefficients $a_n, \ldots, a_0$ in consecutive pairs of locations, all 15 b.p.
Result: Value p of polynomial, 15 b.p., in HL, where

$$p = \sum_{i=0}^{n} a_i x^i.$$

Exit: Result in HL, a_0 in DE, A = 00.
Uses: All registers, subroutine at 2440.
Note: See 6.3.

'HL: = sin(HL) 15 b.p.' at 2470

Entry: Argument x, 15 b.p. in radians in HL, $|x| < 1$.
Result: $\sin(x)$, 15 b.p., in HL.
Exit: Result in HL.
Uses: All registers; subroutines at 2440, 2452.
Note: Intended for $|x| \le \pi/4$. Error in this range less than ± 0.0004. See 6.3, 8.5.

'HL: = cos(HL) 15 b.p.' at 2490
    Entry: Argument x, 15 b.p., in radians in HL, $0 < |x| < 1$.
    Result: $\cos(x)$, 15 b.p., in HL.
    Exit: Result in HL.
    Uses: All registers; subroutines at 0CF1, 0D6F, 0FF1, 2440, 2470.
    Note: Intended for $0 < |x| \leq \pi/4$. Error in this range less than ± 0.0004. See
    6.3.

'HL: = tan(HL) 15 b.p.' at 24D9
    Entry: Argument x, 15 b.p., in radians in HL, $0 < |x| < \pi/4$.
    Result: $\tan(x)$, 15 b.p., in HL.
    Exit: Result in HL.
    Uses: All registers; subroutines at 0CF1, 0D6F, 0FCD, 0FF1, 2440, 2470, 2490.
    Note: Error less than ± 0.0007. See 6.3.

'Degrees to radians' at (i) 24C1 and at (ii) 24C4
    Entry: (i)   Integer number of degrees d in A, $|d| \leq 57$ (decimal);
              (ii)   Number of degrees d in HL, 8 b.p., $|d| < 57.3$.
    Result: Equivalent number of radians, 15 b.p., in HL.
    Exit: Result in HL.
    Uses: All registers; subroutines at 2400, 2420.

'Radians to degrees' at 2500
    Entry: Number of radians r in HL, 15 b.p., $-1 \leq r < +1$.
    Result: Equivalent number of degrees, 8 b.p., in HL.
    Exit: Result in HL; r, 15 b.p., in BC.
    Uses: All registers; subroutines at 2400, 2420.

6.2.4 Floating-point arithmetic

'Normalize up' at (i) 25A1 and at (ii) 25A3
    Entry: (i) x in AHL, where $-2^{22} \leq x < 2^{22}$
            (ii) p (integer) in B; x in AHL as for (i).
    Result: y in AHL, q in B such that *either* $y = x = 0$ and $q = 0$, *or* $2^{21} \leq y$
    $< 2^{22}$ or $-2^{22} \leq y < -2^{21}$ and (i) $y = x \times 2^q$ or (ii) $y \times 2^p = x \times 2^q$. See 4.7.2.
    Exit: Results q in B and y in AHL.
    Uses: A,B,H,L.

'Normalize down' at 25CB
    Entry: x in AHL; p in B.
    Result: x, p unchanged in AHL, B if $-2^{22} \leq x < 2^{22}$; $x/2$ (rounded) in AHL,
    $p + 1$ in B otherwise. See 4.7.2.
    Exit: Results in B, AHL.
    Uses: A,B,C,H,L; subroutine at 2577.

The subroutines listed below are introduced and described in 4.7.4.

'Store'	$M^4[BC] := DEHL$	at 2608
'Fetch'	$DEHL := M^4[BC]$	at 2619
'Multiply'	$DEHL: \times M^4[BC]$	at 264B
'Negate'	$DEHL: -$	at 265B
'Negate'	$M^4[DE]: -$	at 266A
'Reciprocal'	$DEHL: /$	at 26D9
'Divide'	$DEHL: / M^4[BC]$	at 26EC
'Add'	$DEHL := M^4[HL] + M^4[DE]$	at 26F7
'Subtract'	$DEHL := M^4[HL] - M^4[DE]$	at 2731
'Read'	$DEHL := $ in f.p. number	at 2745
'Print'	F.p. print (DEHL)	at 2B80

The external (decimal) formats for the last two are described in 6.2.1 and 6.2.2 above.

6.3   MOVING UP FROM THE LEVEL OF MACHINE CODE

The monitor enables hexadecimal (that is, binary) information to be put into the system, copied from one part of it to another, altered and displayed; and programs to be entered, left and resumed. The assembler allows programs expressed in a readable form to be put into the machine directly; and, with the disassembler, programs and parts of programs can be displayed in the same readable form—readable, that is, by human beings. Yet none of this software does anything to enhance the programmer's *power of expression*; that is still limited by the instruction set of the particular processor. However, the instruction set includes provision for *subroutines*, and it is through the development of a *resident subroutine library* that we have a direct opportunity of allowing programs—or at least some parts of some programs—to be expressed at a 'higher level' than that of the majority of the machine instructions. A 'resident' subroutine, one held in PROM at a fixed location, effectively adds a powerful new instruction to the instruction set. Thus with the floating-point subroutines in PROM, the 8080 instruction 'JS2731' (CD 31 27) means 'assign the f.p. difference of two specified f.p. numbers to the f.p. accumulator'—an operation involving the execution of very many simpler instructions. We have seen in a simple example—the temperature conversion program in 4.7.6—how, when the right subroutines are available, and particularly when these subroutines have been designed as an integrated set, a program can reduce to little more than a succession of subroutine calls separated, perhaps, by instructions for fetching and storing parameters.

The reader who finds the floating-point subroutines useful will almost certainly wish to extend the set to include the 'standard functions' of the well-known 'high-level programming languages'—square root, sine, arctan, log and so on. The specification of any of these new subroutines, if it is to be consistent with the existing set, is obvious. For example, 'cosine' will replace the value x, say, in the f.p. accumulator by $\cos(x)$. In symbols

'DEHL$: = \cos(DEHL)$'

or, more compactly,

'DEHL:cos'.

The fixed-point subroutines given here include a double-length square root (at 0BE0) and a 15 b.p. polynomial (at 2452). These make use of algorithms which can be adapted for the floating-point subroutines.

The square-root algorithm is an application of Newton's iterative method. If y_0 is an approximation to a root y of $f(x) = 0$, where f is a well-behaved function, then

$$y_1 = y_0 - \frac{f(y_0)}{f'(y_0)}$$

is a better one.

In the particular case in hand, if y_0 is an approximation to $\sqrt{x}$ then $y_1 = \frac{1}{2}(y_0 + \frac{x}{y_0})$ is better. In the form of a subroutine:

$$y := y_0$$
$$01:b := y$$
$$a := x$$
$$a:/y$$
$$a:+y$$
$$a:/2$$
$$y := a$$
$$y - b$$
$$\text{JNZ(L01)}$$
$$\text{RET}$$

Here 'JNZ' means 'jump back if the two successive iterates, y and b, are still distinguishable'—see 4.7.7. The fixed-point version at 0BE0 terminates when y, b differ in the least significant bit only or are equal. The initial 'guess' y_0 is not critical; any value in the middle of the result range can be used. In order to give as many significant figures as possible within a double-length value, the subroutine computes $2^7 \times \sqrt{x}$; or $\sqrt{x}$ to 7 b.p. The step '$a:/y$' is achieved by a call of 'HL: = (BC/DE) × 2^A' with A = 0E ($p_0 = 14$; see 4.5.5.1). The absolute error of the result is within $\pm 4 \times 10^{-3}$. In fact if $2^7 \sqrt{x}$ is an integer then the result is exact; otherwise the relative error is within ± 0.16 p.c. for small x and within ± 0.003 p.c. for large x.

The implementation of the algorithm for a floating-point argument and result can be approached in a number of ways. The most obvious, perhaps, is to program the steps each by a call on one of the existing f.p. subroutines. Another way is to consider the argument as having an exponent and a mantissa. If the exponent is odd, we prepare the number by subtracting one from the exponent and shifting the mantissa up one place. Then we halve the exponent and take the square-root of the mantissa. The mantissa is a triple-length number with 22 binary places. A subroutine for dealing with such numbers will need some care in the writing, but when it has been made it will be considerably faster and more compact than a 'fully floating' version.

The method used by the subroutine at 2452 for the evaluation of a polynomial is called *nested multiplication*. A cubic expression $a_3x^3+a_2x^2+a_1x+a_0$ contains six multiplications and three additions. But if it is expressed as $((a_3x+a_2)x+a_1)x+a_0$ it reduces to three multiplications and three additions. A polynomial of degree n,

$$p = \sum_{i=0}^{i=n} a_i x^i$$

needs only n (not $\frac{1}{2}n(n+1)$) multiplications when evaluated by nested multiplication:

$$
\left.
\begin{array}{l}
i:=n \\
p:=a_n \\
01:i-0 \\
\quad RZ \\
\quad i:-1 \\
\quad p:\times x \\
\quad p:+a_i \\
\quad J(L01)
\end{array}
\right\}
\quad \text{or} \quad
\left\{
\begin{array}{l}
i:=n \\
p:=0 \\
01:p:+a_i \\
\quad i-0 \\
\quad RZ \\
\quad i:-1 \\
\quad p:\times x \\
\quad J(L01)
\end{array}
\right.
$$

The subroutine at 2452 uses the second of these variants. The first variant is possibly more convenient for a floating-point polynomial:

ST: = HL	Address of a_n
ST: = BC	Address of x
ST: = AF	Degree n in A
B: = H	
C: = L	
JS2619	Fetch a_n
01:AF: = ST	i
BC: = ST	Address of x
A − 00	
JZ(L02)	
ST: = BC	
ST: = AF	
JS264B	$p:\times x$
BC: = 17FC	
JS2608	Store p
AF: = ST	
A:−1	$i:-1$
BC: = ST	
HL: = ST	
4× HL:+1	(cf. 5.5)
ST: = HL	
ST: = BC	
ST: = AF	
DE: = 17FC	
JS26F7	$p:+a_i$
J(L01)	
02:BC: = ST	(clear stack)
RET	

Note: The use of M⁴17FC, the location used by the monitor for the safe-keeping of the program counter and stack pointer values, would be dangerous practice in an ordinary subroutine. It is justified, and indeed good practice, in a proven resident subroutine as (i) the monitor will not be required to save register-values while such a subroutine is in operation, and (ii) the use of RAM, other than of the stack, by resident subroutines should be held within bounds as narrow as possible.

The fixed-point 'sine' subroutine at 2470 uses the fixed-point polynomial sub-routine to evaluate a truncated Taylor series—see 8.5. This is an obvious, and quite a good, approximation for arguments in $|x| \leq \pi/4$ given to 15 b.p. But it is by no means the best approach when the argument is a floating-point variable of un-restricted range. Methods for the approximation of trigonometric and other functions, by economized Chebyshev series, by continued fractions or by other means, are discussed in many books on numerical techniques. The programmer who has to produce a set of subroutines for a microprocessor will have to consider the particular circumstances in which they are to be used; it may or may not be good enough to adapt the techniques of the subroutines on the nearest big computer.

As well as, or perhaps instead of, a set of subroutines for arithmetic, trigo-nometry and other functions, a set for some other type of operation may be required. For example, a copy of the system on which most of the work described in this book was done has additional PROM space containing a set of subroutines for a graphical display. Any such set should, if possible, be designed as a unity so that, for example, the results of one subroutine are left in the places where another subroutine expects its data, and, in numerical work, the subroutines are 'compatible' as regards binary places, length of numbers and so on.

Whatever the actual sets of resident subroutines are, there will be a large number—one or two hundred or even more—of subroutine-call instructions like 'JS2731' (CD 31 27), which will have a special significance within the system. Although 'JS2731' means exactly what it says at the machine-code level, namely 'jump to the subroutine at 2731', at our higher level of expression made possible by the existence of the subroutine library it is as inadequate as, for example, 'D6 12' is in conveying the idea of 'subtraction'. We may consider it worthwhile to introduce a new written form into the assembler, one for each of the subroutines; as a start, there are the descriptive titles used in the lists of 6.2. These certainly make the temperature-conversion program of 4.7.6 more readable:

```
DEHL: = in f.p. number
BC: = 1300
M4[BC]: = DEHL
DEHL: = in f.p. number
BC: = 1304
M4[BC]: = DEHL
DEHL: = in f.p. number
BC: = 1308
M4[BC]: = DEHL
```

```
01:New line
    DEHL: = in f.p. number
    BC: = 130C
    M4[BC]: = DEHL
    HL: = 130C
    DE: = 1300
    DEHL: = M4[HL] − M4[DE]
    BC: = 1304
    DEHL: × M4[BC]
    BC: = 1308
    DEHL:/M4[BC]
    F.p. print (DEHL)
    J(L01)
```

With a few cosmetic changes, such as shortening the text for f.p. read and not using lower-case letters (which, as every computer mythologist knows, do not occur in real programs for real computers), we have a program which could be read by an assembler not unduly bigger than the original. There is still one line per machine instruction, however; and because of the need for parameter-fetching there is a considerable amount of repetitive detail. The first three lines are, with one change of address, repeated three more times in the program. Each group of three lines represents what, at the higher level, is seen as a single operation—reading a value and assigning it to a specified location. This can be expressed in a manner consistent with existing notations as, for example, 'M4(1300: = READ'. The assembler, still growing, can be made to read this piece of text and generate the nine bytes of machine code 'CD 45 27 01 00 13 CD 08 26'. Our temperature-conversion program reduces to:

```
    M4(1300): = READ
    M4(1304): = READ
    M4(1308): = READ
01:NEWLINE
    M4(130C): = READ
    DEHL: = M4(130C) − M4(1300)
    DEHL: × M4(1304)
    DEHL:/M4(1308)
    PRINT(DEHL)
    J(L01)
```

This version of the program, which is the first high-level version in the sense of having one line for several machine instructions, is still recognizably intended for the 8080 or 8085 or Z80 since the proper names of registers appear in it. It also has explicit, absolute addresses. The next version, in which symbolic names have replaced these names and addresses, is the first *machine-independent* version. Its level is that of the 'autocodes' which were widely used in the nineteen-fifties; it would have been accepted by an autocode compiler with very little change.

```
    W0: = READ
    W1: = READ
    W2: = READ
01:NEWLINE
    W3: = READ
    R: = W3 – W0
    R: × W1
    R: /W2
    PRINT(R)
    J(L01)
```

This text contains no indication that it is an 8080 program, or a microprocessor program, or a program for any particular kind of computer—although it does perhaps suggest a computer with an accumulator. But it can certainly be *translated* into the machine-code program of 4.7.6, or a similar program for some other processor, by an extended assembler which by this stage has earned for itself the more dignified title of *compiler* or *translator*.

Having achieved machine independence, we may wish to go on to improve matters even more by writing constants as immediate operands, leaving the compiler to attend to the matter of their storage:

```
01:NEWLINE
    W3: = READ
    R: = W3 – 32
    R: × 5
    R: /9
    PRINT(R)
    J(L01)
```

Then, remembering that techniques for the translation of arithmetic expressions have been known since 1951, we can move to a higher level of expression still:

```
01:NEWLINE
    F: = READ
    C: = (F – 32) × 5/9
    PRINT(C)
    J(L01)
```

This needs only slight attention from the make-up department to be accepted as BASIC, or FORTRAN, or ALGOL, or PL/1. When the program's inherent *structure* is made explicit:

$$\textbf{repeat}(new\ line;\ F: = read;$$
$$C: = (F-32) \times 5/9;\ print(C))$$

we have, apart from the fact that it is non-terminating, something which would pass for a high-level program anywhere.

The stages by which the program of 4.7.6 can be replaced as a source program for the microprocessor system by each successive program above may be envisaged in at least two different ways. We can see each stage as providing a new level of expression to *supersede* a class of expressions at the earlier level; or we can see each stage as providing *additional* expressive power. In the one case there might be a new compiler for each stage, the last one perhaps being not much bigger and not much more complicated than the first. In the other case, the full realization of all the levels of expression in one compiler might require a more ponderous piece of software than we should like to see carried by our system.

If the first approach is taken, the end result is likely to be two compilers: one for dealing, at machine-code level, with programs involving detailed control of machine operations, and the other for dealing with the kind of program that can be conveniently expressed in high-level terms. In other words, there will be an assembly language and a high-level language, just as there is on a big machine, and they will be disjoint.

The second approach, if the compiler can be kept under proper control as regards size and speed, will lead to something new and very worth-while for the microprocessor user. This is a compiler for a 'multi-level language' which will admit low-level and high-level expressions equally; a language in which it will be possible to program the output of a measured pulse to a peripheral device and the calculations on the readings from instruments with equal facility.

6.4 MOVING DOWN TO THE LEVEL OF MACHINE CODE

At whatever level a program, or part of a program, is expressed, its implementation will be the execution of a sequence of machine instructions.

We have seen in 5.4 an example of one kind of process by which a high-level text can be used in the generation of a machine-code program. The ALGOL60 procedure *Shellsort* was translated into the form of an 8080 subroutine. The translation process was presented, not as the strict application of pre-defined transformational rules, but informally in a number of intuitive steps. At various stages, decisions as to the types and ranges of the several quantities concerned had to be put into effect. These decisions determine the applicability of the resultant subroutine; they have to be made whether the translation is done 'by hand', as in 5.4, or mechanically, as discussed below. The procedure as given sorts n elements $a_1, \ldots, a_n$ into numerical order, each element being of the numerical type *real*. No limit is implied for n; its value is of type *integer*, consistent with its use in counting (cf. 4.7.7). Different versions of the subroutine follow from different decisions as to what maximum value of n is to be permitted. The usual implementation of *real* is by floating-point arithmetic; but there may well be a need for subroutines to sort simpler types of values, not distinguished in the high-level language. Accordingly, the first version of the sorting subroutine is written for unsigned single-length integers (or fixed-point numbers to a common number of binary places) and variations for other types of value are suggested. Finally, as regards subscripts, the ALGOL implies only that the elements are *numbered*; each version of the subroutine requires them to be *located* at regularly spaced addresses.

Suppose now that we have a compiler or translator program capable of reading the ALGOL text directly and generating a corresponding machine-code subroutine. Which of the many variants, of which those suggested in 5.4 are only a selection, do we expect the compiler to produce? Specifically, how is it going to decide what limit to put on *n*, what kind of values the elements shall have, and how they are expected to be stored? In default of any information beyond that of the ALGOL text itself, presumably it should be a version using double-length integer arithmetic on the counters and floating-point representation for the elements, assumed consecutively stored. This would allow any set of f.p. numbers in RAM to be sorted; that is all that can reasonably be expected. A version for double-length integral elements would be produced if the ALGOL text were to specify *integer array a*. Because there are only the two numerical types *real* and *integer* in ALGOL60, it is not possible to express a requirement for any other version in that particular high-level language. Some other high-level languages—ALGOL68, PASCAL, PL/1—admit rather more numerical types and to that extent may be more suitable than ALGOL60, BASIC and FOR-TRAN as starting-points for the design of a high-level language for a microprocessor. However—and this applies particularly to ALGOL68 and PL/1—if we try to work from one of these we may well find that the specification of necessary *restrictions* on the use of the language demands as much work as would have been required for the *extension* of one of the others.

Several compilers for different versions of several of these languages have been made, the most frequently occurring name being BASIC. Those which allow the specification of both integral and floating-point arithmetic can be very useful indeed where numerical work has to be done. A few, with all the superficial appearance of high-level compilers and nothing but integral arithmetic, are little more than toys. Some of them, by their nature and by the nature of the languages they serve, exclude any expression of such programs as those for the PROM programmer (8.8, 0360–03FD), which require careful timing and detailed specification of operations on non-standard peripherals. Others may allow these programs, but only after a good deal of 'conceptual dislocation'. The ideas in terms of which the programs are conceived have to be replaced by other ideas stemming from the language in which they must be expressed, resulting in an unnatural and obscure expression of what is perfectly clear in machine code.

A programmer with a good understanding of his favourite high-level language will, in the absence of his ideal compiler for that language on his favourite microprocessor, find little difficulty in translating and adapting any reasonably short programs and procedures to machine-code level in the manner of 5.7. If this work becomes dull, there is always scope for individual expression in tailoring the object program. (What has happened to the nested-loop structure of *Shellsort* in 5.7?)

In Chapter 7, the problem of the design of a language in which both high-level and low-level expression are possible will be discussed.

7

Software: organization, language, structure

7.1 MICROPROCESSORS IN CONTEXT

Microprocessors have put back programming twenty-five years. So we were assured by a most eminent authority at the 1977 IFIP Congress. Unfortunately, it is not entirely true.

In 1952 the word 'software' had not been invented. A new computer would have been programmed from scratch without help or distraction from other computers and their software. Twenty-five years later, a new microprocessor arriving in the world finds itself surrounded by computers, many of them enormous and many of them weighed down by the accumulated software of a quarter of a century's undisciplined growth. Not only that, but if it is the newest in a line of microprocessors it will have its own inheritance of two or three years' software. Now it is probably unjust to compare all this software (which, of course, includes Chapter 8) with the 90,000 ox-years' work in the Augean stables, but it would be a Herculean task indeed to go through the existing software on even one large machine and cut it down to its proper useful size. If it could be done for any machine we might be left with a model for future adaptation to microprocessors. While it remains undone we should be warned against imitating the perpetuated mistakes and the extravagances of existing practice. A 1978 advertisement proposes a system comprising a simulator program written in FORTRAN requiring a substantial FORTRAN compiler, a working store of 24K words, a disc unit and an interactive terminal, and all as an aid to the development of low-level programs for a microprocessor. If the big computer would otherwise be unemployed this might have some social value, but it really is absurd to involve such a vast array of software and hardware in something which is far more effectively done with the very modest facilities of the microprocessor system alone.

Software grew most rapidly during the nineteen-sixties, the age of the large, centralized computer 'The Computer', an awesome being, enthroned at the centre of the universe, approached only by its three shifts of acolytes, granting audience at its own pleasure to those who fulfil the rites of protocol. At the beginning of this period a FORTRAN compiler had about 20,000 instructions, and a good ALGOL

197

compiler rather less. A year or two later we hear of languages for which compilers of more than a quarter of a million instructions have been written. The Computer was not satisfied with compilers alone—there were assemblers, editors, loaders, simulators, emulators, operating systems, . . . many hundreds of thousands, if not millions, of instructions. This software was not cheap—the cost of some choice pieces was reckoned in man-centuries (the ceiling of the Sistine Chapel cost four man-years). Nor was it always well designed or constructed—one notorious example was a software package some of whose successive monthly 'releases' each represented the correction of a thousand errors. There was no need to answer the irreverent few who questioned the wisdom of all this. The software could accumulate because The Computer could grow, not only in size but in power and influence.

It was the rapid development of semiconductor technology that broke The Computer's despotic hold on information processing. The *minicomputers* met not only the need for independent, decentralized computing but also that for information processing outside the scope of the central machine with its numerous users competing for attention. This is in all those applications—'real time', 'process control', 'physical system'—in which the computer has to interact with an environment in which it is not the master.

Microprocessors—very large scale integrated circuits—and the associated storage and interface components are versatile, adaptable, portable and remarkably powerful. They have become very cheap; their running costs are extremely low and their overheads negligible. They create an entirely new situation in which a great deal of computing can be done locally and independently and in absolute security. Where once there was only the central machine, there can be hundreds or even thousands of local machines, perhaps many copies of each of a number of different models. Clearly, the development of software in circumstances like this is not going to emulate that of the last twenty-five years; software will need to be economical and free of unnecessary accretions.

Exercises

You have a type-X microcomputer system. You acquire some programs, say x bytes altogether, which run on the rival type-Y microcomputer. You want to use these programs. Knowing the value of your own time, what is the smallest value of x for which you would *buy* a type-Y machine? For what range of values of x could you be persuaded to use and pay for a Y-to-X cross-compiler–simulator on a type-Z mini- or macro-computer? If you buy the type-Y, what will the type-X be doing while you use it? Does it matter? On the other hand, what do you do if you are in thrall to an organization which has 'standardized' on the type-X?

It seems likely that microprocessor development will lead to many new types of c.p.u., with correspondingly many instruction sets. Although, no doubt, many existing and future processors are destined to vanish without trace, it would be disastrous to allow any one processor or any one instruction set to pre-empt future improvement. The ideal is not yet in sight.

As programmers we are likely to meet a variety of machines, machine codes, and higher-level languages. Although our everyday work may be confined to one or two processors, the advantage of being able to read and understand programs written for any of a number of different systems is obvious. One of the most curious phenomena of programming history has been 'language inertia'. This continues to show itself in two principal ways. First, a significant number of programmers who have learnt their trade in one language alone seem to become incapable of adapting to any other language or style of programming; and second, a number of inessential and superficial aspects of certain early languages persist and in the face of all reasoned argument become features of the successors of these languages. In order to avoid the inhibiting effects of this phenomenon for the future we should encourage those who are not yet beyond the reach of new ideas to acquire a second language, and hope that a new generation of polyglot programmers will present less of an impedance to reasonable progress than their predecessors.

7.2   SOME CONSIDERATIONS IN THE PLANNING AND DESIGN OF SOFTWARE

It is unlikely that any one specification of basic software, still less of 'higher' software, will satisfy more than a minority of potential users. There is no such thing as a typical group of users, or typical model system.

The software of Chapter 8, and the speculation of this chapter, are products of what many would regard as a specialized, even artificial, environment, namely the 'computer science' department of the school of mathematics of a provincial English university which, in common with many others no doubt, has forcibly been made aware that money occurs in nature rather less abundantly than does silicon.

Students reading 'computer science with mathematics' in this department have three years in which to learn some mathematics, to learn something of what is of permanent value in computing history and current practice, to acquire facility in programming and elementary computer design, and to reach a critical understanding of the tools which have been put at their disposal. Many other students, of mathematics, physical sciences, medical and other subjects, take shorter courses intended to familiarize them with current ideas and to give them some programming experience. A third group of students, part-time adult students attending evening classes and short vacation courses, are concerned to keep themselves up to date with new developments. Those who have attended courses on microprocessors and their applications—industrial design engineers, members of the armed services, directors of commercial companies, medical archaeologists, schoolteachers, printers, shopkeepers—have influenced the content not only of the adult education courses but also of the undergraduate syllabus. Their concern and interest are often even more direct and useful than the usual feedback from former students and their employers.

The impact of the microprocessor on all these courses is likely to be profound. In the past the undergraduate courses tended to avoid computer design, or treated it at a very elementary level in terms of simple logic circuitry unconnected with the computer used for exercises in programming. The computer has been too busy, and is in any case too remote, to provide useful illustration of computer design. Now, for the first time, we have in the microprocessor and its associated components:

(i)   a set of components which follow on conceptually from, and are physically compatible with, the integrated circuits of the TTL and CMOS families which are widely used in the teaching of basic logic design;

(ii) a set of components whose internal design can be appreciated, understood, and criticized by the student and which can be put together to form a complete computer illustrating all those points of computer design and architecture which have traditionally been taught 'off the blackboard';

(iii) the hardware for building a useful computer which can without difficulty carry the programming exercises previously run by the students on the central computer.

In short, the microprocessor system can provide all that is necessary for the teaching of computer science at undergraduate level, with the possible exception of some features of large systems which, if they are not now obsolete or obsolescent, can be treated as special topics. For considerably less money than is ordinarily spent on the provision of centralized facilities, a number of microcomputer systems can be provided in sufficient variety to maintain awareness of the differences between processors and in sufficient quantity to allow each student to have all the programming time he needs as well as the means to carry out experiments in design. Equally, of course, there can be microcomputers enough for those activities of the research staff and postgraduate students which do not necessitate the use of a large machine or its software.

In other organizations—such as those of the adult students mentioned above—although requirements will differ in many respects, it seems reasonable to suppose that there also will be the need for numbers of microcomputers.

In every case, where there are many microcomputers it is probable that some of them will tend to be used for program development while others will tend to be used for 'production' work, that is, for running proven programs. An important question with implications for software design is the extent to which these functions are and are not interchangeable.

The design of the production computer is determined by the union of the demands of the object programs for its several applications. Can, and should, these programs be developed on (a copy of) the same machine, or is there a need for a special 'development system', possibly even based on another processor, to carry out the peculiar tasks of program development? Clearly, the object system (production computer) *must* be part of the development system since the necessary final stage of development is the test run of the object program on the object machine. The question therefore is what *additional* facilities are required for the earlier stages of development.

There has been a tendency among those who pronounce on these matters to exaggerate the difficulties of writing programs and getting them to work, to urge the use of needlessly large, complicated and expensive systems, and yet to encourage the hope that object systems and object programs will be small and cheap. In point of fact the best development system is a computer which is substantially the object machine with two additions: (i) PROMs holding any necessary development software—assembler, disassembler, higher-level interpreter or compiler—and (ii) a secondary storage device for the programs under development—perhaps a PROM programmer used as described in 6.1.4, or a cassette recorder. The principle of economy of means cannot be over-emphasized. A sledgehammer is not needed to crack a nut. A child who can't play his scales properly on a cottage piano is unlikely to do better on a cathedral organ. The development system needs to be no more than the object system extended as described, and the development software should be as simple and unsophisticated as possible consistent with the implementation of its proper function. In this connection it should be noted that, inexpensive as semiconductor storage has become, it is still several hundred times more costly than paper.

7.3   NOTATIONS AND LANGUAGE

Chapters 2 and 3 were concerned with the description and notation of the instruction sets of four microprocessors. Two of these (8080, 8085) are substantially the same. That of the Z80 includes the 8080 set as a *subset,* and its other instructions include many evidently inspired by some in the instruction set of the 6800. The 6800 and 8080 sets are very different from each other.

The listings in Chapter 3 and in 2.10 (end) show that it has been possible to express the principal effects of nearly all of the united set in a consistent, systematic and readable notation. The two or three exceptions are those whose outcome depends on an external signal (a 'reset' or request for interruption). In some cases, notably the 'block' and 'step' instructions of the Z80, the notation requires rather long expressions, and, for the sake of conciseness only, small groups of letters have been used in the lists of Chapter 3 and in actual and projected software.

The usefulness of the notation has been felt in a number of ways, some of which have been listed in 2.2. In addition, the notations introduced in Chapters 4, 5 and 6 show how the scheme allows itself to be extended, informally but yet consistently, to the expression of higher-level program steps and of steps which have not yet been brought down to the level of a particular machine. This has enabled equivalent subroutines to be developed in parallel. Subroutines or programs for any of the processors can be read with equal facility.

Some questions which have been asked concerning the usefulness of the notation and its extensions for other processors and in other software than the low-level assemblers are the following:

Question   Can other microprocessors have their instruction sets expressed in the same notational system?

Answer   Some certainly can—it is impossible to speak for all. Each of the original processors required *ad hoc* extensions to the system as at first conceived, and it is likely that a new processor will call for further *ad hoc* extension. It is important, however, that the core should be unaffected by these embellishments, and that the system should remain as simple and coherent in conception as possible.

Question   For a particular processor, in what software will the notation have a part to play?

Answer   Certainly in software like the 8080 assembler and disassembler. Similar programs for other processors have been made or are being made. The possibility of a compiler at higher levels was suggested in 6.3, and the idea of a 'language' incorporating higher-level expressions is discussed below.

Question   Are translation programs between instruction sets practicable?

Answer   Probably not. The details of the treatment of condition flags make this extremely difficult. In any case it is likely to be easier and cheaper to run a program on a copy of the machine for which it was written than to translate it for, or simulate it on, some other machine.

Question   Is any software for the combined instruction set practicable?

Answer   No. A program is meant for one machine. If multi-processor systems with processors of dissimilar types are envisaged, then a multi-processor program is an assemblage of single-processor sub-programs. However, certain *high-level* expressions may be *machine-independent* and thus capable of translation into any of a number of machine codes.

The design of a high-level programming language for conventional computers is often seen as equivalent to the specification of a high-level instruction set for an abstract machine which will in effect be simulated on the actual machines. This approach, and *a fortiori* the theoretical approach to the design of a machine-independent high-level algorithmic language, although it will certainly be helpful in the clarification of certain sets of ideas, cannot be entirely satisfactory for microprocessors since there is a fundamental need to keep the operation of every instruction of the machine expressible in the language.

There are many illustrations of this difficulty in the text of 8.8. Perhaps the most suitable example for discussion is the PROM-reading program in 03C0–03EB. (*Note:* The subroutines 03D1–03EB are also used by the PROM-programming program at 0360.) This is a rather simple program for communication between the microcomputer and a special peripheral device. It uses techniques, discussed in 5.7, which are used for other devices attached to a parallel interface adapter, and it is typical of the basic software which is developed for such peripherals as analogue/ digital converters, graphical display units, line printers, disc stores and so on. Programs like this cannot be expressed in BASIC or FORTRAN, and if they can be written in some other high-level language their expression is liable to be somewhat stilted (cf. 6.4). It is useful to examine the example in order to decide *at what level* it would most suitably be expressed. We should begin by considering the specification of the program. The peripheral device and those of its terminals which are relevant are shown in Figure 7.1. The device holds 1024 bytes of information supposed numbered consecutively. Whenever it receives a pulse at 'count' it delivers the next of these bytes at the 'data output' terminals. After a pulse at 'reset' the next byte will be the lowest-numbered byte. After all 1024 bytes have been delivered the device puts out the signal 'counter overflow'. All signals are compatible with the 8255 to which the device is connected (Figure 5.8(b)). The program is to read the information of the device into RAM locations (hex) 1000–13FF. The width of the 'reset' and 'count' pulses is not critical. Put this way, the specification is very machine-dependent.

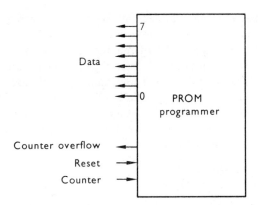

Fig. 7.1

But if the nature of the interface is not mentioned, how far can we go in programming? Not very far. Keeping the full specification in mind, we can try to raise the level of the given program in the manner of 6.3 (the temperature-conversion program). Now it happens that it, and its subroutines, together with the PROM-programming program, were written to occupy the minimum amount of space. An unpleasant consequence of this is that it is rather difficult to express the operations of the subroutines in any compact symbolic notation. For example, the subroutine at 03E3 increments HL, outputs a positive pulse to line 0 of port C of the 8255, and sets the flag Z according to the value of the signal on line 4 of the port C. This is hardly the sort of thing to express in a single statement in a programming language. If the program has to be as small as possible, it seems improbable that a better expression than that of 8.8 could be made. If, however, other criteria such as clarity and elegance of structure are regarded as more important than compactness, then there is more chance of attaining a reasonably high level of expression. The given program can be written without the use of subroutines as follows:

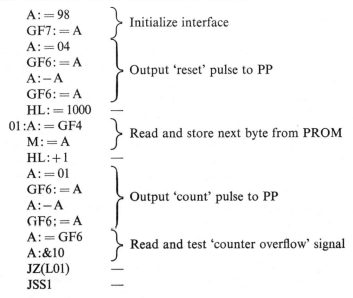

Each bracketed group of machine instructions corresponds to one complete and self-contained operation of the interface. The notes against them represent all that could have been expressed had the specification not prescribed the 8255 interface. We might devise a notation for each type of group, rather as in 6.3, and so produce a higher level expression of the program. The notation will clearly be special to the 8255; had, say, the 6820 or Z80PIO been used the machine-code program would have been different and other special notations would have been needed. Writing, for example, 'GF4.A' for 'Port A of the device with device numbers F4–F7', a possible expression of the program is:

```
        GF4.CONTROL: = 98
        GF4.C.2: = PULSE
        HL: = 1000
 01:M: = GF4.A
        HL: +1
        GF4.C.0: = PULSE
        Z: = #GF4.C.4
        JZ(L01)
        MONITOR
```

With the use of identifiers (symbolic names, cf. 6.3) this might become:

```
        PP.CONTROL: = 98
        PP.RESET: = PULSE
        HL: = 1000
 01:M: = PP.DATA
        HL: +1
        PP.COUNT: = PULSE
        Z: = #PP.OVERFLOW
        JZ(L01)
        MONITOR
```

If this version of the program is to be accepted by a compiler, then clearly the compiler has to have the information that the PROM programmer's 'reset' terminal is connected to the port C, bit 2 of the 8255 whose I/O device numbers are F4–F7, and so on. (Theoretically, perhaps, it could make this allocation, and inform the machine operator to that effect so that the right plug could be made up, but this sort of thing is hardly practical.) If the system is fixed, this information will be implicit in the compiler; any addition of a new peripheral will require an extension to the compiler—and any removal of a peripheral should mean the shortening of the compiler. A compiler which can deal with 'declarations' of peripherals—that is, with information accompanying a program defining what peripherals will be installed in the object system and at what locations—may be justified in some circumstances.

As in 6.3, we might remove the label and express the structure of the program:

```
        PP.CONTROL: = 98;
        PP.RESET: = PULSE;
        HL: = 1000;
```

repeat (M[HL: + 1]: = PP.DATA; PP.COUNT: = PULSE)
until PP.OVERFLOW;
MONITOR

Except for possibly relaxing the insistence on the use of HL as the addressing register, this is, perhaps, as far as one can go. We have a mixture of 8080 instructions and higher-level structures. The program remains machine-dependent, specifically in its first line, and, apart from this first line, it is reasonably comprehensible. Unless one knows the details of the 8255 the value '98' is meaningless. This calls attention to a further difficulty, and that is concerned with interface components generally. Although it is a fairly straightforward device, the 8255 has to be regarded as almost a micro-processor in its own right; the meaning of the control value '98' as distinct from all other possible control values cannot be expressed in one or two ASCII characters. The other parallel interface adapters present their own problems, to say nothing of the serial devices, the special interfaces, and the variety of new components that become available. We do not yet have an overall view of these components that would allow the formulation of a general approach to the high-level expression of their operations. There seems no end to their variety and ingenuity. For the immediate future, each new one is likely to call for as many new kinds of expression as a new microprocessor.

A programmer who has only himself to consider is of course free to accept or reject any or all of the notational ideas suggested to him, and to invent some of his own, in making up his own personal shorthand for the writing down of his own projected programs. But this freedom will become limited both by the restrictive software actually available for his use, which will require the programs to be written, or rewritten, within specific constraints, and by the need to communicate with other people who may not know all his ways with symbols. In other words every programmer will be, sooner or later, writing in a *programming language* which is understood by his colleagues, or has been *implemented* by software on his machine, or both.

One programming language is inherent in the machine itself without software, and that is the machine code comprised of the instruction set. This language is understood by programmers in the sense that they can read descriptions of the instructions and observe the machine's execution of them. However, programs in this language are not read easily since their binary (or octal or hexadecimal) representations contain nothing to remind the reader of the significance of their components. For this reason the instructions are usually represented in writing in a form which suggests their meaning. The program which converts this into binary will normally have additional facilities, such as those introduced in 6.1.2, and be called an assembler. The language accepted by the assembler is the assembly language; it is a low-level language since its program-steps each give rise to one machine instruction only.

Many *high-level languages* have been developed over the years. They are usually characterized by the fact that a high-level statement, or program step, gives rise to many machine-code instructions. A good and well implemented high-level language has considerable attractions for the programmer. Most obviously, it allows a program to be expressed in terms already used in the original description of the problem—

names of variables in the problem can often be used unchanged as identifiers in the program. The language admits expressions (formulae) constructed according to more or less normal rules. Its treatment of subroutines and of repetitive and iterative structures (see 7.4) allows the maintenance of the inherent form of a computation in its expression as a program. Programs which can be written in a good high-level language are so written several times more quickly than in a low-level language, and with considerably fewer mistakes. To the extent that a high-level program is machine-independent, so is the possibility of its use on any machine for which the language has been implemented. The price paid for the use of a high-level language is its compiler and other software for facilitating the development of its programs.

Compilers for some high-level languages on some microprocessors are commercially available. The best of these are well worth having. Some of them, however, seem to be somewhat extravagant in their storage demands; others, as has already been remarked, sacrifice substance for appearance.

There will certainly be many users who will, for a time, find one of these compilers adequate for all their programming needs. Equally, there will be others who will not. Such users will already have discovered the limitations of the low-level assembly languages. Their need, in fact, is for the ability to express programs at a number of levels. One program may be written naturally at high level; another, because it is intimately concerned with an interface, may require low-level expression; a third program may want passages at high and low levels, and at all levels in between. The requirement is for a 'multi-level' programming language, capable of admitting any program that could be expressed in machine code but with each of its parts written at its own proper level. Low-level languages allow all programs, but often at the cost of great inconvenience; high-level languages offer convenience and improve the programmer's effectiveness, but not all of them allow the expression of everything the system may be required to do, and few of them allow that in the most appropriate manner.

If this need is admitted, we have the problem of the orderly development of a low-level language (as exemplified by that described in 6.1.2) to take in the enhancements suggested in 6.3 and 6.4, and in the present chapter. In parallel with this will be the work of implementing the developing language by making compilers or interpreters for its several stages and auxiliary software to ease the programmer's task of writing and correcting programs.

This problem has not been felt on earlier computers to the same extent. This may perhaps be due to the tendency to divide the programmers around a large machine into 'systems programmers', collectively concerned with making the computer as generally useful as possible, and 'applications programmers', whose main interest is the exploitation of the machine and its facilities in the solution of a series of particular problems; the distinction seems to widen the gulf between low-level and high-level programming.

The specification of a complete project for a multi-level language is by no means a trivial matter. Some stages, such as the provision of notations (like 'HL: = C × E') for calls on resident subroutines, can be managed without conceptual difficulties; but others, such as the introduction of symbolic names and numerical constants of various types, require extreme care. The possibility of programs such as the last version of the PROM-reading program will also cause problems.

In the next section the several stages in a possible plan of development will be outlined, together with structural features needed to enable programs to be expressed in good style.

7.4 STRUCTURE AND STYLE

The specification of a multi-level language for a microprocessor must meet certain criteria. First, every instruction in the machine code must be expressible as a statement in the language. Second, at the highest level the expressive power must be comparable with that of the high-level languages currently implemented for the microprocessor. Third, it must be possible to implement the language at each of a series of levels. A program run at any of these implementation levels must run identically at any of the higher levels. The object code generated for a statement defined as corresponding to a single machine instruction must be that instruction and no more, at every level. (The implementation of higher-level statements will not be so severely prescribed.) Fourth, the specification must not make unreasonable demands on space for the compiler at any level.

Clearly, the basis of the language must be in a listing of the notations for the instructions of the machine such as those given in Chapter 3. In addition, at the lowest level it must be possible to label instructions and to write references to labels in place of addresses.

The first extension suggested in 6.3 was that of the 'semantic' subroutine calls. This requires careful consideration of the sets of subroutines for which this provision is to be made; each set for a particular family of operations (such as floating-point arithmetic) should be planned as a whole, with mutual compatibility in mind. The written form for each subroutine call should match the others, and those of the instructions, in style; and it should, if at all possible, be cast in an existing mould. Attention to these points should go a long way to simplifying the implementation of this stage as well as to keeping down the size of the compiler.

The second suggestion of 6.3, that of admitting expressions standing for several machine instructions each—a subroutine call and parameter-handling instructions— poses no new problems; but again coherence, style and structure are important. Inevitably, these 'macros' will make hidden use of registers. The programmer will need to be informed of these, as he needs to know what registers are disturbed in an ordinary subroutine call.

Neither of these extensions is in any way necessary for other kinds of extension to be made. Some users may feel they need them, others not. In any case, at this point the language, as a programming language, is very simple conceptually. Its statements are each in one of perhaps four or five basic forms; one of these is 'aopb', where the third component, or the second and third components, may be null; another is 'J mode cond addr' and another, for the 'odd' operations, is just 'Identifier'. The components include the names of registers, flags, interrupt masks, the store, the set of input–output ports as identifiers; and one-bit, two-hex-digit, four-hex-digit, and reference-to-label quantities as values. The *syntax* should be simply definable in, for example, the style of the ALGOL60 report or one of its derivatives; and the *semantics* need be little more than information corresponding to one of the sections of Chapter 3 with additions for the subroutines. (It is sufficient for our purposes here to be able to define what instructions are to correspond to each statement in the language; there is no need to attempt to define the semantics of the machine code.) The further extensions suggested in 6.3—the introduction of identifiers with restricted scope and of constant values in forms other than hexadecimal—need to be considered after certain *structural* questions have been decided.

The main question here concerns the way in which the language is to be used. Throughout this book the assumption has been that a program, or a modular part of a program, is written away from the computer, and then tested as a whole on the machine. Some programmers, with some kinds of programs, prefer to work 'interactively', writing and testing at the same time, at the keyboard of the console device. Languages such as APL and BASIC seem well adapted to this kind of use; the block structure of ALGOL60 and its derivatives works against it. Other things being equal, the choice between interactive and detached programming is a matter for the programmer's temperament, although the evidence seems to be that the latter encourages the better quality of style and structure in resultant programs. Unless we go for interactive programming, then, it is the ALGOL60 block structure which is the most likely starting point for the further development of our microprocessor language.

An identifier may be declared as standing for a variable of some given type within the block; in particular, it can be declared as being allocated to the register or flag of the same name in the particular microprocessor and as having a type compatible with the use of that register or flag. Again, it may be declared that digits are to be decimal or hexadecimal throughout the block, or for classes of values within the block. The mechanism as a whole should be machine-independent, but any declaration affecting the name of a register or flag will restrict the applicability of the program to a particular group of machines, or even to one machine. With this extension, the way is open for the admission of the user's names of variables and the use of values expressed in conventional (decimal-based) notation. This is a matter, however, where the semantic definition of the extension requires extreme care if it is not to cause the programmer more trouble than it is worth. If the declarations as suggested are provided for, a further step is for the incorporation of expressions or formulae. Here, perhaps, the most important problem is to ensure unique, unambiguous implementation; the 'looseness' in conventional 'top-down' language definitions must be avoided at all costs.

Whether or not the ALGOL60 block concept is used as suggested above, it can certainly be used in defining structural elements for tidiness in programming. A single 'statement' can be either a single machine instruction, or an instruction of the 'macro' type described above, or a block properly delimited as in ALGOL60. It is then a straightforward matter to define conditional, or choice, statements, or even multiple-choice ('case') statements; and hardly more difficult to introduce counting and iterative structures—the 'for' and '*repeat*' ('*while*' or '*until*') statements, examples of which have been introduced informally in a number of places, including 2.10.

A final extension related to the block concept might be one by which the subroutines were to be transformed into *procedures* with *parameters*. This can lead into very deep water; it would be foolish to put any proposal into a language specification without first considering the consequences for the compiler as well as for the object program.

Of all these possible extensions, and others, there are good reasons for regarding the addition of the structural elements as the most urgently needed. It is, of course, possible to write well-structured programs[1] without them. But until the indiscriminate use of unconditional and conditional jumps gives way to the methodical use of structuring, programs are liable to be tortuous, impossible to read and full of errors. Jump instructions cannot be excluded altogether, however, since, for example, there are peculiarities in the hardware of every processor—privileged addresses are a case in point. And while it has been a good rule to avoid 'goto' statements in programs for well structured problems, there remain situations where 'essential use of the goto' is necessary. There is also the rather disturbing case of the sorting subroutine, Figure 5.5. The procedure on which this was based had three 'nested' loops—that is, three loops one inside the other. The final subroutine has the form of three *interlocking* loops, and that is a form that cannot be expressed using the conventional structuring elements alone. Is it a well structured subroutine? Or has it lost its shape through an ill-founded desire to save bytes? What is the proper structure of the algorithm (as contrasted with any realization of the algorithm)? Is it amenable to proof of correctness? Do your answers depend on whether you still like programming computers, or not?

It is clear that the question of the design of languages for use with microprocessors is by no means settled. While many users will be satisfied for a time with a ready-made 'high-level' compiler whose workings they will never investigate, others will find a challenge in seeking out more suitable means of expression for microcomputer programs than are at present envisaged.

Although the experience of the last 25 years does not exactly encourage optimism, it may not be too fanciful to imagine a reader going on to produce his own book in 2003 on 'Picoprocessor Programming and Software Development' and being able to write that, although the new picoprocessors had put back programming 25 years by being born naked into the world, nevertheless the sound progress of these 25 years had made it possible within months to equip them with the very best in software.

---

[1] O. J. Dahl, E. W. Dijkstra, and C. A. R. Hoare: 'Structured Programming': London: Academic Press: 1972.

8

First software for a small 8080 system

8.1   HISTORY

The software (that is, the collection of programs and subroutines) of this chapter grew with the system on which it was developed. No other computer than the 8080 system itself was used. The first instruction was written on 30 December 1976; the first 4K (monitor, assembler, basic arithmetic) were completed in March 1977 and the remaining 2K (disassembler, floating-point arithmetic) in June 1977. Since those dates one correction has been needed for the monitor and one for the disassembler. The two errors are each interesting enough to merit a brief comment below. The total effort invested in this software cannot be more than three man-months. The main periods of activity were the Christmas and Easter vacations; these were separated by the Spring term during which students and colleagues provided many distractions. This information is given by way of encouragement to those who may find the prospect of writing programs somewhat daunting; it is also given by way of excuse for some of the inelegance of style which will be pointed out when the software is described.

At the time when the first instruction of the package was written, the system in use was an unmodified Intel SDK kit, with the Intel MCS-80 monitor in a 1K-byte ROM, 3K bytes of blank PROM (3×2708), and 1K bytes of RAM (8×2111). A KSR-33 Teletype was available, and connected to the kit's 8251 interface (cf. 1.4.1, 2.8). In the following month a PROM programmer designed by K. R. Brooks[1] was made available, and interfaced to the system through the kit's 8255. In February an additional 1K byte RAM module was added on the wire-wrap area of the SDK board, and the monitor ROM was replaced by a PROM containing the monitor given below and also a PROM programming program. In March a small extension board was installed enabling the system to accommodate 6K of PROM (6×2708).

Development of the software proceeded as follows.

(i)   The first program to be copied into a PROM was the PROM programming program (PPP) itself. With the help of this and the Intel monitor, the bulk of

[1]K. R. Brooks: "Microprocessor-controlled PROM programming": *New Electronics*, **2**, 23 (1976)

the assembler was tested piece by piece in RAM and copied into PROM. The last part of the assembler was put into the free space in the PPP-PROM. At this stage there was only 1K of RAM (1000–13FF), part of which (13E2–13FF) was required as work space by the monitor. This is why the last 30 bytes of each of the main assembler PROMs contain odd subroutines—these spaces were filled in later.

(ii)   The assembler was left while the new monitor was written. This monitor provides slightly better facilities than the Intel ROM monitor in about 15 per cent less space. The saved space (0360–03FF) was sufficient to accommodate a PPP, a PROM-reading program, and subroutines for input and output of character strings. The testing and correction of the new monitor was the most difficult part of this software work, since it had to be done without a working monitor.

(iii)   With the new monitor and the PPP in use, and with the aid of the assembler, the various subroutines which were later used to 'fill up' the four PROMs were developed. By this time the additional 1K bytes of RAM were available and the odd spaces at the bottom of the monitor and assembler PROMs could be used.

(iv)   When the PROM extension mentioned above was added, a further 2K of PROM-space became available. The disassembler was then written and placed in one of the extra PROMs, and finally the floating-point package was designed and tailored to fit the remaining space.

(v)   A number of other programs (for example, a reverse Polish interpreter and a graphics monitor) are held in PROMs. The PROM-reading program enables the PROM programmer to be used as a very fast and convenient input device, so any of these programs can be in RAM within a few seconds.

Several copies of the software PROMs are in use. For the newest 8080 and 8085 systems, however, the 2716 2K PROM rather than the 2708 1K PROM has been used.

The software is described piece by piece below. For each program or subroutine an informal description is given. The informal descriptions are followed by a print-out of the text of the whole package as produced by the disassembler but with a detailed commentary in parallel with the text. The chapter ends with a plain hexadecimal 'dump' of the 6K of PROM.

The following address and device-number allocation applies to the system:

PROM	0000–0FFF and 2400–2BFF
RAM	1000–17FF
8251	(for teletype or video display unit) device numbers FA,FB
8255	(for PROM programmer) device numbers F4,F5,F6,F7.

8.2   THE MONITOR PROM (0000–03FF)

Certain addresses within the range occupied by this PROM require special consideration.

(i)   The 'RESET' address, 0000. When the power for the system is switched on, or the RESET key is operated, the program counter is reset to 0000 and so the instruction at this location is executed. The monitor program, which is meant to provide a firm foundation on which to build other programs, is therefore written to start at 0000.

(ii)   The 'special subroutine' (or 'restart') addresses, 0000, 0008, 0010, 0018, 0020, 0028, 0030, 0038. A subroutine whose first instruction is at one of these locations can be called by an instruction of only one byte (a subroutine at any other location requires to be called by a three-byte instruction). The most frequently called subroutines should be written at these locations. One of them, however, is 0000, the RESET address, which is already spoken for. Another, 0008, called by JSS1 (hex CF), is required for calling the monitor itself from other programs, and so this address has been used for the 'normal' entry to the monitor. We are left with six others, spaced at 8-byte intervals.

8.2.1   The monitor program—main part

The RESET signal is applied not only to the c.p.u. itself but to peripheral interfaces, and in particular to the 8251 which stands between the computer and the console device. The first four instructions (0000–0007) of the monitor at its RESET entry serve to *initialize* this 8251 interface. Among other things they define the format of the message (one character) to be transmitted; detailed information is given by the manufacturers' leaflets on the 8251. From the programming point of view it should be noted that (i) after RESET, the 8251 *must* be initialized, and (ii) if the initialization instructions are executed again after the interface has been used and before another RESET signal is given, their effect is *not* that of re-initialization. Since we cannot (or rather do not) generate a RESET signal by software we should not try to re-enter the monitor at 0000 by software. The proper software entry to the monitor must avoid the 8251 initialization instructions. This is why the monitor is re-entered at 0008, by calling the special subroutine SS1 (JSS1, CF hex).

From 0008 onwards, the monitor must carefully store away in a 'safe place' the contents of all the registers as they were when the instruction 'JSS1' at the exit from the 'user's program' was executed. The block of locations 0010–0066 is occupied by special subroutines, so at 000D there is an unconditional jump to 0067. The instructions at 0008–000C and 0067–007D copy the register information into M17F4 to M17FF, the 'far end' of the system's RAM. Minor difficulties with SP and AF make this rather tricky. The PC value is that stacked as return address by the subroutine call JSS1. Note that the execution of this passage immediately after RESET and interface initialization is redundant, but harmless.

Instructions 007E–0086 cause the teletype to print (or the v.d.u. to display) the message 'MONITOR'. The printing of this message is an indication that the monitor has been entered by RESET or by a software call.

Instructions 0087–00B9 form the main loop of the monitor. First the stack pointer is set to 17F4, so that the stack as used by the monitor will grow away from the safe places reserved for the register contents (above). Then the cue mark '>' is printed (displayed) on a new line, and the monitor is ready to receive an instruction (0090). An instruction can be any one of the seven letters D, G, I, M, R, S, X. If one of these is typed in, the corresponding branch of the monitor will be executed Branches D, I, M, S, X end by jumping to 0087, the beginning of the loop. Branches

G, R end by entering some other (specified) program from which the monitor may in due course be entered again at 0008. If some other key than one of the seven instruction letters is operated, the monitor will print a question mark '?' and loop back to 0087 to allow a further attempt.

8.2.2 Special subroutines

Before discussing the branches of the monitor we should look at the special subroutines, all of which it uses.

At 0038, SS7 'A: = inchar' is a subroutine for reading one character from the console device. On being called, this subroutine loops (0038–003B) until a key is pressed on the keyboard, after which port FB, bit 1 gives a 'one' and port FA delivers the corresponding character to register A. Any parity bit (A_7) is removed, and copies of the input character are left in A and C.

The hardware of the system does not cause an input character to be 'bounced back' or 'echoed' to the printing unit of the teletype or the screen of the v.d.u. Thus a call of SS7 reads a character but does not display it.

The basic output subroutine is SS3, 'outchar (C)', at 0018. As there is insufficient space between 0018 and 0020, this begins with a jump to 0045. Here the execution is held in a loop as long as bit 0 from port FB is 'zero', that is until the printer or v.d.u. is ready to receive a (further) character. As soon as the bit 0 has changed to 'one' the character is output to port FA.

The subroutine at 0010, SS2 'echo' is perhaps a luxury. It is included to give a convenient treatment to certain control characters. Normally it merely outputs the character given to it in register C, but if this character is hex 1B ('escape') it outputs hex 24 ('$'), and if it is hex 0D ('carriage return') it outputs the two characters in succession hex 0D ('carriage return') and hex 0A ('line feed').

The subroutine at 0020, SS4 'in–out', is essentially a call of 'A: = inchar' followed by a call of 'echo'. Thus a call of 'in–out', as well as reading a character into the computer, gives a visible confirmation of the key operation on paper or on the screen. It gives the convenience of 'newline' for one key-operation, and it shows the point where the 'escape' key (see I, D below) is operated.

Some systems have *automatic* 'bounce-back' or 'echo'. However, there are occasions when this is not wanted. The arrangement without automatic echo is to be preferred since echo can be programmed but the disabling of the echo cannot.

The two remaining special subroutines, SS5 and SS6, are very simple. 'ASCII–Hex', given one of the sixteen values 30–39, 41–4F in A, converts it to the corresponding value in 00–0F. 'Hex–ASCII' is the converse operation.

The special subroutines are all called by the monitor; they are all, of course, available to other programs.

8.2.3 The monitor program—branches

(Branches G, R beginning at 00C4, 00CA respectively are discussed after branches I, S, D, M.)

I ('input') at 00E3

This begins by using the subroutine at 01F7 to read a starting address. Thereafter it repeats a loop which reads a pair of hex digits, forming them into a byte; stores this byte at the address; and increments the address by one. Spaces, commas and carriage-return characters typed between bytes are ignored (so the format of the printed record can be controlled) and the operation ends when an 'escape' character is typed in.

S ('substitute') at 0106

This also begins by using the subroutine at 01F7 to read a starting address. If a space or comma is typed (JSS4 at 01D9), the machine prints the value held at the specified address, followed by a hyphen (minus sign, ' − '); if any other character is typed the operation terminates. After ' − ' has been printed the user may type in a pair of hex digits which will be formed into a byte and will overwrite the value previously displayed. Alternatively, or after typing in the hex digits, the user may type (i) a space or comma, in which case the value at the *next* higher address will be displayed and can be accepted or overwritten as before, or (ii) any other character, in which case the operation terminates.

D ('display' or 'dump') at 0133

This is the part of the monitor used to print the hexadecimal dumps given at the end of this chapter. As can be seen, the body of the output consists of lines of sixteen bytes from consecutive locations, separated by spaces, and each beginning with the starting address.

The branch begins by reading two addresses separated by a space or comma. The operation fails if (i) an address is incorrectly typed, (ii) some character other than space or comma follows the first address, or (iii) the second address is lower than the first. If all is well, a loop is entered at 014D which will display the contents of the store from the first given address to the second, inclusive. The loop first prints the address of the next location whose value is to be printed, and then it enters an inner loop (0158–017B) which prints values from consecutive locations until the address concerned is a multiple of sixteen. At that point the inner loop returns to the outer loop. The operation normally continues until the value at the finishing address has been printed, but there is a sequence of instructions (015F–016E) which allows the display to be abandoned at any time. At each passage through this sequence, the keyboard interface is examined (cf. SS7 above). If (i) bit 1 of port FB is a 'one' *and* (ii) the value at port FA is 1B, in other words if the 'escape' key has been operated, then the display will stop immediately and (016C) the main loop of the monitor will be resumed at 0087.

M ('mimic' or 'copy') at 0180

This is a 'block copy' operation of the kind discussed in 5.2. It begins at 0180 by reading three addresses, separated each from the next by a space or comma. They are respectively the source starting address, the source finishing address, and the destination starting address. (The source finishing address is used instead of the number of bytes to be copied required by the examples of 5.2). If the second address is less than the first, there is a failure exit to 0034. If not, the two starting addresses are compared, and depending on the comparison the copying proceeds either forwards (01B2) or backwards (01C4). In the latter case a little computation (01C4–01D6) is necessary to establish new starting and finishing conditions.

The remaining monitor operations, G ('go'), R ('resume') and X ('examine registers'), are related to each other, and are perhaps more difficult to understand than those described above.

Any program (for example, the assembler, or the user's program under test in RAM) should terminate by calling the monitor as if it were a subroutine at 0008, by JSS1 (CF). As explained in 8.2.1 above, this causes the contents of the registers (AF, BC, DE, HL, SP, PC) as they were at the moment of the call to be stored away in the 'safe' locations M17F4–M17FF. These locations are accessible through the operations G, R and X.

R ('resume'), at 00CA

The saved values are restored to the registers, as follows. First, the stack pointer is set to 17F4 so that the values for DE, BC, AF can be unstacked. Then the stack pointer value in MM17FE is restored by way of HL. The program counter value (MM17FC) is now stacked, and the value for HL (MM17FA) restored. The final 'RET' (00E0) completes the restoration of the program counter.

The net effect of all this is that the program which last called the monitor is *resumed* at the instruction immediately after the monitor call, with the values in the registers as they were at the call. (The monitor has behaved as a completely transparent subroutine.)

G ('go'), at 0DC4

The 'go' operation is a variation of R which is used for entering programs at specific points, in particular at their proper entry points. The action described under R above is preceded by the reading of an entry address. This address value is immediately written into MM17FC, overwriting the saved program-counter contents.

A complete 'go' instruction, such as 'G1234' is usually thought of as 'enter the program which starts at 1234', though it is more precisely 'jump to 1234 with the values of the registers as they were before the last subroutine call to 0008'.

The 'transparency' so carefully ensured by the monitor for 'G' and 'R' can be obscured by the operation of 'X', the remaining monitor operation, whose function is to display the saved register contents and to allow them to be selectively changed from the keyboard.

X ('examine registers'), at 0215

This is the most complicated of the monitor operations. It requires several subroutines for its own use. It begins by printing a heading line with the names of the flags and registers, and then it prints the corresponding saved values immediately under the names. Flags appear as bits (0, 1); other values in hexadecimal. The space bar of the keyboard is then treated as a 'tab' key for lining up the carriage (cursor) with any particular value which needs to be modified. A new value typed under an existing value will cause the latter to be overwritten. At any stage 'carriage return' transfers control back to the main loop of the monitor (0087).

The X-branch occupies 0215–021A and 0245–0311, with its subroutines in 0312–0359. In the printing of the saved values, the section for printing the flag values (024D–025F) makes use of a subroutine (0312–031E) which on each of five calls finds and prints a flag value. The section for printing the other registers (0260–0287) is rather more straightforward. The remaining part (0288–02E9) is somewhat intricate. With the carriage (cursor) aligned on the N-flag value *either* five new bit-values can be typed in for the flags, *or* the space bar can be operated to 'tab' to the A-register value, *or* the return key can be used to terminate the operation. The choice is repeated with the A, BC, DE, HL, SP and PC values. New flag values are read and combined into a new flag register value for M17F8 by successive calls on the subroutine in 031F–032C. Each register pair or double-length register is dealt with by a call on the subroutine in 033C–0359. This subroutine deals, at each call, with the three-way choice as for the flags. A point to notice is that the conditional jump at 0348, if it takes place, leaves an unused return address on the stack. Immediately, however, the stack pointer value is reset and so this is of no consequence.

8.2.4 Other subroutines

The following subroutines, used by the monitor and by other software, are held in the monitor PROM.

At 01E6: 'check hex' is used after 'ASCII–hex' or before 'Hex–ASCII'. It has no effect if the value in A is in the range 00 to 0F inclusive; if the value is outside the range, there is a failure exit to the monitor (00B4).

At 0220: 'A: = in byte' reads and checks two hex digits. If all is well they are assembled into a single byte in register A.

At 0204: 'outbyte (A)' splits the byte given in A into 2 hex digits which are then printed.

At 0200: 'CRLF' ('newline') is simply a call on 'echo' with 0D (carriage return) in C.

At 01F7: 'HL: = in address' is simply two calls of 'A: = in byte' with assignments to H and L respectively.

At 005F: 'Outstring (B)': given a value n in B and an address a in HL, this subroutine prints the n characters whose ASCII values are to be found in $M(a)$, $M(a+1)$, . . . , $M(a+n-1)$.

At 03F6: 'Outstring (ESC)': given an address a in HL, this subroutine prints the characters whose ASCII values are in $M(a)$ onwards until it finds the value 1B ('escape'). The subroutine returns at this point without printing any character for 1B.

At 03EC: 'In string (ESC)': given an address a in HL, this subroutine reads a succession of characters and stores their ASCII values in $M(a)$ onwards. When it reads 1B ('escape') it returns, having stored 1B for possible later use by 'outstring (ESC)'.

At 0231:   'HL−DE' sets the condition flags N, Z according to the difference
                  HL−DE of the two *unsigned* double-length integers (normally
                  addresses) given in HL, DE.

$$\text{At exit, } N = 0,\ Z = 1 \text{ if } HL - DE = 0 \quad (HL = DE)$$
$$N = 0,\ Z = 0 \text{ if } HL - DE > 0 \quad (HL > DE)$$
$$N = 1,\ Z = 0 \text{ if } HL - DE < 0 \quad (HL < DE)$$

Finally, at 01F4 there is an unconditional jump to 0010 (first instruction of
'echo') and at 021B there is an unconditional jump to 0038 (first instruction of
'A: = inchar'). These are provided to allow certain programs which were written
originally with the Intel SDK monitor (including the assembler) to be run with the
minimum of alteration with this new monitor.

8.2.5 Programs for the PROM programmer (0360–03EB)

The techniques used here are introduced in 5.7. The two programs, 'program PROM'
at 0360 and 'read PROM' at 03C0, assume that a particular type of PROM programmer for a particular type of PROM (2708 or 8708) is connected in a particular
way to the 8255 whose device numbers are F4–F7. The interface characteristics of
the programmer and its connections are as described in 5.7.

'Program PROM' (entry 0360) operates in three phases. First, the supposedly
blank PROM mounted in the programmer is read a byte at a time. As long as each
byte is found to be hex FF (all ones, the 'erased' condition) the reading proceeds.
If a byte other than FF is read, the program halts (03BA) and the warning light 'not
erased' on the programmer is lit. After a successful check of the whole PROM, the
interface is prepared for writing (0371–0376) and the programming operation begins.
For the 8708 and 2708 this process takes the form of an inner loop (0384–039A)
executed once for each of the 1024 bytes of the PROM inside an outer loop (037D–
039E) which is repeated 200 times. This is required by the physical nature of the
PROM. Within the inner loop is a timing loop which (cf. 5.7) measures the width of
the programming pulse. The final part of the process is checking, which requires the
interface to be prepared for reading (039F–03A2). Each byte of the newly programmed
PROM is read back into register A and compared with its original, still in RAM
(1000–13FF). If any discrepancy is found, the 'error' light on the programmer is lit
(03BB–03BE) and the monitor is called (03BF); an 'X' operation of the monitor will
then reveal (HL) the location of the discrepancy.

The 'read PROM' program (entry 03C0) is mainly (03C7–03CF) a simple loop
which reads the information from a PROM mounted in the PROM programmer
byte by byte into RAM locations 1000 to 13FF (the same locations as are used by
the PPP).

8.3   THE ASSEMBLER (0400–07E2, 0800–0BDF, 0C00–0D6E, 0D85–0DC9)

(See 8.1 above for the reason why 07E3–07FF and 0BE0–0BFF were not used for the
assembler.)

The assembler makes use of the RAM as detailed below:

1000–100F	Store for the characters (ASCII values) of the source instruction currently being processed.
1010–1011	Object-program counter (that is, the address of the location at which the next assembled byte will be stored). Initialized to 1180.
1012–1013	Jump list counter (address of location at which next entry of jump list will be stored).
1014	Marker (initially zero (00); set to 01 by first compiled instruction).
1015–101F	Not used.
1020–103D	X-table (X0 always begins at 1000; $MM(1020+2(h-1))$ is the run-time address of the first element of Xh, $1 \leq h \leq F$.
103E–103F	Address at run-time of first instruction of compiled program.
1040–10BF	Label table: the run-time address of label L is in $MM(1040+2L)$, $0 \leq L \leq 3F$.
10C0–117F	Jump list. A list each of whose entries consists of three bytes. The three bytes are a label and an address at which there is an instruction referring to that label. When, during assembly, a reference to a label which has not yet occurred is found, an entry is added to this list. At FINISH, the list is used, in conjunction with the label table, to supply the missing addresses. There is accommodation for up to 64 (decimal) entries.
1180 onwards	The instructions and constants of the assembled object program. The length of this section is limited by the stack.

The assembler is entered at 0C00, usually by the monitor instruction G0C00. The first part of the assembler is

0C00–0C19:	*Initialization:* The X-table, label table and jump-lists are cleared (set to zero), the marker (1014) is cleared, and a jump is made to
0400–0457:	*The instruction read-routine:* Ignoring any 'space' or 'line-feed' characters, the characters forming a source instruction are read and stored in M1000 onwards. At any stage during this process, a 'delete' character from the keyboard will cause the routine to restart at 0406 having printed ' ?'. The source instruction is terminated with ';' or 'return'. After either of these, the routine prints ';' followed by sufficient spaces to align the carriage (cursor) twenty character-positions from the left-hand margin.

The assembler then processes the newly read instruction (0C20 onwards). After generating up to three object-program bytes, as appropriate, it continues by jumping to one of the several entry points of the output routine.

0460–0485:	*The output routine:* This makes use of a subroutine 'out object byte' (0458–045B, 0486–0499). 'Out object byte' stores a copy of the byte given in A at the end of the object program (1180 onwards) and prints its value followed by a space.

The output routine is entered at several points:

047A — one byte, in A, to be output.
0479 — one byte, to be formed by adding the values in A and C, to be output.
0475 — one byte, in B, to be output.
0472 — two bytes, in A, B, to be output in that order.
0467 — three bytes, in A, B, E, to be output in that order.
0463 — (failure entry) −three zero bytes (00 00 00) to be output.
0460 — if flag Z is set (Z = 1), one byte, in B, to be output;
        if Z not set (Z = 0), three zero bytes (00 00 00) to be output.
047D — no bytes to be output (X or VALUES instruction processed).

After putting out the required number of bytes, the routine checks for the presence of a semicolon ';' immediately after the last character of the processed instruction. If it is not present, '?' is printed. At 0436 the 'new line' prepares for reading another instruction from 0406.

0C20 onwards: processing an instruction

This, the major part of the assembler, is a tree structure with a branch dealing with all instructions beginning with the same letter. The branches begin at the following locations:

A	04A6	F	0CC1	K	07C7	S	08C7
B	0585	G	0633	L	0DA3	V	0D05
C	060A	H	0654	M	0DAF	X	0C2E
D	0616	I	0725	N	09A1	labels	0C93
E	0976	J	074B	R	0895		

Within each branch, successive characters of the instruction are examined, and the branch is left by a jump to the appropriate entry point of the output routine. Notes on the subroutines that may be called by a branch are given below.

A few branches require special comment.

The X-branch can be entered only if the marker is zero. The processing of an X-instruction (declaration of a working-store block) sets up an entry in the X-table. No bytes are output. When the first instruction not beginning with X is encountered, the marker is set to 01 (non-zero) and the starting-addresses of all the (declared) X-blocks are computed (0C59) before that instruction is processed. Subsequently any instruction beginning with X is rejected. The run-time address of the first object byte is immediately after the last X-block.

The V-branch ('VALUES') generates no instruction bytes, but it allows a string of ASCII characters or hexadecimal values to be included with the object program.

The labels branch causes an entry to be placed in the label table. Having checked the colon (':') immediately following the label, the label branch jumps to 04A0 to begin the processing of the labelled instruction.

The F-branch generates no object bytes. It causes the jump list to be scanned and all forward references in the object program to be completed. It ends by calling the monitor (0CEE).

Subroutines for the assembler

'ASCII—Hex (assembler)'—entry 0B00. Given an ASCII value in A, this subroutine produces the corresponding hex digit in A and B; but if the ASCII value is not that of one of the hex digits, the subroutine leaves FF in B.

'Operator'—entry 0B20. Before entry HL points to the next character of the source instruction; the next one, two or three characters are expected to be an operator. On return, if an operator has been found, the result in C and the increment to HL are as follows:

For	':+',	C: = 00,	HL:+1
	':++',	C: = 01,	HL:+2
	':−',	C: = 02,	HL:+1
	':−−',	C: = 03,	HL:+2
	':&',	C: = 04,	HL:+1
	':#',	C: = 05,	HL:+1
	':U',	C: = 06,	HL:+1
	'−',	C: = 07,	HL:+0
	':=',	C: = 08,	HL:+1

If no operator is found, C: = FF. In this case HL incremented by 1 indicates that ':' was found but the next character was not one of +, −, &, #, U, =.

'Construct J'—entry 0B60. The next two characters of the source instruction—expected to be hex digits—are converted from ASCII and combined into a single byte value, in A. If either is not a hex digit, the failure value FF is left in C.

'Single-length register or J'—entry 0B1B. When this subroutine is called the next one or two characters should be (i) the name of a single-length register, or M, or (ii) the increment or decrement value 1, or (iii) two hex digits making a J-byte value. At exit the result is:

(i)   for 'B', C = 00; for 'C', C = 01; for 'D', C = 02; for 'E', C = 03; for 'H', C = 04; for 'L', C = 05; for 'M', C = 06; for 'A', C = 07;

(ii) for '1', C = 09;

(iii) for J, C = 08 and the byte value is in A. HL is incremented by one.

Otherwise, C = FF, the failure value.

'Condition'—entry 0BC0. The next one or two characters of the source instruction should be the name of a condition. At exit the result is:

For NZ, C = 00	For NP, C = 04
Z, C = 01	P, C = 05
NK, C = 02	NN, C = 06
K, C = 03	N, C = 07

Otherwise C = FF, the failure value.

'Form JK'—entry 0A00. The next four characters of the source instruction are expected to be hex digits. If they are, the first two are converted and combined to form the K-byte value in E and the last two form the J-byte value in A.

'Construct JK'—entry 0B80. This is a large, complicated subroutine which deals with the various forms which the assembler allows for an address. The result is usually the lower half of the absolute address (J-byte) in A and the upper half (K-byte) in E.

For the *explicit form* of address, four hex digits 'hhhh', A and E have the values produced by 'form JK'.

For the *label form* '(Lhh)', the address of the label is looked up in the label table. If it is there, it is given in A,E. If it is not, an entry is added to the jump list; the value 'FD' ('forward') is given in E.

For the *X-form* '(Xh)' or '(Xh+hh)' or '(Xh−hh)', the X-table is used to give the address of the X-block concerned and if necessary the displacement is added or subtracted from this.

For the *I-form* '(I+hh)' or '(I−hh)' the address for A,E is computed from the values in MM1010, MM103E and the given displacement. (See the beginning of this section for use of RAM.)

8.4   THE DISASSEMBLER (2800–2B7F)

The disassembler was used to print out the text of the software later in the chapter. For each instruction, first the location is printed, then the operation code (I-byte), and finally the written form. At entry the disassembler expects a starting address in HL and a finishing address in DE. It then works through the store beginning at the starting address and ending immediately before the first instruction whose I-byte is at or after the finishing address.

The disassembler must assume that the text on which it is operating consists only of a succession of instructions. If it is allowed to run into an area of store occupied by other information, such as ASCII text or floating-point numbers, it will print nonsense.

The structure of the disassembler is of a simple counting loop. At each passage through the loop, after the address and I-byte have been printed, the two most significant bits of the I-byte are used to select one of four main branches. Each branch corresponds to a quarter of the Karnaugh map given in Chapter 3. Within each branch, the structure of the disassembler follows the Karnaugh map structure. As the bottom left-hand corner of the map is entirely regular, so the branch for I = 10...... (28A3) is very simple. The top left-hand corner is divided into several segments including a number of a single cell each. Consequently the branch for I = 00...... (2960) involves a succession of segments each for an individual I-byte value.

The written form of an instruction is considered in three parts, one or two of which are missing in some cases. The three are the 'head string', the J or KJ value and the 'tail string'. Thus the instruction 'MM2345: = HL' has all three parts, respectively 'MM', '2345', and '. = HL'; the instruction 'C: = 25' has the first two, respectively 'C: = ' and '25'; and 'K: = 1' is treated as consisting of a tail string only.

The way in which any given instruction is printed is best discovered by reference to the annotated text. In many cases, a branch will end by jumping to an address in the range 2828 to 284F, for the printing of the tail string. And there the reader will find shamelessly exploited a programmers' trick of the kind that gave machine-code programming a bad name twenty and more years ago. The succession of assignments to DE which the disassembler has found in itself between 283A and 284C is a space-saving trick for arriving at 284C with one or other of a limited range of values in register B. A jump to 2838 will assign 02 to B and a succession of useless values to the spare register pair DE. A jump to 2841, the *second* byte of one of these useless assignments, will assign the value 05 to B and a shorter succession of useless values to DE. The use of such a trick is justified only when, as here, there is a need for space-saving, and can be excused only to the extent that it is pointed out and explained.

The disassembler's subroutines, 'Find name of register' (2860), 'Print value of KJ' (286F), 'Find name of register pair' (2940), 'Ordinary register pair' (2936), 'Stacking register pair' (2955), 'Print name of condition' (2A56) are simple and straightforward.

The subroutine 'Find and print symbols for *op*' (2900) is written as a nested pair of subroutines, calling the inner one at 2905, in order to benefit from the single-byte conditional return instruction of the 8080. Written as a single-level subroutine, this would have a three-byte jump instruction at each position occupied by a conditional or unconditional return except the last.

8.5   SUBROUTINES FOR INTEGRAL AND FIXED-POINT ARITHMETIC

Many of these subroutines are introduced in Chapter 4. Here references to sections in that chapter are given, together with any additional comments for which there is insufficient space in 8.8.

07E6/8	'out decimal fraction (HL)'
	Given $X = f \times 2^{16}$ in HL, where $0 \leq X \leq 65,535$, prints an approximation to f with 5 (07E6) or B (07E8) decimal places
0BE0	'HL: = sqrt(BC) $\times 2^7$'
	The algorithm is Newton's (6.3). The value of p_0 (4.5.5.1) for the double-length division is 14 (decimal). The iteration is finished when two successive approximations are either equal (0BF3) or different in the least significant digit only (0BF5–0BFA).
0F18–0F4F	Single-length multiplication—see 4.5.3.
0F50–0F9A	Single-length division—see 4.5.5.
0F9B–0FF0	Double-length division—see 4.5.5.
0FF1/2	'HL:/2'
	0FF1 adds 1 in l.s.b. position for rounding (4.6.4).
2400–243E	Double-length multiplication—the method is the same as that given in 4.5.3 but using double-length registers and operations wherever possible. See also 4.5.4.
2440	Multiplication, 15 b.p.—uses double-length integer multiplication, at 2420, to give $(x \times 2^{15}) \times (y \times 2^{15}) = xy \times 2^{30}$ which is shifted

up one place to give $xy \times 2^{31}$; this in turn is rounded to double length to give $(xy \times 2^{31}) \times 2^{-16} = xy \times 2^{15}$, the required result.

2452   Polynomial, 15 b.p.—see 6.3.

2470   'HL: = sin(HL) 15 b.p.'

Given $x \times 2^{15}$ in HL this evaluates:

$$(2 \times x \times \left(\left(\left(-\frac{x^2}{2 \times 7!} + \frac{1}{2 \times 5!}\right) \times x^2 - \frac{1}{2 \times 3!}\right) \times x^2 + \frac{1}{2}\right) \times 2^{15})$$

Note:

$$-2^{14} \div 7! = -3 \ (\text{FFFD})$$
$$+2^{14} \div 5! = +137 \ (0089)$$
$$-2^{14} \div 3! = -2731 \ (\text{F555})$$
$$+2^{14} \qquad = +16384 \ (4000)$$

2490   'HL: = cos(HL) 15 b.p.'
$$\cos(x) = (1 - \sin^2(x))^{\frac{1}{2}}$$

250A–2567   Triple-length signed integer multiplication—see 4.5.4 and 4.7.3.4.

2568–25A0   Triple-length arithmetic shift down—see 4.7.3.1.

25E4   Rounding, 44 b.p. to 22 b.p.—see 4.7.3.4.

8.6   FLOATING-POINT SUBROUTINES

The triple-length subroutines in 250A–25A1 and 25D7–2602 are intended as auxiliary subroutines for the floating-point set—see 4.7.3. Normalization (25A1–25D7) is described in 4.7.2.

The floating-point arithmetic subroutines (2608–2629, 263E–2744, 24A7–24BF) are described in 4.7.4 and the input and output subroutines (2745–27FF, 2B80–2BFF, 262A–263D) in 4.7.5.

8.7   ERRORS AND SHORTCOMINGS

It was mentioned in 8.1 above that an error in the monitor and another in the disassembler went undetected for several months.

The error in the monitor was, essentially, the omission of the instruction 'SP: = 17F4' at 0081. The purpose of this instruction is to ensure that the return addresses for the call of the 'out string' subroutine and the call of 'out char' inside it are both written into RAM and not thrown at some PROM or into thin air. Before the omission was repaired, the monitor worked correctly most of the time. It so happened that nearly every time the machine was switched on the 'random' value in SP pointed at an address in RAM. On the rare occasions when it did not, and so the message 'MONITOR' was not printed properly, a surge in the mains or a dry joint on the board could be blamed. Then a copy of the monitor PROM was installed in another system. It worked—but only very occasionally. Both the original and the copy worked hardly ever on the second system; both worked nearly every time on the first. When the error in the program was pointed out it immediately became obvious that there was nothing wrong with either machine.

The error in the disassembler was another omission—the instruction hex 37 ('K: = 1') had been overlooked. Presumably no one who used the disassembler during its first eight months had wanted to set the carry flag.

The scars of the corrective surgery, as well as those of various amputations and transplants, will be evident to any experienced programmer who cares to look for them.

Although the software was planned in outline, its details are the result of its growth. A revised edition is now being produced with the needs of higher-level programming in mind (6.3).

There are several places where instruction space in the monitor PROM can be saved. For example, the 22-byte subroutine at 0231 (which seemed quite good at the time) can be replaced by the 6-byte subroutine given in 4.5.2. The space saved is enough to allow the disassembler to be made into a branch of the monitor, and to allow programming and reading of types of PROM additional to the 2708/8708, all within the same 1024 bytes.

The assembler, being the earliest part of the software, is also the most in need of improvement. Its existing facilities can certainly be provided in less than 2K bytes, and some minor additions (e.g. addresses relative to labels, decimal and floating-point values) can probably be fitted in. More important is the restructuring of the assembler as a foundation for the higher-level programming discussed in 6.3; the first 'increment' will be of a second block of 2K bytes.

The arithmetic and miscellaneous subroutines should then fit neatly into 2K bytes, making a total of 8K bytes (8 × 2708 or 4 × 2716) for the whole second edition. The '15 b.p.' subroutines will be omitted, having been superseded by floating-point polynomial and trigonometric subroutines. The obvious shortcomings of the existing subroutines (e.g. the incomplete checking in the decimal integer input, the management of rounding after divisions, and the floating-point output problems mentioned in 4.7.5) should of course be corrected at the same time.

8.8   ANNOTATED TEXT OF SOFTWARE

The following is a listing as produced by the disassembler of the 6K bytes of the software (0000–0FFF and 2400–2BFF).

For instructions the format is: location of I-byte, value of I-byte, written form of instruction. The J- and K-byte values, if any, will be visible in the written form.

For sections of ASCII text (that is, sets of characters stored in ASCII code) the format is: location of first character, quote mark, text, quote mark.

For sections of numerical values (binary constants) the format is: location of first byte, the symbol '#', hexadecimal values (two digits per byte), the symbol '#'.

The text is divided into sections of convenient size for printing, and is arranged in numerical order of address except that:

> 0010–0066 follows 00C3
> 035A–035F follows 0244
> 01E6–0230 follows 035F
> 07E6–07FF follows 0E71
> 24A7–24C0 follows 2744

The annotations are, it is hoped, self-explanatory. They should be read in conjunction with the general descriptions of 8.2 to 8.6.

```
G2800
0000    3E    A:=CF;                    (SS0)  'RESET' entry to monitor
0002    D3    GFB:=A;
0004    3E    A:=27;                           Initialize TTY/VDU interface
0006    D3    GFB:=A;
0008    22    MM17FA:=HL;               (SS1)  Normal entry to monitor
000B    F5    ST:=AF;
000C    E1    HL:=ST;
000D    C3    J0067;

MONITOR
>

G2800
0067    22    MM17F8:=HL;
006A    E1    HL:=ST;
006B    22    MM17FC:=HL;
006E    21    HL:=0000;
0071    39    HL:+SP;
0072    22    MM17FE:=HL;
0075    60    H:=B;
0076    69    L:=C;
0077    22    MM17F6:=HL;
007A    EB    HL:=:DE;
007B    22    MM17F4:=HL;
007E    21    HL:=00BA;
0081    31    SP:=17F4;
0084    CD    JS03F6;
0087    31    SP:=17F4;
008A    CD    JS0200;
008D    0E    C:=3E;
008F    DF    JSS3;
0090    E7    JSS4;
0091    FE    A-44;
0093    CA    JZ0133;
0096    FE    A-47;
0098    CA    JZ00C4;
009B    FE    A-49;
009D    CA    JZ00E3;
00A0    FE    A-4D;
00A2    CA    JZ0180;
00A5    FE    A-52;
00A7    CA    JZ00CA;
00AA    FE    A-53;
00AC    CA    JZ0106;
00AF    FE    A-58;
00B1    CA    JZ0215;
00B4    0E    C:=3F;
00B6    DF    JSS3;
00B7    C3    J0087;

MONITOR
>

00BA    "   MONITOR  "
```

Save register contents:

MM17F4:=DE

MM17F6:=BC

MM17F8:=AF

MM17FA:=HL

MM17FC:=PC

MM17FE:=SP

Print entry message 'MONITOR'

Re-entry after normal monitor instruction: initialize stack pointer; cue-mark '>' on new line

Read next monitor instruction

If 'D' jump to 0133

If 'G' jump to 00C4

If 'I' jump to 00E3

If 'M' jump to 0180

If 'R' jump to 00CA

If 'S' jump to 0106

If 'X' jump to 0215

Failure: print '?'
Loop back for next monitor instruction

```
     G2800
0010    41    B:=C;              (SS2) Entry 'echo'
0011    3E    A:=1B;
0013    B8    A-B;
0014    C3    J0050;
0017    00    NULL;
0018    C3    J0045;             (SS3) Entry 'outchar (C)'
001B    0E    C:=0A;
001D    DF    JSS3;
001F    48    C:=B;
001F    C9    RET;
0020    FF    JSS7;              (SS4) Entry 'in-out'
0021    4F    C:=A;
0022    D7    JSS2;
0023    79    A:=C;
0024    C9    RET;
0025    00    NULL;
0026    00    NULL;
0027    00    NULL;
0028    D6    A:-30;             (SS5) Entry 'ASCII-hex.'
002A    FE    A-0A;
002C    F8    RN;
002D    D6    A:-07;
002F    C9    RET;
0030    C6    A:+30;             (SS6) Entry 'hex.-ASCII'
0032    FE    A-3A;
0034    F8    RN;
0035    C6    A:+07;
0037    C9    RET;
0038    DB    A:=GFB;            (SS7) Entry 'A:=inchar'
003A    E6    A:&02;
003C    CA    JZ0038;
003F    DB    A:=GFA;
0041    E6    A:&7F;
0043    4F    C:=A;
0044    C9    RET;
0045    DB    A:=GFB;            Continuation of SS3
0047    E6    A:&01;
0049    CA    JZ0045;
004C    79    A:=C;
004D    D3    GFA:=A;
004F    C9    RET;
0050    C2    JNZ0055;           Continuation of SS2
0053    0E    C:=24;
0055    DF    JSS3;
0056    3E    A:=0D;
0058    B8    A-B;
0059    CA    JZ001B;
005C    48    C:=B;
005D    C9    RET;
005E    00    NULL;
005F    4E    C:=M;              Entry 'outstring (B)'
0060    DF    JSS3;
0061    23    HL:+1;
0062    05    B:-1;
0063    C2    JNZ005F;
0066    C9    RET;
```

MONITOR
>

```
        G2800
        00C4   CD   JS01F7;           'G'    MM17FC:=input address
        00C7   22   MM17FC:=HL;
        00CA   F3   I:=0;             'R'
        00CB   CD   JS0200;                  Newline
        00CE   31   SP:=17F4;    ⎞
        00D1   D1   DE:=ST;      ⎟                                    ⎧ DE:=MM17F4
        00D2   C1   BC:=ST;      ⎟                                    ⎪ BC:=MM17F6
        00D3   F1   AF:=ST;      ⎟                                    ⎪ AF:=MM17F8
        00D4   2A   HL:=MM17FE;  ⎬    Restore register contents:      ⎨ SP:=MM17FE
        00D7   F9   SP:=HL;      ⎟                                    ⎪ HL:=MM17FA
        00D8   2A   HL:=MM17FC;  ⎟                                    ⎪ PC:=MM17FC
        00DB   E5   ST:=HL;      ⎟                                    ⎩
        00DC   2A   HL:=MM17FA;  ⎠
        00DF   FB   I:=1;
        00E0   C9   RET;
        00E1   00   NULL;
        00E2   00   NULL;
        00E3   CD   JS01F7;           'I'    HL:=input address
        00E6   CD   JS0200;                  Newline
        00E9   E7   JSS4;                    In-out
        00EA   FE   A-20;
        00EC   CA   JZ00E9;
        00EF   FE   A-2C;
        00F1   CA   JZ00E9;                  Ignore space, comma, carriage return
        00F4   FE   A-0D;
        00F6   CA   JZ00E9;
        00F9   FE   A-1B;
        00FB   CA   JZ0087;                  Finish on 'escape'
        00FE   CD   JS0221;                  Read second character and form byte
        0101   77   M:=A;        ⎞           Store, and increment addressing register
        0102   23   HL:+1;       ⎠
        0103   C3   J00E9;                   Loop back for next input
        0106   CD   JS01F7;           'S'    HL:=input address
        0109   E7   JSS4;                    In-out
        010A   FE   A-20;
        010C   CA   JZ0114;
        010F   FE   A-2C;
        0111   C2   JNZ0087;                 Finish if not space or comma
        0114   7E   A:=M;                    Display contents of addressed location
        0115   CD   JS0204;
        0118   0E   C:=2D;                   Display '−'
        011A   DF   JSS3;
        011B   E7   JSS4;                    In-out
        011C   47   B:=A;
        011D   EF   JSS5;                    ASCII-hex.
        011E   FE   A-00;        ⎞
        0120   FA   JN012E;      ⎬           Skip to 012E if not hex.
        0123   FE   A-10;        ⎟
        0125   F2   JNN012E;     ⎠
        0128   CD   JS0225;                  Otherwise, complete byte
        012B   77   M:=A;                    Store new value
        012C   E7   JSS4;                    In-out
        012D   47   B:=A;
        012E   78   A:=B;
        012F   23   HL:+1;                   Increment addressing register
        0130   C3   J010A;                   Loop back to continue or finish

        MONITOR
        >
```

```
        G2800
        0133   CD    JS01F7;          'D'
        0136   E5    ST:=HL;                    Read starting address to stack
        0137   E7    JSS4;                      Read and print separator
        0138   FE    A-20;
        013A   CA    JZ0142;
        013D   FE    A-2C;
        013F   C2    JNZ00B4;                   Fail if separator not space or comma
        0142   CD    JS01F7;                    Read finishing address
        0145   D1    DE:=ST;
        0146   CD    JS0231;                    Fail if less than starting address
        0149   FA    JN00B4;
        014C   EB    HL:=:DE;                   HL has current address; DE finishing address
        014D   CD    JS0200;                    Newline
        0150   7C    A:=H;
        0151   CD    JS0204;                    Print current address
        0154   7D    A:=L;
        0155   CD    JS0204;
        0158   0E    C:=20;                     Print space
        015A   DF    JSS3;
        015B   7E    A:=M;                      Print current byte
        015C   CD    JS0204;
        015F   DB    A:=GFB;
        0161   E6    A:&02;                     Is there an input from the keyboard?
        0163   CA    JZ016F;                        If not, skip to 016F
        0166   DB    A:=GFA;                        If so read it (cf SS7)
        0168   E6    A:&7F;
        016A   FE    A-1B;
        016C   CA    JZ0087;                    Finish if 'escape' just read
        016F   CD    JS0231;                    Finish if current address
        0172   CA    JZ0087;                        equal to finishing address
        0175   23    HL:+1;                     Increment addressing register
        0176   7D    A:=L;
        0177   E6    A:&0F;                     New current address divisible by sixteen?
        0179   C2    JNZ0158;                       If not, next byte on same line
        017C   C3    J014D;                         If so, newline
        017F   00    NULL;
```

```
MONITOR
>
```

```
    G2800
    0180  CD   JS01F7;         'M'
    0183  E5   ST:=HL;               Source starting address to stack
    0184  E7   JSS4;                 Read and print separator
    0185  FE   A-20;
    0187  CA   JZ018F;
    018A  FE   A-2C;
    018C  C2   JNZ00B4;              Fail if not space or comma
    018F  CD   JS01F7;               Read source finishing address
    0192  D1   DE:=ST;
    0193  CD   JS0231;
    0196  FA   JN00B4;               Fail if source addresses inconsistent
    0199  E5   ST:=HL;
    019A  D5   ST:=DE;
    019B  E7   JSS4;                 Read and print separator
    019C  FE   A-20;
    019E  CA   JZ01A6;
    01A1  FE   A-2C;
    01A3  C2   JNZ00B4;              Fail if not space or comma
    01A6  CD   JS01F7;               Destination start address to stack
    01A9  E5   ST:=HL;
    01AA  D1   DE:=ST;
    01AB  E1   HL:=ST;
    01AC  CD   JS0231;               Compare starting addresses
    01AF  FA   JN01C4;               Jump to 01C4 for 'backward' copying
    01B2  42   B:=D;
    01B3  4B   C:=E;                 BC has destination address
    01B4  D1   DE:=ST;               DE has source finishing address
    01B5  7E   A:=M;
    01B6  02   M[BC]:=A;
    01B7  C5   ST:=BC;
    01B8  CD   JS0231;               Copying loop (Section 5.2) finishing after last source address has
    01BB  C1   BC:=ST;               been copied
    01BC  CA   JZ0087;
    01BF  03   BC:+1;
    01C0  23   HL:+1;
    01C1  C3   J01B5;

    MONITOR
      >
```

```
    G2800
  01C4   EB   HL:=:DE;           'Backward' copying—see Section 5.2
  01C5   44   B:=H;
  01C6   4D   C:=L;
  01C7   7A   A:=D;
  01C8   2F   A:#;
  01C9   67   H:=A;              Instructions in 01C5 to 01CE inclusive equivalent to 'HL:−DE'
  01CA   7B   A:=E;
  01CB   2F   A:#;
  01CC   6F   L:=A;
  01CD   23   HL:+1;
  01CE   09   HL:+BC;
  01CF   EB   HL:=:DE;
  01D0   E3   HL:=:ST;
  01D1   EB   HL:=:DE;
  01D2   19   HL:+DE;
  01D3   44   B:=H;
  01D4   4D   C:=L;
  01D5   E1   HL:=ST;
  01D6   EB   HL:=:DE;
  01D7   7E   A:=M;
  01D8   02   M[BC]:=A;          Instructions 01D3 to 01E3 similar to those in 01B2 to 01C1
  01D9   C5   ST:=BC;
  01DA   CD   JS0231;
  01DD   C1   BC:=ST;
  01DE   CA   JZ0087;
  01E1   0B   BC:-1;
  01E2   2B   HL:-1;
  01E3   C3   J01D7;

MONITOR
>
```

```
      G2800
      01E6   FE    A-00;                    Entry 'check hex.'
      01E8   FA    JN01F1;
      01EB   FE    A-10;
      01ED   F2    JNN01F1;
      01F0   C9    RET;
      01F1   C3    J00B4;
      01F4   C3    J0010;                   Alternative entry for 'echo' (SS2)
      01F7   CD    JS0220;                  Entry 'HL:=input address'
      01FA   67    H:=A;
      01FB   CD    JS0220;
      01FE   6F    L:=A;
      01FF   C9    RET;
      0200   0E    C:=0D;                   Entry 'Newline' ('CRLF')
      0202   D7    JSS2;
      0203   C9    RET;
      0204   47    B:=A;                    Entry 'Outbyte (A)'
      0205   0F    A:@R;
      0206   0F    A:@R;
      0207   0F    A:@R;
      0208   0F    A:@R;
      0209   E6    A:&0F;
      020B   F7    JSS6;
      020C   4F    C:=A;
      020D   DF    JSS3;
      020E   78    A:=B;
      020F   E6    A:&0F;
      0211   F7    JSS6;
      0212   4F    C:=A;
      0213   DF    JSS3;
      0214   C9    RET;
      0215   CD    JS0200;         'X'      Newline
      0218   C3    J0245;                   Continue at 0245
      021B   C3    J0038;                   Alternative entry for 'A:=inchar' (SS7)
      021E   00    NULL;
      021F   00    NULL;
      0220   E7    JSS4;                    Entry 'A:=inbyte'
      0221   EF    JSS5;
      0222   CD    JS01E6;
      0225   87    A:+A;
      0226   87    A:+A;
      0227   87    A:+A;
      0228   87    A:+A;
      0229   57    D:=A;
      022A   E7    JSS4;
      022B   EF    JSS5;
      022C   CD    JS01E6;
      022F   82    A:+D;
      0230   C9    RET;

      MONITOR
      >
```

```
   G2800
   0231   44   B:=H;                    Entry 'HL—DE'
   0232   4A   C:=D;
   0233   78   A:=B;
   0234   B9   A-C;
   0235   C2   JNZ023D;
   0238   45   B:=L;
   0239   4B   C:=E;
   023A   78   A:=B;
   023B   B9   A-C;
   023C   C8   RZ;
   023D   A9   A:#C;
   023E   FA   JNO35A;
   0241   78   A:=B;
   0242   91   A:-C;
   0243   C9   RET;
   0244   00   NULL;

MONITOR
>


   G2800
   035A   79   A:=C;                    Continuation of 'HL—DE'
   035B   F6   A:U7F;
   035D   C9   RET;
   035E   00   NULL;
   035F   00   NULL;

MONITOR
>
```

```
      G2800
      0245   06    B:=28;                    Continuation of 'X'
      0247   21    HL:=02EA;
      024A   CD    JS005F;                   Print heading line
      024D   3A    A:=M17F8;
      0250   A7    A:&A;
      0251   CD    JS0313;
      0254   CD    JS0313;
      0257   CD    JS0312;                   Print values of flags
      025A   CD    JS0312;
      025D   CD    JS0312;
      0260   0E    C:=20;
      0262   DF    JSS3;
      0263   DF    JSS3;
      0264   3A    A:=M17F9;
      0267   CD    JS0204;                   Print value of A (M17F9)
      026A   21    HL:=17F6;
      026D   CD    JS032D;                          BC (MM17F6)
      0270   21    HL:=17F4;
      0273   CD    JS032D;                          DE (MM17F4)
      0276   21    HL:=17FA;
      0279   CD    JS032D;                          HL (MM17FA)
      027C   21    HL:=17FE;
      027F   CD    JS032D;                          SP (MM17FE)
      0282   21    HL:=17FC;
      0285   CD    JS032D;                          PC (MM17FC)
      0288   CD    JS0200;                   Newline
      028B   E7    JSS4;                     Read and print input character
      028C   FE    A-20;
      028E   CA    JZ02B1;                   If space, skip to 02B1
      0291   FE    A-0D;
      0293   CA    JZ0087;                   If return, finish operation
      0296   CD    JS0324;  ⎫
      0299   CD    JS0322;  ⎪
      029C   CD    JS031F;  ⎪
      029F   CD    JS031F;  ⎪
      02A2   82    A:+D;    ⎬                If neither, assign as new value for 'N' flag and read and assign
      02A3   82    A:+D;    ⎪                new values for other flags
      02A4   87    A:+A;    ⎪
      02A5   3C    A:+1;    ⎪
      02A6   CD    JS0322;  ⎭
      02A9   82    A:+D;
      02AA   82    A:+D;
      02AB   32    M17F8:=A;                 New value for F in M17F8
      02AE   C3    J02B5;
```

```
      MONITOR
      >
```

```
    G2800
    02B1    DF    JSS3;                    Spaces if flag values not altered
    02B2    DF    JSS3;
    02B3    DF    JSS3;
    02B4    DF    JSS3;
    02B5    0E    C:=20;                   Spaces to align with A display
    02B7    DF    JSS3;
    02B8    DF    JSS3;
    02B9    E7    JSS4;                    Read and print input character
    02BA    FE    A-20;
    02BC    CA    JZ02C8;                  If space, skip to 02C8
    02BF    CD    JS0221;         ⎫       If not, complete reading of byte, and assign to store for A (M17F9)
    02C2    32    M17F9:=A;       ⎬
    02C5    C3    J02C9;          ⎭
    02C8    DF    JSS3;                    Spaces if A value not altered
    02C9    21    HL:=17F6;       ⎫
    02CC    CD    JS033C;         │
    02CF    21    HL:=17F4;       │
    02D2    CD    JS033C;         │
    02D5    21    HL:=17FA;       ⎬       Any alterations for BC, DE, HL, SP, PC are dealt with by the
    02D8    CD    JS033C;         │        subroutine at 033C
    02DB    21    HL:=17FE;       │
    02DE    CD    JS033C;         │
    02E1    21    HL:=17FC;       ⎭
    02E4    CD    JS033C;
    02E7    C3    J0087;                   Finish

    MONITOR
    >


    02EA    "NZHPK    A      BC      DE      HL      SP      PC      "
```

```
      G2800
      0312    87    A:+A;              Entry 'outbit(A6)'
      0313    47    B:=A;              Entry 'outbit(A7)'
      0314    3E    A:=30;
      0316    F2    JNN031A;
      0319    3C    A:+1;
      031A    4F    C:=A;
      031B    DF    JSS3;
      031C    78    A:=B;
      031D    87    A:+A;
      031E    C9    RET;
      031F    82    A:+D;              Entry 1 to 'inbit'
      0320    82    A:+D;
      0321    87    A:+A;
      0322    57    D:=A;              Entry 2 to 'inbit'
      0323    E7    JSS4;
      0324    D6    A:-30;             Entry 3 to 'inbit'
      0326    C8    RZ;
      0327    FE    A-01;
      0329    C8    RZ;
      032A    C3    J00B4;
```

```
      032D    0E    C:=20;             Entry 'outreg'
      032F    DF    JSS3;
      0330    DF    JSS3;
      0331    23    HL:+1;
      0332    7E    A:=M;              Outputs two spaces, followed by value of MM(HL) as
      0333    CD    JS0204;            four-hex.-digit integer
      0336    2B    HL:-1;
      0337    7E    A:=M;
      0338    CD    JS0204;
      033B    C9    RET;
```

```
      033C    0E    C:=20;             Entry 'inreg'
      033E    DF    JSS3;
      033F    DF    JSS3;                  Output two spaces
      0340    E7    JSS4;
      0341    FE    A-20;                  Read and print input character
      0343    CA    JZ0356;
      0346    FE    A-0D;                  If space, skip to 0356
      0348    CA    JZ0087;
      034B    CD    JS0221;                If return, finish operation
      034E    23    HL:+1;
      034F    77    M:=A;
      0350    CD    JS0220;             Otherwise, complete reading of four-hex.-digit integral value and
      0353    2B    HL:-1;             assign this value to MM(HL)
      0354    77    M:=A;
      0355    C9    RET;
```

```
      0356    DF    JSS3;
      0357    DF    JSS3;
      0358    DF    JSS3;
      0359    C9    RET;                  Spaces for alignment
      035A    79    A:=C;
      035B    F6    A:U7F;
      035D    C9    RET;
      035E    00    NULL;
      035F    00    NULL;
```

      MONITOR
      >

```
      G2800
      0360    CD    JS03D1;          Program entry 'Program PROM'. Initialize
      0363    DB    A:=GF4;            Read byte from PROM
      0365    3C    A:+1;
      0366    C2    JNZ03B6;          Jump to failure routine if value not FF
      0369    CD    JS03E4;           Test
      036C    CA    JZ0363;           Loop back until all of PROM checked
      036F    3E    A:=88;
      0371    D3    GF7:=A;           Prepare interface for writing
      0373    3E    A:=01;
      0375    D3    GF5:=A;           Set 'write enable' of PROM
      0377    21    HL:=1000;         RAM base address
      037A    E5    ST:=HL;
      037B    06    B:=C8;            Repetition counter (C8 hex.=200 decimal)
      037D    3E    A:=04;
      037F    CD    JS03DD;           'Reset' pulse to counter in programmer
      0382    E1    HL:=ST;
      0383    E5    ST:=HL;
      0384    7E    A:=M;             Next byte from RAM
      0385    D3    GF4:=A;           Byte to PROM data terminals
      0387    00    NULL;
      0388    00    NULL;            Set-up time
      0389    3E    A:=02;
      038B    D3    GF6:=A;           Rising edge of programming pulse
      038D    3E    A:=35;
      038F    3D    A:-1;             Time count for pulse width
      0390    C2    JNZ038F;
      0393    D3    GF6:=A;           Trailing edge of programming pulse
      0395    CD    JS03E3;           Inctest
      0398    CA    JZ0384;           Loop back for next byte until all done
      039B    05    B:-1;
      039C    C2    JNZ037D;          Repeat until done 200 times
      039F    3E    A:=98;            Prepare interface for reading
      03A1    D3    GF7:=A;
      03A3    E1    HL:=ST;
      03A4    DB    A:=GF4;           Read next byte from PROM
      03A6    BE    A-M;              Compare with original in RAM
      03A7    C2    JNZ03BB;          Jump to failure routine if different
      03AA    CD    JS03E3;           Inctest
      03AD    C2    JNZ03A4;          Loop back until all checked
      03B0    76    HALT;             Operation complete
      03B1    00    NULL;
      03B2    00    NULL;
      03B3    00    NULL;            (unused)
      03B4    00    NULL;
      03B5    00    NULL;
      03B6    3E    A:=02;            Failure: 'not erased'
      03B8    D3    GF5:=A;
      03BA    76    HALT;             Failure: 'error'
      03BB    3E    A:=04;
      03BD    D3    GF5:=A;
      03BF    CF    JSS1;

      MONITOR
      >
```

```
    G2800
    03C0    00    NULL;                    Program entry 'Read PROM'
    03C1    CD    JS03D1;                       Initialize interface
    03C4    21    HL:=1000;                     Set RAM base address
    03C7    DB    A:=GF4;                        Read byte from PROM
    03C9    77    M:=A;                          Store in RAM
    03CA    CD    JS03E3;                        Inctest
    03CD    CA    JZ03C7;                        Loop back until all done
    03D0    CF    JSS1;                          Call monitor
    03D1    3E    A:=98;                   Entry 'Initialize interface'
    03D3    D3    GF7:=A;
    03D5    3E    A:=04;
    03D7    CD    JS03DD;
    03DA    C9    RET;
    03DB    3E    A:=01;                   Entry 'Pulse A0 to interface'
    03DD    D3    GF6:=A;                  Entry 'Pulse to interface'
    03DF    97    A:-A;
    03E0    D3    GF6:=A;
    03E2    C9    RET;
    03E3    23    HL:+1;                   Entry 'Inctest'
    03E4    CD    JS03DB;                  Entry 'Test'
    03E7    DB    A:=GF6;
    03E9    E6    A:&10;
    03EB    C9    RET;
    03EC    FF    JSS7;                    Entry 'Instring(ESC)'
    03ED    77    M:=A;
    03EE    FE    A-1B;
    03F0    C8    RZ;
    03F1    DF    JSS3;
    03F2    23    HL:+1;
    03F3    C3    JO3EC;
    03F6    4E    C:=M;                    Entry 'Outstring(ESC)'
    03F7    79    A:=C;
    03F8    FE    A-1B;
    03FA    C8    RZ;
    03FB    DF    JSS3;
    03FC    23    HL:+1;
    03FD    C3    JO3F6;

    MONITOR
    >
```

```
G2800
0400   21   HL:=1180;                        (Instruction read routine)
0403   22   MM1010:=HL;                       Initialize object-program counter
0406   21   HL:=1000;                         Initialize source-character address
0409   16   D:=0E;                            Maximum instruction length is fourteen
040B   CD   JS021B;  CRTIN                     Read (not print) character
040E   FE   A-20;
0410   CA   JZ040B;
0413   FE   A-0A;
0415   CA   JZ040B;                           Ignore space or line-feed
0418   FE   A-7F;
041A   CA   JZ0431;                           Abandon instruction if 'delete' read
041D   FE   A-3B;
041F   CA   JZ043E;
0422   FE   A-0D;
0424   CA   JZ043E;                           Instruction terminated by ';' or return
0427   77   M:=A;                             Store source character
0428   23   HL:+1;                            Advance address
0429   4F   C:=A;
042A   CD   JS01F4;  CRTOUT                    Echo accepted character
042D   15   D:-1;                             Count down; loop back if <14 characters read; otherwise fail
042E   C2   JNZ040B;
0431   0E   C:=3F;
0433   CD   JS01F4;                           Print '?'
0436   0E   C:=0D;
0438   CD   JS01F4;                           New line
043B   C3   J0406;                            Loop back for next instruction
043E   36   M:=FF;                            Store hex. FF as terminator
0440   0F   C:=3B;
0442   CD   JS01F4;                           Output';'
0445   7A   A:=D;
0446   C6   A:+05;
0448   57   D:=A;
0449   0E   C:=20;                            Output sufficient spaces to align carriage at twentieth position
044B   CD   JS01F4;
044E   15   D:-1;
044F   C2   JNZ0449;
0452   21   HL:=1000;                         Reset source-character address
0455   C3   J0C20;                            Jump to 0C20 to process instruction
0458   C5   ST:=BC;                   Entry  'out object byte'
0459   C3   J0486;                            Continue at 0486
045C   00   NULL;
045D   00   NULL;
045E   00   NULL;
045F   00   NULL;
```

MONITOR
>

```
      G2800                          (Output routine)
      0460   CA   JZ0475;            If Z=1 then skip to 0475
      0463   3E   A:=00;             Prepare three null bytes
      0465   47   B:=A;
      0466   5F   E:=A;
      0467   CD   JS0458;            Out object byte
      046A   78   A:=B;
      046B   CD   JS0458;            Out object byte
      046E   7B   A:=E;
      046F   C3   J047A;             Skip to 047A
      0472   CD   JS0458;            Out object byte
      0475   78   A:=B;
      0476   C3   J047A;             Skip to 047A
      0479   81   A:+C;
      047A   CD   JS0458;            Out object byte
      047D   23   HL:+1;
      047E   7E   A:=M;              Fetch next source symbol
      047F   3C   A:+1;
      0480   C2   JNZ0431;           Fail if not terminator, hex. FF
      0483   C3   J0436;             Rejoin main loop of instruction read routine
      0486   E5   ST:=HL;            (Continuation of 'out object byte')
      0487   2A   HL:=MM1010;        Fetch object-program counter
      048A   77   M:=A;              Store new object byte
      048B   23   HL:+1;
      048C   22   MM1010:=HL;        Store incremented object-program counter
      048F   E1   HL:=ST;
      0490   CD   JS0204;            Print object byte
      0493   0E   C:=20;
      0495   CD   JS01F4;            Print space
      0498   C1   BC:=ST;
      0499   C9   RET;
      049A   00   NULL;
      049B   3E   A:=3C;             ('A:+1')
      049D   C3   J047A;             One byte (3C) to be output
```

MONITOP
>


```
      G2800
      04A0   7E   A:=M;              (First character, not 'X')
      04A1   FE   A-41;
      04A3   C2   JNZ0580;           Jump to 0580 if not 'A'
      04A6   23   HL:+1;             ('A')
      04A7   7E   A:=M;              Next character
      04A8   FE   A-3A;
      04AA   CA   JZ09D1;            Jump to 09D1 if ':'
      04AD   C3   J09B8;             If not continue at 09B8
```

MONITOR
>

```
     G2800
     04B0   79   A:=C;                    ('Aop')
     04B1   FE   A-FF;
     04B3   CA   JZ0463;                  Fail if operator not found
     04B6   FE   A-08;
     04B8   CA   JZ04F1;                  Jump to 04F1 for 'A:='
     04BB   59   E:=C;
     04BC   CD   JS0E1B;                  Single-length register or J-value
     04BF   47   B:=A;
     04C0   79   A:=C;
     04C1   FE   A-FF;
     04C3   CA   JZ0463;                  Fail if no terminator
     04C6   FE   A-08;
     04C8   CA   JZ04E8;                  Jump to 04E8 for 'AopJ'
     04CE   FE   A-09;
     04CD   CA   JZ04D9;                  Jump to 04D9 for 'Aop1'
     04D0   7B   A:=E;                    ('Aopr')
     04D1   87   A:+A;                    Form I
     04D2   87   A:+A;
     04D3   87   A:+A;
     04D4   C6   A:+80;
     04D6   C3   J0479;                   One byte to be output
     04D9   7B   A:=E;                    ('Aop1')
     04DA   FE   A-00;
     04DC   CA   JZ049B;                  Jump to 049B for 'A:+1'
     04DF   FE   A-02;
     04E1   06   B:=3D;
     04E3   C3   J0460;                   One byte (3D) to be output for 'A:-1'
     04E6   00   NULL;
     04E7   00   NULL;
     04E8   7B   A:=E;                    ('AopJ')
     04E9   87   A:+A;                    Form I
     04EA   87   A:+A;
     04EB   87   A:+A;
     04EC   C6   A:+C6;
     04EE   C3   J0472;                   Two bytes to be output
     04F1   CD   JS0E1B;                  ('A:=') Single-length register or J-value
     04F4   47   B:=A;
     04F5   FE   A-47;
     04F7   CA   JZ0528;                  Jump to 0528 for 'A:=G'
     04FA   79   A:=C;
     04FB   FE   A-08;
     04FD   C2   JNZ0505;                 Jump to 0505 if not J-value
     0500   3E   A:=3E;                   ('A:=J')
     0502   C3   J0472;                   Two bytes (3E J) to be output

     MONITOR
     >
```

```
   G2800
0505   FE   A-FF;              ('A:=r')
0507   CA   JZ050F;            If no register jump to 050F
050A   3E   A:=78;
050C   C3   J0479;            One byte to be output
050F   23   HL:+1;
0510   7E   A:=M;              Next character
0511   FE   A-FF;
0513   C2   JNZ051A;          If not terminator jump to 051A
0516   2B   HL:-1;            ('A:=M')
0517   C3   J050A;            Jump back to output one byte
051A   FE   A-5B;
051C   CA   JZ0532;           If '[' jump to 0532
051F   CD   JS0B80;           Construct JK
0522   47   B:=A;             ('A:=Mkkjj')
0523   3E   A:=3A;
0525   C3   J0467;            Three bytes (3A J K) to be output
0528   23   HL:+1;            ('A:=G')
0529   CD   JS0B60;           Construct J
052C   47   B:=A;             ('A:=Gjj')
052D   3E   A:=DB;
052F   C3   J0472;            Two bytes (DB J) to be output
0532   23   HL:+1;            ('A:=M[')
0533   7E   A:=M;             Next character
0534   FE   A-42;
0536   CA   JZ054E;           If 'B' jump to 054E
0539   FE   A-44;             ('A:=M[D'?)
053B   C2   JNZ0463;          Fail if not 'D'
053F   23   HL:+1;
053F   7E   A:=M;             Next character
0540   FE   A-45;
0542   C2   JNZ0463;          Fail if not 'E'
0545   06   B:=1A;            Value for I
0547   23   HL:+1;
0548   7E   A:=M;
0549   FE   A-5D;
054B   C3   J0460;            ('A:=M[DE]') One byte (1A) to be output
054E   23   HL:+1;            ('A:=M[B')
054F   7E   A:=M;             Next character
0550   FE   A-43;
0552   C2   JNZ0463;          Fail if not 'C'
0555   06   B:=0A;            Value for I
0557   C3   J0547;            Check ']' and output 0A for 'A:=M[BC]'
```

MONITOR
>

```
    G2800
    055A    23    HL:+1;                 ('AF')
    055B    7E    A:=M;                  Third character
    055C    FE    A-3A;
    055E    C2    JNZ0463;               Fail if not ':'
    0561    23    HL:+1;
    0562    7E    A:=M;                  Fourth character
    0563    FE    A-3D;
    0565    C2    JNZ0463;               Fail if not '='
    0568    23    HL:+1;
    0569    7E    A:=M;                  Fifth character
    056A    FE    A-53;
    056C    C2    JNZ0463;               Fail if not 'S'
    056F    23    HL:+1;
    0570    7E    A:=M;                  Sixth character
    0571    FE    A-54;
    0573    06    B:=F1;
    0575    C3    J0460;                 ('AF:=ST') One byte (F1) to be output
    0578    FE    A-43;                  ('DE')
    057A    06    B:=27;
    057C    C3    J0460;                 ('DEC') One byte (27) to be output
    057F    00    NULL;
```

```
MONITOR
>
```

```
        G2800
        0580   FE   A-42;              (First character)
        0582   C2   JNZ0605;           Jump to 0605 if not B
        0585   23   HL:+1;             ('B')
        0586   7E   A:=M;              Second character
        0587   FE   A-43;
        0589   CA   JZ05CE;            If 'C' jump to 05CE
        058C   1E   E:=40;             (r or r₁ will be B)
        058E   FE   A-3A;
        0590   C2   JNZ0463;           Fail if not ':'
        0593   23   HL:+1;             ('r:')
        0594   7E   A:=M;              Third character
        0595   FE   A-2B;
        0597   CA   JZ05BD;            If '+' jump to 05BD
        059A   FE   A-2D;
        059C   CA   JZ05C3;            If '−' jump to 05C3
        059F   FE   A-3D;
        05A1   C2   JNZ0463;           Fail if not '='
        05A4   CD   JS0B1B;            ('r:=') single-length register or J
        05A7   47   B:=A;
        05A8   79   A:=C;
        05A9   FE   A-08;
        05AB   C2   JNZ05B4;           Jump to 05B4 if not J
        05AE   7B   A:=E;              ('r:=jj')
        05AF   C6   A:+C6;
        05B1   C3   J0472;             Two bytes to be output
        05B4   E6   A:&F8;
        05B6   C2   JNZ0463;           Fail if not r₂
        05B9   7B   A:=E;           ⎫  ('r₁:=r₂') One byte to be output
        05BA   C3   J0479;          ⎬
        05BD   7B   A:=E;           ⎭  ('r:+')
        05BE   C6   A:+C4;
        05C0   C3   J05C6;
        05C3   7B   A:=E;              ('r:−')
        05C4   C6   A:+C5;
        05C6   47   B:=A;
        05C7   23   HL:+1;
        05C8   7E   A:=M;              Next character
        05C9   FE   A-31;
        05CB   C3   J0460;             ('r:+1' or 'r:−1') One byte to be output

        MONITOR
        >
```

```
     G2800
     05CE   23    HL:+1;                ('BC')
     05CF   7E    A:=M;                 Third character
     05D0   FE    A-3A;
     05D2   C2    JNZ0463;              Fail if not ':'
     05D5   0E    C:=00;                Base I=00 for BC
     05D7   23    HL:+1;
     05D8   7E    A:=M;                 Fourth character
     05D9   FE    A-2B;
     05DB   CA    JZ0960;               If '+' jump to 0960
     05DE   FE    A-2D;
     05E0   CA    JZ0966;               If '−' jump to 0966
     05E3   FE    A-3D;
     05E5   C2    JNZ0463;              Fail if not '='
     05E8   23    HL:+1;
     05E9   7E    A:=M;                 Fifth character
     05EA   FE    A-53;
     05EC   CA    JZ05F8;               If 'S' jump to 05F8
     05EF   0C    C:+1;                 Modify I for 'immediate load'
     05F0   C3    J0764;                Continue at 0764
     05F3   79    A:=C;                 (unused)
     05F4   3C    A:+1;
     05F5   C3    J0467;
     05F8   23    HL:+1;                ('BC:=S')
     05F9   7E    A:=M;                 Sixth character
     05FA   FE    A-54;
     05FC   C2    JNZ0463;              Fail if not 'T'
     05FF   79    A:=C;                 ('unstack' instruction)
     0600   C6    A:+C1;                Result C1, D1, E1 or F1
     0602   C3    J047A;                One byte to be output

     MONITOR
     >
```

```
        G2800
        0605   FE   A-43;            (first character)
        0607   C2   JNZ0611;         Jump to 0611 if not 'C'
        060A   23   HL:+1;           ('C')
        060B   7E   A:=M;            Second character
        060C   1E   E:=48;           (r or r₁ will be C)
        060E   C3   J058E;           Continue at 058E
        0611   FE   A-44;            (first character)
        0613   C2   JNZ062E;         Jump to 062E if not 'D'
        0616   23   HL:+1;           ('D')
        0617   7E   A:=M;            Second character
        0618   FE   A-45;
        061A   CA   JZ0622;          Jump to 0622 if 'E'
        061D   1E   E:=50;           (r or r₁ will be D)
        061F   C3   J058E;           Continue at 058E
        0622   23   HL:+1;           ('DE')
        0623   7E   A:=M;            Third character
        0624   FE   A-3A;
        0626   C2   JNZ0578;         Jump to 0578 if not ':'
        0629   0E   C:=10;           ('DE:') Base I=10 for DE
        062B   C3   J05D7;           Continue at 05D7 (read DE for BC)
        062E   FE   A-47;            (first character)
        0630   C2   JNZ064F;         Jump to 064F if not G
        0633   23   HL:+1;           ('G')
        0634   CD   JS0B60;          Construct J
        0637   47   B:=A;
        0638   23   HL:+1;
        0639   7E   A:=M;            Next character
        063A   FE   A-3A;
        063C   C2   JNZ0463;         Fail if not ':'
        063F   23   HL:+1;
        0640   7E   A:=M;            Next character
        0641   FE   A-3D;
        0643   C2   JNZ0463;         Fail if not '='
        0646   23   HL:+1;
        0647   7E   A:=M;            Next character
        0648   FE   A-41;
        064A   3E   A:=D3;
        064C   CA   JZ0472;          ('Gjj:=A') Two bytes (D3 J) to be output
        064F   FE   A-48;            (first character)
        0651   C2   JNZ0720;         Jump to 0720 if not H
        0654   23   HL:+1;           ('H')
        0655   7E   A:=M;            Second character
        0656   FE   A-3A;
        0658   C2   JNZ0660;         Jump to 0660 if not ':'
        065B   1E   E:=60;           (r or r₁ will be H)
        065D   C3   J0593;           Continue at 0593
```

MONITOR
>

```
      G2800
      0660   FE   A-4C;                    ('H') (second character)
      0662   C2   JNZ0987;                 Jump to 0987 if not 'L'
      0665   23   HL:+1;                    ('HL')
      0666   7E   A:=M;                     Third character
      0667   FE   A-3A;
      0669   C2   JNZ0463;                 Fail if not ':'
      066C   23   HL:+1;
      066D   7E   A:=M;                     Fourth character
      066E   FE   A-2D;
      0670   CA   JZ06BC;                  If '−' jump to 06BC
      0673   FE   A-2B;
      0675   C2   JNZ06C5;                 If not '+' jump to 06C5
      0678   23   HL:+1;                    ('HL:+')
      0679   7E   A:=M;                     Fifth character
      067A   FE   A-31;
      067C   C2   JNZ0684;                 Jump to 0684 if not '1'
      067F   3E   A:=23;
      0681   C3   J047A;                   ('HL:+1') One byte (23) to be output
      0684   FE   A-42;                    ('HL:+') (fifth character)
      0686   C2   JNZ0692;                 Jump to 0692 if not 'B'
      0689   23   HL:+1;                    ('HL:+B')
      068A   7E   A:=M;                     Sixth character
      068B   FE   A-43;
      068D   06   B:=09;
      068F   C3   J0460;                   One byte (09) to be output for 'HL:+BC'
      0692   FE   A-44;                    ('HL:+') (fifth character)
      0694   C2   JNZ06A0;                 Jump to 06A0 if not 'D'
      0697   23   HL:+1;                    ('HL:+D')
      0698   7E   A:=M;                     Sixth character
      0699   FE   A-45;
      069B   06   B:=19;
      069D   C3   J0460;                   One byte (19) to be output for 'HL:+DE'
      06A0   FE   A-48;                    ('HL:+') (fifth character)
      06A2   C2   JNZ06AE;                 Jump to 06AE if not 'H'
      06A5   23   HL:+1;                    ('HL:+H')
      06A6   7E   A:=M;                     Sixth character
      06A7   FE   A-4C;
      06A9   06   B:=29;
      06AB   C3   J0460;                   One byte (29) to be output for 'HL:+HL'
      06AE   FE   A-53;                    ('HL:+') (fifth character)
      06B0   C2   JNZ0463;                 Fail if not 'S'
      06B3   23   HL:+1;                    ('HL:+S')
      06B4   7E   A:=M;                     Sixth character
      06B5   FE   A-50;
      06B7   06   B:=39;
      06B9   C3   J0460;                   One byte (39) to be output for 'HL:+SP'
      06BC   23   HL:+1;                    ('HL:−')
      06BD   7E   A:=M;                     Fifth character
      06BE   FE   A-31;
      06C0   06   B:=2B;
      06C2   C3   J0460;                   One byte (2B) to be output for 'HL:−1'

      MONITOR
      >
```

```
      G2800
      06C5   FE   A-3D;              ('HL:') (fourth character)
      06C7   C2   JNZ0463;           Fail if not '='
      06CA   23   HL:+1;             ('HL:=')
      06CB   7E   A:=M;              Fifth character
      06CC   FE   A-3A;
      06CE   C2   JNZ06EF;           Jump to 06EF if not ':'
      06D1   23   HL:+1;             ('HL:=:')
      06D2   7E   A:=M;              Sixth character
      06D3   FE   A-53;
      06D5   C2   JNZ06E1;           Jump to 06E1 if not 'S'
      06D8   23   HL:+1;             ('HL:=:S')
      06D9   7E   A:=M;              Seventh character
      06DA   FE   A-54;
      06DC   06   B:=E3;
      06DE   C3   J0460;             One byte (E3) to be output for 'HL:=:ST'
      06E1   FE   A-44;              ('HL:=:') (sixth character)
      06E3   C2   JNZ0463;           Fail if not 'D'
      06E6   23   HL:+1;             ('HL:=:D')
      06E7   7E   A:=M;              Seventh character
      06E8   FE   A-45;
      06EA   06   B:=EB;
      06EC   C3   J0460;             One byte (EB) to be output for 'HL:=:DE'
      06EF   FE   A-53;              ('HL:=') (fifth character)
      06F1   C2   JNZ0700;           Jump to 0700 if not 'S'
      06F4   23   HL:+1;             ('HL:=S')
      06F5   7E   A:=M;              Sixth character
      06F6   FE   A-54;
      06F8   06   B:=E1;
      06FA   C3   J0460;             One byte (E1) to be output for 'HL:=ST'
      06FD   00   NULL;              (unused)
      06FE   00   NULL;
      06FF   00   NULL;
      0700   FE   A-4D;              ('HL:=') (fifth character)
      0702   C2   JNZ0716;           Jump to 0716 if not 'M'
      0705   23   HL:+1;             ('HL:=M')
      0706   7E   A:=M;              Sixth character
      0707   FE   A-4D;
      0709   C2   JNZ0463;           Fail if not 'M'
      070C   23   HL:+1;             ('HL:=MM')
      070D   CD   JS0B80;            Construct JK
      0710   47   B:=A;
      0711   3E   A:=2A;
      0713   C3   J0467;             Three bytes (2A J K) to be output for 'HL:=MMkkjj'
      0716   CD   JS0B80;            ('HL:=') Construct JK
      0719   47   B:=A;
      071A   3E   A:=21;
      071C   C3   J0467;             Three bytes (21 J K) to be output for 'HL:=kkjj'
      071F   00   NULL;

      MONITOR
      >
```

```
        G2800
        0720   FE   A-49;                  (first character)
        0722   C2   JNZ0746;               Jump to 0746 if not 'I'
        0725   23   HL:+1;                  ('I')
        0726   7E   A:=M;                   Second character
        0727   FE   A-3A;
        0729   C2   JNZ0463;               Fail if not ':'
        072C   23   HL:+1;
        072D   7E   A:=M;                   Third character
        072E   FE   A-3D;
        0730   C2   JNZ0463;               Fail if not '='
        0733   23   HL:+1;
        0734   7E   A:=M;                   Fourth character
        0735   FE   A-30;
        0737   C2   JNZ073F;               Jump to 073F if not '0'
        073A   3E   A:=F3;                  ('I:=0')
        073C   C3   J047A;                  One byte (F3) to be output
        073F   FE   A-31;                   ('I:=')
        0741   06   B:=FB;
        0743   C3   J0460;                  One byte (FB) to be output for 'I:=1'
        0746   FE   A-4A;                   (First character)
        0748   C2   JNZ07C2;               Jump to 07C2 if not 'J'
        074B   23   HL:+1;                  ('J')
        074C   7E   A:=M;                   Second character
        074D   FE   A-53;
        074F   C2   JNZ078B;               Jump to 078B if not 'S'
        0752   23   HL:+1;                  ('JS')
        0753   7E   A:=M;                   Third character
        0754   CD   JS0BC0;                 Condition
        0757   79   A:=C;
        0758   FE   A-FF;
        075A   CA   JZ076C;                 Jump to 076C if no condition
        075D   87   A:+A;                   ('JScnd')
        075E   87   A:+A;
        075F   87   A:+A;                   Form I-byte
        0760   C6   A:+C4;
        0762   4F   C:=A;
        0763   23   HL:+1;
        0764   C5   ST:=BC;
        0765   CD   JS0B80;                 Construct JK
        0768   C1   BC:=ST;
        0769   C3   J07DE;                  Continue at 07DE
        076C   7E   A:=M;                   ('JS') (third character)
        076D   FE   A-53;
        076F   C2   JNZ0783;               Jump to 0783 if not 'S'
        0772   23   HL:+1;                  ('JSS')
        0773   7E   A:=M;                   Fourth character
        0774   D6   A:-30;
        0776   FE   A-08;
        0778   F2   JNN0463;               Fail if not an octal digit
        077B   87   A:+A;                   Form I-byte
        077C   87   A:+A;
        077D   87   A:+A;
        077E   C6   A:+C7;
        0780   C3   J047A;                  One byte to be output for 'JSSs'
        0783   0E   C:=CD;                  ('JS') (third character)
        0785   C3   J0764;                  Continue at 0764 with 'CD' as I-byte
        0788   00   NULL;
        0789   00   NULL;
        078A   00   NULL;

        MONITOR
        >
```

```
      G2800
      078B   CD   JSOBC0;              ('J') Condition
      078E   79   A:=C;
      078F   FE   A-FF;
      0791   CA   JZ079C;              Jump to 079C if no condition
      0794   87   A:+A;                ('Jcnd')
      0795   87   A:+A;
      0796   87   A:+A;
      0797   C6   A:+C2;               Form I-byte
      0799   C3   J0762;               Continue at 0762
      079C   7E   A:=M;                ('J') (second character)
      079D   FE   A-5B;
      079F   CA   JZ07AB;              If '[' jump to 07AB
      07A2   CD   JSOB80;              ('J') Construct JK
      07A5   47   B:=A;
      07A6   3E   A:=C3;
      07A8   C3   J0467;               Output three bytes (C3 J K) for 'Jkkjj'
      07AB   23   HL:+1;               ('J[')
      07AC   7E   A:=M;                Third character
      07AD   FE   A-48;
      07AF   C2   JNZ0463;             Fail if not 'H'
      07B2   23   HL:+1;
      07B3   7E   A:=M;                Fourth character
      07B4   FE   A-4C;
      07B6   C2   JNZ0463;             Fail if not 'L'
      07B9   23   HL:+1;
      07BA   7E   A:=M;                Fifth character
      07BB   FE   A-5D;
      07BD   06   B:=E9;
      07BF   C3   J0460;               One byte (E9) to be output for 'J[HL]'
      07C2   FE   A-4B;                (first character)
      07C4   C2   JNZ0D9E;             Jump to 0D9E if not 'K'
      07C7   23   HL:+1;               ('K')
      07C8   7E   A:=M;                Second character
      07C9   FE   A-3A;
      07CB   C2   JNZ0463;             Fail if not ':'
      07CE   23   HL:+1;
      07CF   7E   A:=M;                Third character
      07D0   FE   A-3D;
      07D2   C2   JNZ0980;             Jump to 0980 if not '='
      07D5   23   HL:+1;               ('K:=')
      07D6   7E   A:=M;
      07D7   FE   A-31;
      07D9   06   B:=37;
      07DB   C3   J0460;               One byte (37) to be output for 'K:=1'
      07DE   47   B:=A;                (from 0769)
      07DF   79   A:=C;
      07E0   C3   J0467;               Three bytes to be output
      07E3   00   NULL;
      07F4   00   NULL;
      07F5   00   NULL;

      MONITOR
      >
```

```
G2800
0800    3E    A:=70;              (Unused)
0802    C3    J0593;
0805    FE    A-5B;               ('M') (second character)
0807    C2    JNZ0847;            Jump to 0847 if not '['
080A    23    HL:+1;              ('M[')
080B    7E    A:=M;               Third character
080C    FE    A-42;
080E    C2    JNZ081D;            Jump to 081D if not 'B'
0811    23    HL:+1;              ('M[B')
0812    7E    A:=M;               Fourth character
0813    FE    A-43;
0815    C2    JNZ0463;            Fail if not 'C'
0818    06    B:=02;              Set I=02
081A    C3    J082B;              Continue at 082B
081D    FE    A-44;              ('M[') (third character)
081F    C2    JNZ0463;            Fail if not 'D'
0822    23    HL:+1;              ('M[D')
0823    7E    A:=M;               Fourth character
0824    FE    A-45;
0826    C2    JNZ0463;            Fail if not 'E'
0829    06    B:=12;              Set I=12
082B    23    HL:+1;
082C    7E    A:=M;               Fifth character
082D    FE    A-5D;
082F    C2    JNZ0463;            Fail if not ']'
0832    23    HL:+1;
0833    7E    A:=M;               Sixth character
0834    FE    A-3A;
0836    C2    JNZ0463;            Fail if not ':'
0839    23    HL:+1;
083A    7E    A:=M;               Seventh character
083B    FE    A-3D;
083D    C2    JNZ0463;            Fail if not '='
0840    23    HL:+1;
0841    7E    A:=M;               Eighth character
0842    FE    A-41;
0844    C3    J0460;              If 'A', one byte (02 or 12) to be output

MONITOR
>
```

```
      G2800
      0847   FE   A-4D;                ('M') (second character)
      0849   C2   JNZ0872;             Jump to 0872 if not 'M'
      084C   23   HL:+1;               ('MM')
      084D   CD   JS0B80;              Construct JK
      0850   47   B:=A;
      0851   23   HL:+1;
      0852   7E   A:=M;                Next character
      0853   FE   A-3A;
      0855   C2   JNZ0463;             Fail if not ':'
      0858   23   HL:+1;
      0859   7E   A:=M;                Next character
      085A   FE   A-3D;
      085C   C2   JNZ0463;             Fail if not '='
      085F   23   HL:+1;
      0860   7E   A:=M;                Next character
      0861   FE   A-48;
      0863   C2   JNZ0463;             Fail if not 'H'
      0866   23   HL:+1;
      0867   7E   A:=M;                Next character
      0868   FE   A-4C;
      086A   C2   JNZ0463;             Fail if not 'L'
      086D   3E   A:=22;
      086F   C3   J0467;               Three bytes (22 J K) to be output for 'MMkkjj:=HL'
      0872   CD   JS0B80;              ('M') Construct JK
      0875   47   B:=A;
      0876   23   HL:+1;
      0877   7E   A:=M;                Next character
      0878   FE   A-3A;
      087A   C2   JNZ0463;             Fail if not ':'
      087D   23   HL:+1;
      087E   7E   A:=M;                Next character
      087F   FE   A-3D;
      0881   C2   JNZ0463;             Fail if not '='
      0884   23   HL:+1;
      0885   7E   A:=M;                Next character
      0886   FE   A-41;
      0888   C2   JNZ0463;             Fail if not 'A'
      088B   3E   A:=32;
      088D   C3   J0467;               Three bytes (32 J K) to be output for 'Mkkjj:=A'
```

MONITOR
>

```
      G2800
      0890  FE  A-52;            (first character)
      0892  C2  JNZ08C2;         Jump to 08C2 if not 'R'
      0895  23  HL:+1;           ('R')
      0896  7E  A:=M;            Second character
      0897  FE  A-FF;
      0899  C2  JNZ08A2;         Jump to 08A2 if not terminator
      089C  3E  A:=C9;           ('R')
      089E  2B  HL:-1;
      089F  C3  J047A;           One byte (C9) to be output for 'R'
      08A2  CD  JS08C0;          ('R') Condition
      08A5  79  A:=C;
      08A6  FE  A-FF;
      08A8  CA  JZ08B3;          Jump to 08B3 if no condition
      08AB  87  A:+A;            ('Rcnd')
      08AC  87  A:+A;
      08AD  87  A:+A;
      08AE  C6  A:+C0;           Form I-byte
      08B0  C3  J047A;           One byte to be output
      08B3  7E  A:=M;            ('R') (second character)
      08B4  FE  A-45;
      08B6  C2  JNZ0463;         Fail if not 'E'
      08B9  23  HL:+1;
      08BA  7E  A:=M;            Third character
      08BB  FE  A-54;
      08BD  06  B:=C9;
      08BF  C3  J0460;           One byte (C9) to be output for 'RET'
```

MONITOR
>

```
        G2800
        08C2   FE    A-53;              (first character)
        08C4   C2    JNZ0971;           Jump to 0971 if not 'S'
        08C7   23    HL:+1;             ('S')
        08C8   7E    A:=M;              Second character
        08C9   FE    A-50;
        08CB   C2    JNZ090D;           Jump to 090D if not 'P'
        08CE   23    HL:+1;             ('SP')
        08CF   7E    A:=M;              Third character
        08D0   FE    A-3A;
        08D2   C2    JNZ0463;           Fail if not ':'
        08D5   23    HL:+1;
        08D6   7E    A:=M;              Fourth character
        08D7   FE    A-3D;
        08D9   C2    JNZ08F5;           Jump to 08F5 if not '='
        08DC   23    HL:+1;             ('SP:=')
        08DD   7E    A:=M;              Fifth character
        08DE   FE    A-48;
        08E0   C2    JNZ08EC;           Jump to 08EC if not 'H'
        08E3   23    HL:+1;             ('SP:=H')
        08E4   7E    A:=M;              Sixth character
        08E5   FE    A-4C;
        08E7   06    B:=F9;
        08E9   C3    J0460;             One byte (F9) to be output for 'SP:=HL'
        08EC   CD    JS0B80;            ('SP:=') Construct JK
        08EF   47    B:=A;
        08F0   3E    A:=31;
        08F2   C3    J0467;             Three bytes (31 J K) to be output for 'SP:=kkjj'
        08F5   FE    A-2B;              ('SP:') (fourth character)
        08F7   C2    JNZ08FF;           Jump to 08FF if not '+'
        08FA   06    B:=33;             ('SP:+')
        08FC   C3    J0906;             Continue at 0906 with I=33
        08FF   FE    A-2D;              ('SP:') (fourth character)
        0901   C2    JNZ0463;           Fail if not '−'
        0904   06    B:=3B;             Set I=3B
        0906   23    HL:+1;
        0907   7E    A:=M;              Fifth character
        0908   FE    A-31;
        090A   C3    J0460;             One byte (33 or 3B) to be output for 'SP:±1'
```

MONITOR
>

```
G2800
090D  FE   A-54;              ('S') (second character)
090F  C2   JNZ0463;           Fail if not 'T'
0912  23   HL:+1;             ('ST')
0913  7E   A:=M;              Third character
0914  FE   A-3A;
0916  C2   JNZ0463;           Fail if not ':'
0919  23   HL:+1;
091A  7E   A:=M;              Fourth character
091B  FE   A-3D;
091D  C2   JNZ0463;           Fail if not '='
0920  23   HL:+1;
0921  7E   A:=M;              Fifth character
0922  FE   A-42;
0924  C2   JNZ0930;           Jump to 0930 if not 'B'
0927  23   HL:+1;             ('ST:=B')
0928  7E   A:=M;              Sixth character
0929  FE   A-43;
092B  06   B:=C5;
092D  C3   J0460;             One byte (C5) to be output for 'ST:=BC'
0930  FE   A-44;              ('ST:=') (fifth character)
0932  C2   JNZ093E;           Jump to 093E if not 'D'
0935  23   HL:+1;             ('ST:=D')
0936  7E   A:=M;              Sixth character
0937  FE   A-45;
0939  06   B:=D5;
093B  C3   J0460;             One byte (D5) to be output for 'ST:=DE'
093E  FE   A-48;              ('ST:=') (fifth character)
0940  C2   JNZ094C;           Jump to 094C if not 'H'
0943  23   HL:+1;             ('ST:=H')
0944  7E   A:=M;              Sixth character
0945  FE   A-4C;
0947  06   B:=E5;
0949  C3   J0460;             One byte (E5) to be output for 'ST:=HL'
094C  FE   A-41;              ('ST:=') (fifth character)
094E  C2   JNZ0463;           Fail if not 'A'
0951  23   HL:+1;             ('ST:=A')
0952  7E   A:=M;              Sixth character
0953  FE   A-46;
0955  06   B:=F5;
0957  C3   J0460;             One byte (F5) to be output for 'ST:=AF'

MONITOR
>
```

```
     G2800
     095A  D1    DE:=ST;              (from 0A82)
     095B  C3    J0ABB;               Continue at 0ABB
     095E  00    NULL;
     095F  00    NULL;

     0960  79    A:=C;                ('BC:+') (or other register pair)
     0961  C6    A:+03;               Modify I for 'increment'
     0963  C3    J0969;
     0966  79    A:=C;                ('BC:-') (or other register pair)
     0967  C6    A:+0B;               Modify I for 'decrement'
     0969  47    B:=A;
     096A  23    HL:+1;
     096B  7E    A:=M;                Fifth character
     096C  FE    A-31;
     096E  C3    J0460;               If '1', one byte to be output
```

MONITOR
>

```
     G2800
     0971  FE    A-45;                (first character)
     0973  C2    JNZ099C;             Jump to 099C if not 'E'
     0976  23    HL:+1;               ('E')
     0977  7E    A:=M;                Second character
     0978  1E    E:=58;               (r or r₁ will be E)
     097A  C3    J058E;               Continue at 058E
     097D  00    NULL;
     097E  00    NULL;
     097F  00    NULL;

     0980  FE    A-23;                ('K:')
     0982  06    B:=3F;
     0984  C3    J0460;               One byte (3F) to be output for 'K:#'
     0987  FE    A-41;                ('H') (second character)
     0989  C2    JNZ0463;             Fail if not 'A'
     098C  23    HL:+1;               ('HA')
     098D  7E    A:=M;                Third character
     098E  FE    A-4C;
     0990  C2    JNZ0463;             Fail if not 'L'
     0993  23    HL:+1;               ('HAL')
     0994  7E    A:=M;                Fourth character
     0995  FE    A-54;
     0997  06    B:=76;
     0999  C3    J0460;               One byte (76) to be output for 'HALT'
     099C  FE    A-4E;                (first character)
     099E  C2    JNZ0CF8;             Jump to 0CF8 if not 'N'
     09A1  23    HL:+1;               ('N')
     09A2  7E    A:=M;                Second character
     09A3  FE    A-55;
     09A5  C2    JNZ0463;             Fail if not 'U'
     09A8  23    HL:+1;               ('NU')
     09A9  7E    A:=M;                Third character
     09AA  FE    A-4C;
     09AC  C2    JNZ0463;             Fail if not 'L'
     09AF  23    HL:+1;               ('NUL')
     09B0  7E    A:=M;                Fourth character
     09B1  FE    A-4C;
     09B3  06    B:=00;
     09B5  C3    J0460;               One byte (00) to be output for 'NULL'
```

MONITOR
>

```
     G2800
  09B8   FE    A-46;            (second character)
  09BA   CA    JZ055A;          Jump to 055A if 'F'
  09BD   FE    A-4B;
  09BF   C2    JNZ09E5;         Jump to 09E5 if not 'K'
  09C2   23    HL:+1;           ('AK')
  09C3   7E    A:=M;            Next character
  09C4   FE    A-3A;
  09C6   C2    JNZ0463;         Fail if not ':'
  09C9   23    HL:+1;           ('AK:')
  09CA   7E    A:=M;            Next character
  09CB   01    BC:=171F;        Possible object bytes are 17, 1F
  09CE   C3    J09EE;           Continue at 09EE
  09D1   23    HL:+1;           ('A:')
  09D2   7E    A:=M;            Next character
  09D3   FE    A-23;
  09D5   C2    JNZ09EB;         Jump to 09EB if not '#'
  09D8   23    HL:+1;           ('A:#')
  09D9   7E    A:=M;            Next character
  09DA   2B    HL:-1;
  09DB   3C    A:+1;
  09DC   C2    JNZ09E4;         Jump to 09E4 if not terminator
  09DF   3E    A:=2F;           ('A:#')
  09E1   C3    J047A;           One byte (2F) to be output
  09E4   2B    HL:-1;           ('A:#')
  09E5   CD    JS0B20;          Operator
  09E8   C3    J04B0;           Continue at 04B0
  09EB   01    BC:=070F;        ('A:') Possible object bytes are 07, 0F
  09EE   FE    A-40;            Third character
  09F0   C2    JNZ09E4;         Jump to 09E4 if not '@'
  09F3   23    HL:+1;
  09F4   7E    A:=M;            Next character
  09F5   FE    A-4C;
  09F7   CA    JZ0475;          ('A:@L') One byte (07) to be output
  09FA   FE    A-52;
  09FC   41    B:=C;
  09FD   C3    J0460;           ('A:@R') One byte (0F) to be output

  MONITOR
  >
```

```
     G2800
  0A00   CD    JS0B60;     Entry  'Form JK'
  0A03   5F    E:=A;              Value of K in E
  0A04   23    HL:+1;
  0A05   CD    JS0B60;            Construct J
  0A08   C9    RET;               Value of J in A

  MONITOR
  >
```

```
      G2800
      0A09   FE   A-00;          (continuation from 0B86)
      0A0B   FA   JN0A12;        Jump to 0A12 if not hex. digit
      0A0E   CD   JS0A00;        Form JK
      0A11   C9   RET;           Return with J in A, K in E
      0A12   79   A:=C;          (not hex. digit)
      0A13   FE   A-28;
      0A15   C2   JNZ0463;       Fail if not '('
      0A18   23   HL:+1;         ('(')
      0A19   7E   A:=M;          Next character
      0A1A   FE   A-4C;
      0A1C   C2   JNZ0A56;       Jump to 0A56 if not 'L'
      0A1F   23   HL:+1;         ('(L')
      0A20   CD   JS0B60;        Construct J
      0A23   E5   ST:=HL;
      0A24   26   H:=00;         Find corresponding entry in label table
      0A26   6F   L:=A;
      0A27   4F   C:=A;
      0A28   29   HL:+HL;
      0A29   EB   HL:=:DE;
      0A2A   21   HL:=1040;      (Label-table base)
      0A2D   19   HL:+DE;
      0A2E   5F   E:=M;
      0A2F   23   HL:+1;
      0A30   56   D:=M;          Entry in DE
      0A31   7B   A:=E;
      0A32   FE   A-00;
      0A34   C2   JNZ0A3D;
      0A37   7A   A:=D;
      0A38   FE   A-00;
      0A3A   CA   JZ0A40;        If entry blank, jump to 0A40
      0A3D   C3   J0AB3;         (Entry found) Continue at 0AB3
      0A40   2A   HL:=MM1010;    (Forward reference)
      0A43   23   HL:+1;
      0A44   EB   HL:=:DE;       DE has location of current J in object program
      0A45   2A   HL:=MM1012;    Jump-list counter
      0A48   71   M:=C;          Make entry in jump list (see notes)
      0A49   23   HL:+1;
      0A4A   73   M:=E;
      0A4B   23   HL:+1;
      0A4C   72   M:=D;
      0A4D   23   HL:+1;
      0A4E   22   MM1012:=HL;    Advanced jump-list counter
      0A51   16   D:=FD;         'FD' marks forward reference as such
      0A53   C3   J0AB3;         Continue at 0AB3

      MONITOR
      >
```

```
    G2800
    0A56   FE    A-58;                    ('(')
    0A58   C2    JNZ0AC0;                 Jump to 0AC0 if not 'X'
    0A5B   23    HL:+1;                    ('(X')
    0A5C   7E    A:=M;                     Next character
    0A5D   4F    C:=A;
    0A5E   CD    JS0B00;                   ASCII–hex.
    0A61   78    A:=B;
    0A62   FE    A-00;
    0A64   FA    JN0463;                   Fail if not hex. digit
    0A67   E5    ST:=HL;                       .
    0A68   CA    JZ0A85;                   Jump to 0A85 if '0'
    0A6B   21    HL:=101E;                 Base address of X-table
    0A6E   5F    E:=A;
    0A6F   16    D:=00;
    0A71   19    HL:+DE;
    0A72   19    HL:+DE;                   Address of X-table entry
    0A73   4E    C:=M;
    0A74   23    HL:+1;
    0A75   46    B:=M;                     X-block starting address
    0A76   60    H:=B;
    0A77   69    L:=C;
    0A78   EB    HL:=:DE;
    0A79   E1    HL:=ST;
    0A7A   D5    ST:=DE;
    0A7B   23    HL:+1;
    0A7C   7E    A:=M;                     Next character
    0A7D   FE    A-29;
    0A7F   C2    JNZ0A8B;                  Jump to 0A8B if not ')'
    0A82   C3    J095A;                    ('(Xh)') Continue at 095A
    0A85   21    HL:=1000;                 ('(X0') X0 starting address
    0A88   C3    J0A78;                    Continue at 0A78
    0A8B   FE    A-2B;                     ('(Xh' (next character)
    0A8D   C2    JNZ0A95;                  Jump to 0A95 if not '+'
    0A90   0E    C:=00;                    ('(Xh+')
    0A92   C3    J0A9C;                    Continue at 0A9C with C=00

    MONITOR
    >
```

```
    G2800
    0A95    FE    A-2D;              ('(Xh') (next character)
    0A97    C2    JNZ0463;           Fail if not '—'
    0A9A    0E    C:=01;             Continue with C=01 (marker for sign)
    0A9C    23    HL:+1;
    0A9D    CD    JS0B60;            Construct J (displacement)
    0AA0    E3    HL:=:ST;           X-block starting address in HL
    0AA1    5F    E:=A;
    0AA2    16    D:=00;             Displacement in DE
    0AA4    79    A:=C;              Sign of displacement
    0AA5    FE    A-00;
    0AA7    CA    JZ0AB1;            Skip to 0AB1 if displacement positive
    0AAA    7A    A:=D;              DE:—
    0AAB    2F    A:#;
    0AAC    57    D:=A;
    0AAD    7B    A:=E;
    0AAE    2F    A:#;
    0AAF    5F    E:=A;
    0AB0    13    DE:+1;
    0AB1    19    HL:+DE;            Add displacement to starting address
    0AB2    EB    HL:=:DE;           Absolute JK value
    0AB3    E1    HL:=ST;
    0AB4    23    HL:+1;
    0AB5    7E    A:=M;              Next character
    0AB6    FE    A-29;
    0AB8    C2    JNZ0463;           Fail if not ')'
    0ABB    7B    A:=E;
    0ABC    5A    E:=D;
    0ABD    C9    RET;               Return with J in A, K in E
    0ABE    00    NULL;
    0ABF    00    NULL;
```

```
    MONITOR
    >
```

```
      G2800
      0AC0   FE   A-49;              ('(')
      0AC2   C2   JNZ0463;           Fail if not 'I'
      0AC5   23   HL:+1;             ('(I')
      0AC6   7E   A:=M;              Next character
      0AC7   FE   A-2B;
      0AC9   C2   JNZ0AD1;           Jump to 0AD1 if not '+'
      0ACC   0E   C:=00;             Set C=00 as sign marker
      0ACE   C3   J0AD8;             Continue at 0AD8
      0AD1   FE   A-2D;
      0AD3   C2   JNZ0463;           Fail if not '−'
      0AD6   0E   C:=01;             Set C=01 as sign marker
      0AD8   23   HL:+1;
      0AD9   CD   JS0B60;            Construct J
      0ADC   E5   ST:=HL;
      0ADD   5F   E:=A;
      0ADE   16   D:=00;             Displacement in DE
      0AE0   79   A:=C;
      0AE1   FE   A-00;
      0AE3   CA   JZ0AED;            Skip to 0AED if displacement positive
      0AE6   7A   A:=D;              DE: −
      0AE7   2F   A:#;
      0AE8   57   D:=A;
      0AE9   7B   A:=E;
      0AEA   2F   A:#;
      0AEB   5F   E:=A;
      0AEC   13   DE:+1;
      0AED   2A   HL:=MM103E;        Run-time location of start of object program
      0AF0   19   HL:+DE;
      0AF1   EB   HL:=:DE;
      0AF2   2A   HL:=MM1010;        Object-program counter
      0AF5   19   HL:+DE;
      0AF6   23   HL:+1;             Plus 3 for length of current instruction
      0AF7   23   HL:+1;
      0AF8   23   HL:+1;
      0AF9   11   DE:=EE80;          Minus 1180 for compile-time base
      0AFC   19   HL:+DE;
      0AFD   C3   J0AB2;             Continue at 0AB2

      MONITOR
      >



      G2800
      0B00   D6   A:-30;             Entry 'ASCII–hex. for assembler'
      0B02   FA   JN0B14;
      0B05   FE   A-0A;
      0B07   FA   JN0B19;
      0B0A   D6   A:-11;
      0B0C   FA   JN0B14;
      0B0F   FE   A-06;
      0B11   FA   JN0B17;
      0B14   06   B:=FF;
      0B16   C9   RET;               No hex. digit—value FF in B
      0B17   C6   A:+0A;
      0B19   47   B:=A;
      0B1A   C9   RET;               Hex. digit—value in A and in B
      0B1B   23   HL:+1;             Entry 'Single-length register or J'
      0B1C   23   HL:+1;
      0B1D   C3   J0B89;             Continue at 0B89

      MONITOR
      >
```

```
G2800
0B20   0E   C:=00;            Entry 'operator'
0B22   7E   A:=M;             Next character
0B23   FE   A-3A;
0B25   CA   JZ0B2F;           If ':' jump to 0B2F
0B28   FE   A-2D;
0B2A   CA   JZ0B52;           If '−' jump to 0B52
0B2D   0D   C:-1;
0B2E   C9   RET;              Failure—return with C=FF
0B2F   23   HL:+1;            (':')
0B30   7E   A:=M;             Next character
0B31   FE   A-2B;
0B33   CA   JZ0B55;           If '+' jump to 0B55
0B36   0C   C:+1;             (':')
0B37   0C   C:+1;
0B38   FE   A-2D;
0B3A   CA   JZ0B55;           If '−' jump to 0B55
0B3D   0C   C:+1;
0B3E   0C   C:+1;
0B3F   FE   A-26;
0B41   C8   RZ;               Return with C=04 for ':&'
0B42   0C   C:+1;
0B43   FF   A-23;
0B45   C8   RZ;               Return with C=05 for ':#'
0B46   0C   C:+1;
0B47   FE   A-55;
0B49   C8   RZ;               Return with C=06 for ':U'
0B4A   0C   C:+1;
0B4B   0C   C:+1;
0B4C   FE   A-3D;
0B4E   C8   RZ;               Return with C=08 for ':='
0B4F   0E   C:=FF;            Failure—return with C=FF
0B51   C9   RET;
0B52   0E   C:=07;            ('−')
0B54   C9   RET;              Return with C=07 for '−'
0B55   47   B:=A;             (':+') or (':−')
0B56   23   HL:+1;
0B57   7E   A:=M;             Next character
0B58   B8   A-B;
0B59   C2   JNZ0B5E;          Jump to 0B5E if not '+' or '−'
0B5C   0C   C:+1;             (':++') or (':−−')
0B5D   C9   RET;              Return with C=01 for ':++', C=03 for ':−−'
0B5F   2B   HL:-1;            (':+') or (':−')
0B5F   C9   RET;              Return with C=00 for ':+', C=02 for ':−'

MONITOR
>
```

```
        G2800
        0B60   7E    A:=M;              Entry 'construct J'
        0B61   CD    JSOB00;                ASCII–hex.
        0B64   78    A:=B;
        0B65   3C    A:+1;
        0B66   CA    JZ0B7B;            Jump to 0B7B if no hex. digit
        0B69   50    D:=B;
        0B6A   23    HL:+1;
        0B6B   7E    A:=M;              Next character
        0B6C   CD    JSOB00;                ASCII–hex.
        0B6F   78    A:=B;
        0B70   3C    A:+1;
        0B71   CA    JZ0B7B;            Jump to 0B7B if no hex. digit
        0B74   7A    A:=D;              Shift up upper digit
        0B75   87    A:+A;
        0B76   87    A:+A;
        0B77   87    A:+A;
        0B78   87    A:+A;
        0B79   80    A:+B;              Add in lower digit
        0B7A   C9    RET;               Return with J-value
        0B7B   0E    C:=FF;             (Not hex.)
        0B7D   7E    A:=M;
        0B7E   C9    RET;               Return with character in A and C=FF
        0B7F   00    NULL;
        0B80   7E    A:=M;              Entry 'construct JK'
        0B81   4F    C:=A;
        0B82   CD    JSOB00;                ASCII–hex.
        0B85   78    A:=B;
        0B86   C3    J0A09;             Continue at 0A09

MONITOR
        >
```

```
        G2800
        0B89   7E    A:=M;              (continued from 0B1D)
        0B8A   FE    A-FF;
        0B8C   2B    HL:-1;
        0B8D   C2    JNZ0BB6;           Jump to 0BB6 if more than one character left
        0B90   7E    A:=M;
        0B91   0E    C:=00;
        0B93   D6    A:-42;
        0B95   C8    RZ;                Return with C=00 for 'B'
        0B96   0C    C:+1;
        0B97   3D    A:-1;
        0B98   C8    RZ;                Return with C=01 for 'C'
        0B99   0C    C:+1;
        0B9A   3D    A:-1;
        0B9B   C8    RZ;                Return with C=02 for 'D'
        0B9C   0C    C:+1;
        0B9D   3D    A:-1;
        0B9E   C8    RZ;                Return with C=03 for 'E'
        0B9F   0C    C:+1;
        0BA0   D6    A:-03;
        0BA2   C8    RZ;                Return with C=04 for 'H'
        0BA3   0C    C:+1;
        0BA4   D6    A:-04;
        0BA6   C8    RZ;                Return with C=05 for 'L'
        0BA7   0C    C:+1;
        0BA8   3D    A:-1;
        0BA9   C8    RZ;                Return with C=06 for 'M'
        0BAA   0C    C:+1;
        0BAB   C6    A:+0C;
        0BAD   C8    RZ;                Return with C=07 for 'A'
        0BAE   0C    C:+1;
        0BAF   0C    C:+1;
        0BB0   C6    A:+10;
        0BB2   C8    RZ;                Return with C=09 for 'I'
        0BB3   0E    C:=FF;
        0BB5   C9    RET;               Failure—return with C=FF
        0BB6   0E    C:=08;
        0BB8   CD    JS0B60;            Construct J
        0BBB   C9    RET;               Return with C=08 and value of J in A
        0BBC   00    NULL;
        0BBD   00    NULL;
        0BBE   00    NULL;
        0BBF   00    NULL;

        MONITOR
        >
```

```
      G2800
OBCO  FE  A-4E;          Entry 'condition'
OBC2  C2  JNZOD85;       Jump to 0D85 if not 'N'
OBC5  OE  C:=07;
OBC7  23  HL:+1;
OBC8  7E  A:=M;          Next character
OBC9  FE  A-47;
OBCB  F2  JNNOBDO;       Jump to 0BD0 if letter after 'F'
OBCE  2B  HL:-1;
OBCF  C9  RET;           Return with C=07 for 'N'
OBDO  OD  C:-1;
OBD1  FE  A-4E;
OBD3  C8  RZ;            Return with C=06 for 'NN'
OBD4  OD  C:-1;
OBD5  OD  C:-1;
OBD6  FE  A-50;
OBD8  C8  RZ;            Return with C=04 for 'NP'
OBD9  OD  C:-1;
OBDA  OD  C:-1;
OBDB  FE  A-4B;
OBDD  C3  JOD97;         Continue at 0D97

MONITOR
>
```

```
      G2800
OBEO  26  H:=30;         Entry 'HL:=sqrt(BC)×2⁷'
OBE2  EB  HL:=:DE;
OBE3  3E  A:=0E;
OBE5  C5  ST:=BC;
OBE6  D5  ST:=DE;
OBE7  CD  JSOF9B;        HL:=(BC/DE)×2ᴬ
OBEA  D1  DE:=ST;
OBEB  C1  BC:=ST;
OBEC  19  HL:+DE;
OBED  CD  JSOFF1;        HL:/2 (unsigned, rounded)
OBFO  CD  JSOC1A;        HL−DE
OBF3  C8  RZ;
OBF4  E5  ST:=HL;
OBF5  CD  JSOCF1;        HL:−DE
OBF8  23  HL:+1;
OBF9  7C  A:=H;
OEFA  B5  A:UL;
OBFB  E1  HL:=ST;
OBFC  C2  JNZOBE2;
OBFF  C9  RET;

MONITOR
>
```

```
      G2800
0C00  06    B:=00;            Program entry 'Assembler'
0C02  21    HL:=1020;
0C05  70    M:=B;
0C06  23    HL:+1;            Clear X-table and label table
0C07  7D    A:=L;
0C08  FE    A-C0;
0C0A  C2    JNZ0C05;
0C0D  78    A:=B;
0C0E  32    M1014:=A;         Initialize marker and jump-list counter
0C11  21    HL:=10C0;
0C14  22    MM1012:=HL;
0C17  C3    J0400;            Jump to instruction read routine
0C1A  C5    ST:=BC;           Entry 'HL−DE(transparent to BC)'
0C1B  CD    JS0231;           HL−DE
0C1E  C1    BC:=ST;
0C1F  C9    RET;
```

```
MONITOR
>
```

```
      G2800
0C20  3A    A:=M1014;         (process instruction)
0C23  FE    A-00;
0C25  C2    JNZ0C8A;          Jump to 0C8A if marker set
0C28  7E    A:=M;             First character of source instruction
0C29  FE    A-58;
0C2B  C2    JNZ0C59;          Jump to 0C59 if not 'X'
0C2E  23    HL:+1;            ('X')
0C2F  7E    A:=M;             Next character
0C30  CD    JS0B00;           ASCII−hex.
0C33  78    A:=B;
0C34  FE    A-00;
0C36  FA    JN0463;           Fail if not hex.
0C39  E5    ST:=HL;
0C3A  26    H:=00;
0C3C  6F    L:=A;
0C3D  29    HL:+HL;
0C3E  EB    HL:=:DE;
0C3F  21    HL:=1020;
0C42  19    HL:+DE;           Address of entry in X-table
0C43  E3    HL:=:ST;
0C44  23    HL:+1;
0C45  7E    A:=M;             Next character
0C46  FE    A-3A;
0C48  C2    JNZ0463;          Fail if not ':'
0C4B  23    HL:+1;
0C4C  CD    JS0B60;           Construct J
0C4F  E3    HL:=:ST;
0C50  77    M:=A;        ⎫
0C51  23    HL:+1;       ⎪
0C52  3E    A:=00;       ⎬  Store J-value in X-table—with zero upper byte
0C54  77    M:=A;        ⎪
0C55  E1    HL:=ST;      ⎭
0C56  C3    J047D;            Jump to output routine (no output bytes)
```

```
MONITOR
>
```

```
        G2800
        0C59    3E    A:=01;                (not 'X')
        0C5B    32    M1014:=A;             Set marker (no more X-blocks)
        0C5E    E5    ST:=HL;
        0C5F    2A    HL:=MM1020;           Length of X0 block
        0C62    EB    HL:=:DE;
        0C63    21    HL:=1000;             Base address of RAM for object program (X0)
        0C66    19    HL:+DE;
        0C67    22    MM1020:=HL;           Address of X1
        0C6A    21    HL:=1020;             Address of X-table
        0C6D    4E    C:=M;
        0C6E    23    HL:+1;                Fetch X-table entry (address of X-block)
        0C6F    46    B:=M;
        0C70    23    HL:+1;
        0C71    5E    E:=M;
        0C72    23    HL:+1;                Fetch X-table entry (length of X-block)
        0C73    56    D:=M;
        0C74    EB    HL:=:DE;
        0C75    09    HL:+BC;
        0C76    EB    HL:=:DE;
        0C77    72    M:=D;
        0C78    2B    HL:-1;                Store X-table entry (address of next X-block)
        0C79    73    M:=E;
        0C7A    7C    A:=H;
        0C7B    FE    A-10;
        0C7D    C2    JNZ0C6D;
        0C80    7D    A:=L;
        0C81    FE    A-3E;
        0C83    C2    JNZ0C6D;              Repeat until sixteenth entry done
        0C86    E1    HL:=ST;
        0C87    C3    J04A0;                Continue at 04A0
        0C8A    7E    A:=M;                 (marker set) First character
        0C8B    FE    A-58;
        0C8D    CA    JZ0463;               Fail if 'X'
        0C90    C3    J04A1;                Continue at 04A1

        MONITOR
        >
```

```
      G2800
      0C93   CD   JSOB60;        (label) Construct J
      0C96   FE   A-40;
      0C98   F2   JNN0463;          Fail if out of range
      0C9B   E5   ST:=HL;
      0C9C   2A   HL:=MM103E;       Run-time location of start of object program
      0C9F   EB   HL:=:DE;
      0CA0   2A   HL:=MM1010;       Object-program counter
      0CA3   19   HL:+DE;
      0CA4   EB   HL:=:DE;
      0CA5   21   HL:=EE80;         Minus 1180 for compile-time base
      0CA8   19   HL:+DE;
      0CA9   EB   HL:=:DE;          Run-time location of label in DE
      0CAA   06   B:=00;
      0CAC   4F   C:=A;             Label
      0CAD   21   HL:=1040;         Base of label table
      0CB0   09   HL:+BC;
      0CB1   09   HL:+BC;
      0CB2   73   M:=E;
      0CB3   23   HL:+1;
      0CB4   72   M:=D;             Label entered in label table
      0CB5   E1   HL:=ST;
      0CB6   23   HL:+1;
      0CB7   7E   A:=M;             Next character
      0CB8   FE   A-3A;
      0CBA   C2   JNZ0463;          Fail if not ':'
      0CBD   23   HL:+1;
      0CBE   C3   J04A0;            Continue at 04A0
      0CC1   21   HL:=10C0;         ('F') Base address of jump list
      0CC4   3A   A:=M1012;         Jump-list counter (lower half)
      0CC7   BD   A-L;
      0CC8   C2   JNZ0CD2;
      0CCB   3A   A:=M1013;         Jump-list counter (upper half)
      0CCE   BC   A-H;
      0CCF   CA   JZ0CEE;           Jump to 0CEE if all done
      0CD2   7E   A:=M;
      0CD3   E5   ST:=HL;
      0CD4   26   H:=00;
      0CD6   6F   L:=A;
      0CD7   29   HL:+HL;
      0CD8   EB   HL:=:DE;
      0CD9   21   HL:=1040;         Base of label table
      0CDC   19   HL:+DE;
      0CDD   5E   E:=M;
      0CDE   23   HL:+1;
      0CDF   56   D:=M;             Absolute address of label in DE
      0CE0   E1   HL:=ST;
      0CE1   23   HL:+1;
      0CE2   4E   C:=M;
      0CE3   23   HL:+1;
      0CE4   46   B:=M;             Address of J-byte to be filled in, in BC
      0CE5   7B   A:=E;
      0CE6   02   M[BC]:=A;         J-byte filled in
      0CE7   03   BC:+1;
      0CE8   7A   A:=D;
      0CE9   02   M[BC]:=A;         K-byte filled in
      0CEA   23   HL:+1;
      0CEB   C3   J0CC4;            Loop back to 0CC4
      0CEE   CF   JSS1;             Assembly complete—call monitor
      0CEF   00   NULL;
      0CF0   00   NULL;
```

MONITOR
>

```
     G2800
     OCF1   7D    A:=L;               Entry 'HL:-DE'
     OCF2   93    A:-E;
     OCF3   6F    L:=A;
     OCF4   7C    A:=H;
     OCF5   9A    A:--D;
     OCF6   67    H:=A;
     OCF7   C9    RET;

     MONITOR
     >
```

```
     G2800
     OCF8   FE    A-46;               (first character)
     OCFA   C2    JNZ0D00;            Jump to 0D00 if not 'F'
     OCFD   C3    J0CC1;              If 'F' jump to 0CC1
     0D00   FE    A-56;               (first character)
     0D02   C2    JNZ0C93;            Jump to 0C93 if not 'V'
     0D05   CD    JS0200;             ('V') New line (console)
     0D08   CD    JS0D66;             In-out
     0D0B   FE    A-22;
     0D0D   C2    JNZ0D1E;            Jump to 0D1E if not quotation mark
     0D10   CD    JS0D66;             (' " ') In-out
     0D13   FE    A-22;
     0D15   CA    JZ0436;             Jump to 0436 if (closing) quotation mark
     0D18   CD    JS0D59;             Store byte
     0D1B   C3    J0D10;              Loop back to 0D10
     0D1E   FE    A-23;
     0D20   C2    JNZ0463;            Fail if not '#'
     0D23   CD    JS0D66;             In-out
     0D26   CD    JS0B00;             ASCII-hex.
     0D29   78    A:=B;
     0D2A   FE    A-00;
     0D2C   FA    JN0463;             Fail if not hex.
     0D2F   87    A:+A;
     0D30   87    A:+A;
     0D31   87    A:+A;
     0D32   87    A:+A;
     0D33   57    D:=A;               Upper half
     0D34   CD    JS0D66;             In-out
     0D37   CD    JS0B00;             ASCII-hex.
     0D3A   78    A:=B;
     0D3B   FE    A-00;
     0D3D   FA    JN0463;             Fail if not hex.
     0D40   82    A:+D;               Lower half
     0D41   CD    JS0D59;             Store byte
     0D44   CD    JS0D66;             In-out
     0D47   FE    A-20;
     0D49   CA    JZ0D44;
     0D4C   FE    A-0D;
     0D4E   CA    JZ0D44;             Ignore space or return
     0D51   FE    A-23;
     0D53   C2    JNZ0D26;            Loop back if not '#'
     0D56   C3    J0436;              Jump to 0436 (in main loop)

     MONITOR
     >
```

```
      G2800
      0D59   C5    ST:=BC;          Entry 'Store byte'
      0D5A   E5    ST:=HL;
      0D5B   2A    HL:=MM1010;      Object-program counter
      0D5E   77    M:=A;
      0D5F   23    HL:+1;
      0D60   22    MM1010:=HL;
      0D63   E1    HL:=ST;
      0D64   C1    BC:=ST;
      0D65   C9    RET;
      0D66   CD    JS021B;          Entry 'in-out'
      0D69   4F    C:=A;
      0D6A   CD    JS01F4;
      0D6D   79    A:=C;
      0D6E   C9    RET;
      0D6F   C5    ST:=BC;          Entry 'HL:=sqrt(HL)×2⁸'
      0D70   D5    ST:=DE;
      0D71   44    B:=H;
      0D72   4D    C:=L;
      0D73   78    A:=B;
      0D74   E6    A:&C0;
      0D76   C2    JNZ00B4;         Fail if out of range
      0D79   CD    JS0BE0;          HL:=sqrt(BC), 7 b.p.
      0D7C   29    HL:+HL;          8 b.p.
      0D7D   D1    DE:=ST;
      0D7E   C1    BC:=ST;
      0D7F   C9    RET;
      0D80   00    NULL;
      0D81   00    NULL;
      0D82   00    NULL;
      0D83   00    NULL;
      0D84   00    NULL;

      MONITOR
      >
```

```
      G2800
 OD85  OE    C:=05;                  (from 0BC2)
 OD87  FE    A-50;
 OD89  C8    RZ;                     Return with C=05 for 'P'
 OD8A  OD    C:-1;
 OD8B  OD    C:-1;
 OD8C  FE    A-4B;
 OD8E  C8    RZ;                     Return with C=03 for 'K'
 OD8F  OD    C:-1;
 OD90  OD    C:-1;
 OD91  FE    A-5A;
 OD93  C8    RZ;                     Return with C=01 for 'Z'
 OD94  OD    C:-1;
 OD95  OD    C:-1;
 OD96  C9    RET;                    Failure—return with C=FF
 OD97  C8    RZ;                     Return with C=02 for 'NK'
 OD98  OD    C:-1;
 OD99  OD    C:-1;
 OD9A  C3    JODC5;                  Continue at 0DC5
 OD9D  00    NULL;
 OD9E  FE    A-4C;                   (first character)
 ODA0  C2    JNZODAA;                Jump to 0DAA if not 'L'
 ODA3  23    HL:+1;                  ('L')
 ODA4  7E    A:=M;                   Second character
 ODA5  1E    E:=68;                  (r or r₁ will be L)
 ODA7  C3    JO58E;                  Continue at 058E
 ODAA  FE    A-4D;                   (first character)
 ODAC  C2    JNZ0890;                Jump to 0890 if not 'M'
 ODAF  23    HL:+1;                  ('M')
 ODB0  7E    A:=M;                   Second character
 ODB1  FE    A-3A;
 ODB3  C2    JNZ0805;                Jump to 0805 if not ':'
 ODB6  23    HL:+1;                  ('M:')
 ODB7  23    HL:+1;
 ODB8  7E    A:=M;                   Fourth character
 ODB9  FE    A-4D;
 ODBB  CA    JZ0463;                 Fail if 'M'
 ODBE  2B    HL:-1;
 ODBF  2B    HL:-1;
 ODC0  1E    E:=70;                  (r or r₁ will be M)
 ODC2  C3    JO593;                  Continue at 0593
 ODC5  FE    A-5A;                   (from 0D9A)
 ODC7  C8    RZ;                     Return with C=00 for 'NZ'
 ODC8  OD    C:-1;
 ODC9  C9    RET;                    Failure—return with C=FF


MONITOR
>
```

```
    G2800
    0DCA    16    D:=2B;            Entry 'out decimal integer (HL)'
    0DCC    7C    A:=H;
    0DCD    FE    A-80;
    0DCF    C2    JNZ0DD9;
    0DD2    7D    A:=L;
    0DD3    FE    A-00;
    0DD5    CA    JZ0E4E;           Jump to 0E4E if HL=8000
    0DD8    7C    A:=H;
    0DD9    FE    A-00;
    0DDB    F2    JNN0DE6;          Skip to 0DE6 unless value is negative
    0DDE    14    D:+1;             (negative)
    0DDF    14    D:+1;             Change '+' to '−'
    0DE0    2F    A:#;
    0DE1    67    H:=A;
    0DE2    7D    A:=L;
    0DE3    2F    A:#;
    0DE4    6F    L:=A;
    0DE5    23    HL:+1;            Negate value
    0DE6    01    BC:=D8F0;
    0DE9    CD    JS0E5D;           Divide by 10000
    0DEC    01    BC:=2710;
    0DEF    09    HL:+BC;
    0DF0    7B    A:=E;             ASCII form of d₄
    0DF1    FE    A-30;
    0DF3    C2    JNZ0DF9;          Skip to 0DF9 if quotient non-zero
    0DF6    5A    E:=D;             Move sign and suppress non-significant zero
    0DF7    16    D:=20;
    0DF9    D5    ST:=DE;
    0DFA    01    BC:=FC18;
    0DFD    CD    JS0E5D;           Divide by 1000
    0E00    01    BC:=03E8;
    0E03    09    HL:+BC;
    0E04    53    D:=E;             ASCII form of d₃
    0E05    01    BC:=FF9C;
    0E08    CD    JS0E5D;           Divide by 100
    0E0B    01    BC:=0064;
    0E0E    09    HL:+BC;           ASCII form of d₂ in E
    0E0F    26    H:=30;
    0E11    7D    A:=L;
    0E12    FE    A-0A;
    0E14    FA    JN0E1D;           Divide by 10 (single-length)
    0E17    D6    A:-0A;
    0E19    24    H:+1;             ASCII form of d₁ in H
    0E1A    C3    J0E12;
```

```
MONITOR
>
```

```
     G2800
     0E1D   C6   A:+30;
     0E1F   6F   L:=A;              ASCII form of d₀ in L
     0E20   C1   BC:=ST;
     0E21   78   A:=B;
     0E22   FE   A-20;
     0E24   C2   JNZ0E3F;           Suppress any non-significant zeroes, moving sign next to most
     0E27   7A   A:=D;                 significant digit
     0E28   FE   A-30;
     0E2A   C2   JNZ0E3F;
     0E2D   51   D:=C;
     0E2E   48   C:=B;
     0E2F   7B   A:=E;
     0E30   FE   A-30;
     0E32   C2   JNZ0E3F;
     0E35   5A   E:=D;
     0E36   51   D:=C;
     0E37   7C   A:=H;
     0E38   FE   A-30;
     0E3A   C2   JNZ0E3F;           Print characters forming decimal value right-justified in field of
     0E3D   63   H:=E;                 six positions
     0E3E   5A   E:=D;
     0E3F   79   A:=C;
     0E40   48   C:=B;
     0E41   47   B:=A;
     0E42   DF   JSS3;
     0E43   48   C:=B;
     0E44   DF   JSS3;
     0E45   4A   C:=D;
     0E46   DF   JSS3;
     0E47   4B   C:=E;
     0E48   DF   JSS3;
     0E49   4C   C:=H;
     0E4A   DF   JSS3;
     0E4B   4D   C:=L;
     0E4C   DF   JSS3;
     0E4D   C9   RET;
     0E4E   21   HL:=0E57;          Special treatment for extreme negative value (which cannot be
     0E51   06   B:=06;                negated)
     0E53   CD   JS005F;
     0E56   C9   RET;

     MONITOR
     >


     0E57   "-32768"
```

```
    G2800
    0E5D    1E    E:=30;            Entry 'divide' for decimal output
    0E5F    09    HL:+BC;
    0E60    7C    A:=H;
    0E61    FE    A-00;
    0E63    F8    RN;
    0E64    1C    E:+1;
    0E65    C3    JOE5F;
    0E68    26    H:=00;            Entry 'out decimal integer (A)'
    0E6A    6F    L:=A;                   Change value to double length in HL and jump to 0DCA
    0E6B    FE    A-00;
    0E6D    F2    JNNODCA;
    0E70    25    H:-1;
    0E71    C3    JODCA;

MONITOR
>

    G2800
    07E6    06    B:=05;            Entry 'out decimal fraction (HL), 5 d.p.'
    07E8    0E    C:=2E;            Entry 'out decimal fraction (HL), B d.p.'
    07EA    DF    JSS3;                   Print decimal point
    07EB    97    A:-A;
    07EC    29    HL:+HL;
    07ED    8F    A:++A;                  Multiply HL by ten, forming integral part of result in A and
    07EE    4F    C:=A;                   fractional part of result in HL
    07EF    54    D:=H;
    07F0    5D    E:=L;
    07F1    29    HL:+HL;
    07F2    8F    A:++A;
    07F3    29    HL:+HL;
    07F4    8F    A:++A;
    07F5    19    HL:+DE;
    07F6    89    A:++C;                  Next digit in A
    07F7    C6    A:+30;                  ASCII form of digit
    07F9    4F    C:=A;
    07FA    DF    JSS3;                   Print digit
    07FB    05    B:-1;
    07FC    C2    JNZ07EB;                Repeat until specified number of digits printed
    07FF    C9    RET;

MONITOR
>
```

```
        G2800
        0E74    11      DE:=0000;       Entry 'A:=in decimal integer'
        0E77    E7      JSS4;             Read first character
        0E78    FE      A-2B;
        0E7A    CA      JZOE83;           If '+' skip to 0E83
        0E7D    FE      A-2D;
        0E7F    C2      JNZOE84;          If not sign skip to 0E84
        0E82    14      D:+1;             If '−' set negative marker
        0E83    E7      JSS4;             Read character after sign
        0E84    EF      JSS5;             ASCII–hex.
        0E85    CD      JS01E6;           Check hex.
        0E88    5F      E:=A;
        0E89    E7      JSS4;             Read next character
        0E8A    FE      A-30;
        0E8C    FA      JNOEB4;
        0E8F    FE      A-3A;
        0E91    F2      JNNOEB4;          Jump to 0EB4 if not a decimal digit
        0E94    D6      A:-30;            Binary value of digit
        0E96    47      B:=A;
        0E97    7B      A:=E;
        0E98    FE      A-0D;
        0E9A    F2      JNNOOB4;          Fail if previous value thirteen or more
        0E9D    87      A:+A;
        0E9E    4F      C:=A;
        0E9F    87      A:+A;             Multiply previous value by ten and add in new digit
        0EA0    87      A:+A;
        0EA1    81      A:+C;
        0EA2    80      A:+B;
        0EA3    5F      E:=A;
        0EA4    FE      A-00;
        0EA6    F2      JNNOE89;          Repeat while within range
        0EA9    87      A:+A;
        0EAA    C2      JNZOOB4;  ⎫
        0EAD    15      D:-1;     ⎬       Fail for +128 and ±129 but accept −128
        0EAE    C2      JNZOOB4;  ⎭
        0EB1    E7      JSS4;     ⎫
        0EB2    7B      A:=E;     ⎬       Read terminating character (A=80)
        0EB3    C9      RET;      ⎭
        0EB4    7B      A:=E;
        0EB5    15      D:-1;
        0EB6    F8      RN;               Return with positive value
        0FB7    2F      A:#;              Negate A
        0EB8    3C      A:+1;
        0EB9    C9      RET;              Return with negative value
```

MONITOR
>

```
G2800
OEBA   21    HL:=0000;        Entry 'HL:=in decimal integer'
OEBD   54    D:=H;
OEBE   E7    JSS4;            Read first character
OEBF   FE    A-2B;
OEC1   CA    JZOECA;          If '+' skip to OECA
OEC4   FE    A-2D;
OEC6   C2    JNZOECB;         If not sign skip to OECB
OEC9   14    D:+1;            If '−' set negative marker
OECA   E7    JSS4;            Read character after sign
OECB   EF    JSS5;            ASCII–hex.
OECC   CD    JS01E6;          Check hex.
OECF   6F    L:=A;
OEDO   E7    JSS4;            Read next character
OED1   FE    A-30;
OED3   FA    JNOFOD;
OED6   FE    A-3A;
OED8   F2    JNNOFOD;         Jump to OFOD if not a decimal digit
OEDB   D6    A:-30;           Binary value of digit
OEDD   5F    E:=A;
OEDE   01    BC:=F333;        −3277 (decimal)
OEE1   09    HL:+BC;
OEE2   7C    A:=H;
OEE3   FE    A-00;
OEE5   F2    JNNOOB4;         Fail if previous value 3277 or more
OEE8   01    BC:=OCCD;        +3277 (decimal)
OEEB   09    HL:+BC;
OEEC   29    HL:+HL;
OEED   44    B:=H;
OEEE   4D    C:=L;
OEEF   29    HL:+HL;  ⎫
OEFO   29    HL:+HL;  ⎬      Multiply previous value by ten and add in new digit
OEF1   09    HL:+BC;  ⎭
OEF2   06    B:=00;
OEF4   4B    C:=E;
OEF5   09    HL:+BC;
OEF6   7C    A:=H;
OEF7   FE    A-00;
OEF9   F2    JNNOEDO;         Repeat while within range
OEFC   FE    A-80;
OEFE   C2    JNZOOB4;   ⎫
OF01   7D    A:=L;      ⎪
OF02   FE    A-00;      ⎬     Fail for +32768, ±32769 but accept −32768
OF04   C2    JNZOOB4;   ⎪
OF07   15    D:-1;      ⎪
OF08   C2    JNZOOB4;   ⎭
OFOB   E7    JSS4;            Read terminating character
OFOC   C9    RET;             (HL=8000)
OFOD   15    D:-1;
OFOE   F8    RN;              Return with positive value
OFOF   7C    A:=H;
OF10   2F    A:#;
OF11   67    H:=A;
OF12   7D    A:=L;            Negate HL
OF13   2F    A:#;
OF14   6F    L:=A;
OF15   23    HL:+1;
OF16   C9    RET;             Return with negative value
OF17   00    NULL;
```

MONITOR
>

```
       G2800
       0F18    79      A:=C;           Entry 'Sign correction (C)'
       0F19    FE      A-00;
       0F1B    F0      RNN;
       0F1C    7C      A:=H;
       0F1D    93      A:-E;
       0F1E    67      H:=A;
       0F1F    C9      RET;
       0F20    21      HL:=0000;       Entry 'HL:=C×E (unsigned)'
       0F23    79      A:=C;
       0F24    54      D:=H;
       0F25    06      B:=08;
       0F27    29      HL:+HL;
       0F28    07      A:@L;
       0F29    D2      JNKOF2D;
       0F2C    19      HL:+DE;
       0F2D    05      B:-1;
       0F2E    C2      JNZOF27;
       0F31    C9      RET;
       0F32    7B      A:=E;           Entry 'Sign correction (E)'
       0F33    FE      A-00;
       0F35    F0      RNN;
       0F36    7C      A:=H;
       0F37    91      A:-C;
       0F38    67      H:=A;
       0F39    C9      RET;
       0F3A    CD      JSOF20;         Entry 'HL:=C×E (signed)'
       0F3D    CD      JSOF18;
       0F40    CD      JSOF32;
       0F43    C9      RET;
       0F44    F5      ST:=AF;         Entry 'DE:=D×E (unsigned)'
       0F45    C5      ST:=BC;
       0F46    E5      ST:=HL;
       0F47    4A      C:=D;
       0F48    CD      JSOF20;
       0F4B    EB      HL:=:DE;
       0F4C    F1      HL:=ST;
       0F4D    C1      BC:=ST;
       0F4E    F1      AF:=ST;
       0F4F    C9      RET;
```

MONITOR
>

```
     G2800
0F50    0C      C:+1;              Entry 'HL:=(B/D)×2ᶜ (unsigned)'
0F51    7A      A:=D;
0F52    B8      A-B;
0F53    F2      JNNOF5D;
0F56    0C      C:+1;
0F57    87      A:+A;
0F58    F2      JNNOF52;
0F5B    1F      AK:@R;
0F5C    0D      C:-1;
0F5D    57      D:=A;
0F5E    21      HL:=0000;          (see section 4.5.5)
0F61    29      HL:+HL;
0F62    7C      A:=H;
0F63    FE      A-00;
0F65    FA      JNOOE4;
0F68    78      A:=B;
0F69    BA      A-D;
0F6A    FA      JNOF6F;
0F6D    92      A:-D;
0F6E    23      HL:+1;
0F6F    87      A:+A;
0F70    47      B:=A;
0F71    0D      C:-1;
0F72    C2      JNZOF61;
0F75    C9      RET;
0F76    1E      E:=00;             Entry 'HL:=(B/D)×2ᶜ (signed)'
0F78    78      A:=B;
0F79    FE      A-00;
0F7B    F2      JNNOF82;           Absolute value of dividend
0F7E    2F      A:#;
0F7F    3C      A:+1;
0F80    47      B:=A;
0F81    1C      E:+1;
0F82    7A      A:=D;
0F83    FE      A-00;
0F85    F2      JNNOF8C;           Absolute value of divisor
0F88    2F      A:#;
0F89    3C      A:+1;
0F8A    57      D:=A;
0F8B    1D      E:-1;
0F8C    CD      JSOF50;            Unsigned division
0F8F    7B      A:=E;
0F90    FE      A-00;              Sign check
0F92    C8      RZ;                Return with positive quotient
0F93    7C      A:=H;
0F94    2F      A:#;
0F95    67      H:=A;
0F96    7D      A:=L;              Change sign of HL
0F97    2F      A:#;
0F98    6F      L:=A;
0F99    23      HL:+1;
0F9A    C9      RET;               Return with negative quotient

MONITOR
   >
```

```
G2800
0F9B    EB    HL:=:DE;          Entry 'HL:=(BC/DE)×2^A (unsigned)'
0F9C    C5    ST:=BC;
0F9D    D1    DE:=ST;
0F9E    47    B:=A;
0F9F    04    B:+1;
0FA0    CD    JS0C1A;               HL−DE
0FA3    F2    JNN0FAF;
0FA6    04    B:+1;
0FA7    29    HL:+HL;
0FA8    D2    JNK0FA0;
0FAB    CD    JS0FF2;              HL:/2 (unsigned, truncated)
0FAE    05    B:-1;
0FAF    EB    HL:=:DE;
0FB0    E5    ST:=HL;
0FB1    21    HL:=0000;            (see section 4.5.6)
0FB4    29    HL:+HL;
0FB5    DA    JK00B4;
0FB8    F3    HL:=:ST;
0FB9    CD    JS0C1A;              HL−DE
0FBC    FA    JN0FC5;
0FBF    CD    JS0CF1;              HL:−DE
0FC2    E3    HL:=:ST;
0FC3    23    HL:+1;
0FC4    E3    HL:=:ST;
0FC5    29    HL:+HL;
0FC6    E3    HL:=:ST;
0FC7    05    B:-1;
0FC8    C2    JNZ0FB4;
0FCB    C1    BC:=ST;
0FCC    C9    RET;
0FCD    F5    ST:=AF;           Entry 'HL:=(BC/DE)×2^A (signed)'
0FCE    26    H:=00;
0FD0    78    A:=B;
0FD1    A7    A:&A;
0FD2    F2    JNN0FDC;             Absolute value of dividend
0FD5    2F    A:#;
0FD6    47    B:=A;
0FD7    79    A:=C;
0FD8    2F    A:#;
0FD9    4F    C:=A;
0FDA    03    BC:+1;
0FDB    24    H:+1;
0FDC    7A    A:=D;
0FDD    A7    A:&A;
0FDE    F2    JNN0FE8;             Absolute value of divisor
0FE1    2F    A:#;
0FE2    57    D:=A;
0FE3    7B    A:=E;
0FE4    2F    A:#;
0FE5    5F    E:=A;
0FE6    13    DE:+1;
0FE7    25    H:-1;
0FE8    F1    AF:=ST;
0FE9    E5    ST:=HL;
0FEA    CD    JS0F9B;              Unsigned division
0FED    F1    AF:=ST;
0FEE    C3    J0F90;               Jump to 0F90 for sign correction
```

MONITOR
>

```
   G2800
OFF1   23    HL:+1;            Entry 'HL:/2 (unsigned, rounded)'
OFF2   7D    A:=L;            Entry 'HL:/2 (unsigned, truncated)'
OFF3   E6    A:&FE;
OFF5   0F    A:@R;
OFF6   6F    L:=A;
OFF7   7C    A:=H;
OFF8   1F    AK:@R;
OFF9   67    H:=A;
OFFA   D0    RNK;
OFFB   7D    A:=L;
OFFC   EE    A:#80;
OFFE   6F    L:=A;
OFFF   C9    RET;

MONITOR
>
```

```
      G2800
      2400   3E    A:=10;             Entry 'DEHL:=BC×DE (unsigned)'
      2402   F5    ST:=AF;
      2403   97    A:-A;
      2404   67    H:=A;
      2405   6F    L:=A;
      2406   EB    HL:=:DE;
      2407   29    HL:+HL;
      2408   EB    HL:=:DE;
      2409   1F    AK:@R;
      240A   A7    A:&A;
      240B   29    HL:+HL;
      240C   D2    JNK2410;           (see section 4.5.3)
      240F   13    DE:+1;
      2410   F2    JNN2418;
      2413   09    HL:+BC;
      2414   D2    JNK2418;
      2417   13    DE:+1;
      2418   F3    HL:=:ST;
      2419   25    H:-1;
      241A   E3    HL:=:ST;
      241B   C2    JNZ2406;
      241E   F1    AF:=ST;
      241F   C9    RET;
      2420   21    HL:=0000;          Entry 'DEHL:=BC×DE (signed)'
      2423   78    A:=B;
      2424   A7    A:&A;
      2425   F2    JNN2429;
      2428   19    HL:+DE;            Sign correction for BC
      2429   7A    A:=D;
      242A   A7    A:&A;
      242B   F2    JNN242F;
      242E   09    HL:+BC;            Sign correction for DE
      242F   7C    A:=H;
      2430   2F    A:#;
      2431   67    H:=A;
      2432   7D    A:=L;
      2433   2F    A:#;
      2434   6F    L:=A;
      2435   23    HL:+1;             Total sign correction negated
      2436   E5    ST:=HL;
      2437   CD    JS2400;            DEHL:=BC×DE (unsigned)
      243A   EB    HL:=:DE;
      243B   C1    BC:=ST;
      243C   09    HL:+BC;            Sign correction
      243D   EB    HL:=:DE;
      243E   C9    RET;
      243F   00    NULL;
      2440   CD    JS2420;            Entry 'HL:=BC×DE (all 15 b.p.)'
      2443   EB    HL:=:DE;
      2444   29    HL:+HL;
      2445   EB    HL:=:DE;
      2446   29    HL:+HL;
      2447   D2    JNK244B;
      244A   13    DE:+1;             DEHL shifted up one place
      244B   29    HL:+HL;
      244C   D2    JNK2450;
      244F   13    DE:+1;
      2450   EB    HL:=:DE;           Result rounded to double-length
      2451   C9    RET;

      MONITOR
      >
```

```
       G2800
       2452   11    DE:=0000;         Entry 'Polynomial (15 b.p.)'   p := 0
       2455   D5    ST:=DE;
       2456   5E    E:=M;
       2457   23    HL:+1;
       2458   56    D:=M;             Next coefficient aᵢ to DE
       2459   23    HL:+1;
       245A   E3    HL:=:ST;
       245B   19    HL:+DE;           p :+ aᵢ
       245C   A7    A:&A;
       245D   CA    JZ246D;           Finish if i—0
       2460   3D    A:-1;             i :— 1
       2461   EB    HL:=:DE;
       2462   F5    ST:=AF;
       2463   C5    ST:=BC;
       2464   CD    JS2440;           HL:=BC × DE (all 15 b.p.)   p :× x
       2467   C1    BC:=ST;
       2468   F1    AF:=ST;
       2469   E3    HL:=:ST;
       246A   C3    J2456;            Jump back for next coefficient
       246D   D1    DE:=ST;
       246E   C9    RET;
       246F   00    NULL;
       2470   E5    ST:=HL;           Entry 'HL:=sin(HL) 15 b.p.'
       2471   EB    HL:=:DE;
       2472   42    B:=D;
       2473   4B    C:=E;
       2474   CD    JS2440;           HL:=BC × DE (15 b.p.)
       2477   44    B:=H;
       2478   4D    C:=L;             Value of argument
       2479   3E    A:=03;            Degree of polynomial
       247B   21    HL:=2488;         Location of coefficients
       247E   CD    JS2452;           Polynomial (15 b.p.)
       2481   EB    HL:=:DE;
       2482   C1    BC:=ST;
       2483   CD    JS2440;           HL:=BC × DE (15 b.p.)
       2486   29    HL:+HL;
       2487   C9    RET;

       MONITOR
       >


       2488   #FD FF 89 00 55 F5 00 40#
```

```
     G2800
    2490   CD    JS2470;        Entry 'HL:=cos(HL) 15 b.p.'
    2493   EB    HL:=:DE;             sin in DE
    2494   42    B:=D;
    2495   4B    C:=E;
    2496   CD    JS2440;              HL:=BC×DE (15 b.p.)
    2499   CD    JS24CF;              HL:/2 (signed, rounded)
    249C   EB    HL:=:DE;
    249D   21    HL:=4000;
    24A0   CD    JS0CF1;              HL:−DE
    24A3   CD    JS0D6F;              HL:=sqrt(HL)×2⁸
    24A6   C9    RET;
```

MONITOR
>

```
     G2800
    24C1   67    H:=A;          Entry 'HL(radians 15 b.p.):=A(degrees 0 b.p.)'
    24C2   2E    L:=00;
    24C4   29    HL:+HL;        Entry 'HL(radians 15 b.p.):=HL(degrees 8 b.p.)'
    24C5   44    B:=H;
    24C6   4D    C:=L;
    24C7   11    DE:=477D;            (π/180, 20 b.p.)
    24CA   CD    JS2440;              HL:=BC×DE(15 b.p.)
    24CD   29    HL:+HL;
    24CE   C9    RET;
    24CF   CD    JS0FF1;        Entry 'HL:/2 (signed, rounded)'
    24D2   7C    A:=H;
    24D3   E6    A:&40;
    24D5   87    A:+A;                Shift down as unsigned and copy sign bit
    24D6   84    A:+H;
    24D7   67    H:=A;
    24D8   C9    RET;
    24D9   CD    JS2470;        Entry 'HL:=tan(HL) 15 b.p.'
    24DC   E5    ST:=HL;              Stack sin
    24DD   CD    JS2493;              cos (late entry)
    24E0   C1    BC:=ST;
    24E1   EB    HL:=:DE;
    24E2   3E    A:=0F;
    24E4   CD    JS0FCD;              tan=sin/cos
    24E7   C9    RET;
    24E8   0E    C:=20;         Entry 'Out signed fraction (HL 15 b.p.)'
    24EA   DF    JSS3;
    24EB   0E    C:=2B;
    24ED   29    HL:+HL;              16 b.p.
    24EE   D2    JNK24F6;
    24F1   CD    JS0F93;              HL:−
    24F4   0E    C:=2D;
    24F6   DF    JSS3;
    24F7   0E    C:=30;
    24F9   DF    JSS3;                Print ' +0' or ' −0'
    24FA   06    B:=04;               Four decimal places
    24FC   CD    JS07E8;              Out decimal fraction
    24FF   C9    RET;
```

MONITOR
>

```
     G2800
    2500   44    B:=H;          Entry 'HL(degrees 8 b.p.):=HL(radians 15 b.p.)'
    2501   4D    C:=L;
    2502   11    DE:=7297;            (180/π, 9 b.p.)
    2505   CD    JS2420;              DEHL:=BC×DE (signed)
    2508   EB    HL:=:DE;
    2509   C9    RET;
```

MONITOR
>

```
        G2800
     250A  F5   ST:=HL;              Entry 'BCDEHL:=BHL × CDE (signed)'
     250B  D5   ST:=DE;
     250C  C5   ST:=BC;
     250D  44   B:=H;
     250E  4D   C:=L;
     250F  CD   JS2400;              DEHL:=BC × DE (unsigned)
     2512  C1   BC:=ST;
     2513  E3   HL:=:ST;
     2514  D5   ST:=DE;
     2515  C5   ST:=BC;
     2516  EB   HL:=:DE;
     2517  48   C:=B;
     2518  79   A:=C;
     2519  17   AK:@L;
     251A  9F   A:--A;
     251B  47   B:=A;
     251C  CD   JS2556;              DEHL:=BC(signed) × DE(unsigned)
     251F  E3   HL:=:ST;
     2520  D5   ST:=DE;
     2521  EB   HL:=:DE;
     2522  4A   C:=D;
     2523  CD   JSOF3A;              HL:=C × E (signed)
     2526  E5   ST:=HL;
     2527  7B   A:=E;
     2528  17   AK:@L;
     2529  9F   A:--A;
     252A  57   D:=A;
     252B  21   HL:=000A;
     252E  39   HL:+SP;
     252F  F9   SP:=HL;
     2530  C1   BC:=ST;
     2531  21   HL:=FFF4;
     2534  39   HL:+SP;
     2535  F9   SP:=HL;
     2536  CD   JS2562;              DEHL:=BC(unsigned) × DE(signed)
     2539  C1   BC:=ST;
     253A  EB   HL:=:DE;
     253B  09   HL:+BC;
     253C  44   B:=H;
     253D  4D   C:=L;
     253E  E1   HL:=ST;
     253F  09   HL:+BC;
     2540  44   B:=H;
     2541  4D   C:=L;
     2542  E1   HL:=ST;
     2543  19   HL:+DE;
     2544  D2   JNK2548;
     2547  03   BC:+1;
     2548  54   D:=H;
     2549  5D   E:=L;
     254A  E1   HL:=ST;
     254B  19   HL:+DE;
     254C  D2   JNK2550;
     254F  03   BC:+1;
     2550  54   D:=H;
     2551  5D   E:=L;
     2552  E1   HL:=ST;
     2553  33   SP:+1;
     2554  33   SP:+1;
     2555  C9   RET;
```

```
MONITOR
>
```

```
G2800
 2556   21    HL:=0000;        Entry 'DEHL:=BC(signed) × DE(unsigned)'
 2559   78    A:=B;
 255A   A7    A:&A;
 255B   F2    JNN242F;    ⎫
 255E   19    HL:+DE;     ⎬    Make sign correction for BC if necessary and jump to 242F
 255F   C3    J242F;      ⎭
 2562   21    HL:=0000;        Entry 'DEHL:=BC(unsigned) × DE(signed)'
 2565   C3    J2429;           Avoid sign correction for BC
 2568   F5    ST:=AF;     Entry 'AHL:/2 (truncated)'
 2569   CD    JSOFF2;          HL:/2 (unsigned, truncated)
 256C   F1    AF:=ST;
 256D   07    A:@L;
 256E   1F    AK:@R;
 256F   1F    AK:@R;
 2570   F5    ST:=AF;
 2571   7C    A:=H;
 2572   17    AK:@L;
 2573   0F    A:@R;
 2574   67    H:=A;
 2575   F1    AF:=ST;
 2576   C9    RET;
 2577   D5    ST:=DE;     Entry 'AHL:/2 (rounded)'
 2578   11    DE:=0001;
 257B   19    HL:+DE;
 257C   CE    A:++00;
 257E   CD    JS2568;          AHL:/2 (truncated)
 2581   D1    DE:=ST;
 2582   C9    RET;
 2583   CD    JS2568;     Entry 'AHL:/2ᴮ (truncated)'
 2586   05    B:-1;
 2587   C2    JNZ2583;
 258A   C9    RET;
 258B   05    B:-1;       Entry 'AHL:/2ᴮ (rounded)'
 258C   CA    JZ2595;
 258F   CD    JS2568;          AHL:/2 (truncated)
 2592   C3    J258B;
 2595   D5    ST:=DE;
 2596   11    DE:=0001;
 2599   19    HL:+DE;
 259A   CE    A:++00;
 259C   CD    JS2568;          AHL:/2 (truncated)
 259F   D1    DE:=ST;
 25A0   C9    RET;
```

MONITOR
>

```
      G2800
25A1  06   B:=00;          Entry 'Normalize up (AHL)'
25A3  F5   ST:=AF;         Entry 'Normalize up'
25A4  A7   A:&A;
25A5  C2   JNZ25B2;
25A8  7C   A:=H;
25A9  A7   A:&A;
25AA  C2   JNZ25B2;
25AD  7D   A:=L;
25AE  A7   A:&A;
25AF  CA   JZ25C7;
25B2  F1   AF:=ST;
25B3  F5   ST:=AF;
25B4  E6   A:&E0;
25B6  FE   A-20;
25B8  CA   JZ25C9;
25BB  FE   A-C0;
25BD  CA   JZ25C9;
25C0  F1   AF:=ST;
25C1  29   HL:+HL;
25C2  8F   A:++A;
25C3  05   B:-1;
25C4  C3   J25A3;
25C7  06   B:=00;
25C9  F1   AF:=ST;
25CA  C9   RET;
25CB  4F   C:=A;           Entry 'Normalize down'
25CC  07   A:@L;
25CD  17   AK:@L;
25CE  CE   A:++00;
25D0  1F   AK:@R;
25D1  79   A:=C;
25D2  D0   RNK;
25D3  04   B:+1;
25D4  CD   JS2577;                     AHL:/2 (rounded)
25D7  C9   RET;
25D8  C5   ST:=BC;         Entry 'AHL:-CDE'
25D9  47   B:=A;
25DA  7D   A:=L;
25DB  93   A:-E;
25DC  6F   L:=A;
25DD  7C   A:=H;
25DE  9A   A:--D;
25DF  67   H:=A;
25E0  78   A:=B;
25E1  99   A:--C;
25E2  C1   BC:=ST;
25E3  C9   RET;

      MONITOR
      >
```

```
    G2800
25E4    EB    HL:=:DE;     Entry 'AHL(22 b.p.):=BCDEHL(44 b.p.) rounded'
25E5    50    D:=B;
25E6    59    E:=C;
25E7    01    BC:=0020;
25EA    09    HL:+BC;
25EB    D2    JNK25EF;
25EE    13    DE:+1;
25EF    EB    HL:=:DE;
25F0    29    HL:+HL;
25F1    EB    HL:=:DE;
25F2    29    HL:+HL;
25F3    D2    JNK25F7;
25F6    13    DE:+1;
25F7    EB    HL:=:DE;
25F8    29    HL:+HL;
25F9    EB    HL:=:DE;
25FA    29    HL:+HL;
25FB    D2    JNK25FF;
25FE    13    DE:+1;
25FF    6C    L:=H;
2600    63    H:=E;
2601    7A    A:=D;
2602    C9    RET;
2603    00    NULL;
2604    00    NULL;
2605    00    NULL;
2606    00    NULL;
2607    00    NULL;


MONITOR
>
```

```
      G2800
      2608   F5    ST:=AF;          Entry 'M4[BC]:=DEHL'   (f.p. store)
      2609   7D    A:=L;
      260A   02    M[BC]:=A;
      260B   03    BC:+1;
      260C   7C    A:=H;
      260D   02    M[BC]:=A;
      260E   03    BC:+1;
      260F   7B    A:=E;
      2610   02    M[BC]:=A;
      2611   03    BC:+1;
      2612   7A    A:=D;
      2613   02    M[BC]:=A;
      2614   0B    BC:-1;
      2615   0B    BC:-1;
      2616   0B    BC:-1;
      2617   F1    AF:=ST;
      2618   C9    RET;
      2619   F5    ST:=AF;          Entry 'DEHL:=M4[BC]'   (f.p. fetch)
      261A   0A    A:=M[BC];
      261B   6F    L:=A;
      261C   03    BC:+1;
      261D   0A    A:=M[BC];
      261E   67    H:=A;
      261F   03    BC:+1;
      2620   0A    A:=M[BC];
      2621   5F    E:=A;
      2622   03    BC:+1;
      2623   0A    A:=M[BC];
      2624   57    D:=A;
      2625   0B    BC:-1;
      2626   0B    BC:-1;
      2627   0B    BC:-1;
      2628   F1    AF:=ST;
      2629   C9    RET;
```

```
MONITOR
>
```

G2800

262A	2F	A:#;	(continuation of f.p. print)
262B	3C	A:+1;	
262C	0E	C:=30;	
262E	D6	A:-0A;	
2630	FA	JN2637;	
2633	0C	C:+1;	
2634	C3	J262E;	
2637	C6	A:+3A;	
2639	47	B:=A;	
263A	79	A:=C;	
263B	C3	J27F7;	
263E	CD	JS250A;	(continuation of f.p. multiply)
2641	CD	JS25E4;	Product of mantissae to 22 b.p.
2644	C1	BC:=ST;	
2645	CD	JS25A3;	Normalize up
2648	50	D:=B;	
2649	5F	E:=A;	
264A	C9	RET;	

MONITOR
>

G2800

264B	D5	ST:=DE;	Entry 'DEHL:×M4[BC]' (f.p. multiply)
264C	E5	ST:=HL;	
264D	CD	JS2619;	F.p. fetch
2650	7A	A:=D;	
2651	43	B:=E;	
2652	D1	DE:=ST;	
2653	E3	HL:=:ST;	
2654	84	A:+H;	Sum of exponents
2655	4D	C:=L;	
2656	E1	HL:=ST;	Mantissae in BHL, CDE
2657	F5	ST:=AF;	
2658	C3	J263E;	Jump to 263E to continue
265B	EB	HL:=:DE;	Entry 'DEHL:-' (f.p. negate)
265C	44	B:=H;	
265D	4D	C:=L;	
265E	97	A:-A;	
265F	67	H:=A;	Clear AHL
2660	6F	L:=A;	
2661	CD	JS25D8;	AHL:-CDE
2664	CD	JS25CB;	Normalize down
2667	5F	E:=A;	
2668	50	D:=B;	
2669	C9	RET;	
266A	D5	ST:=DE;	Entry 'M4[DE]:-'
266B	42	B:=D;	
266C	4B	C:=E;	
266D	CD	JS2619;	F.p. fetch
2670	CD	JS265B;	F.p. negate
2673	C1	BC:=ST;	
2674	C5	ST:=BC;	
2675	CD	JS2608;	F.p. store
2678	D1	DE:=ST;	
2679	C9	RET;	

MONITOR
>

```
     G2800
     267A    7A    A:=D;              Entry 'DEHL:= 1/DEHL' (f.p. unsigned)
     267B    2F    A:#;
     267C    3C    A:+1;
     267D    3C    A:+1;
     267E    F5    ST:=AF;
     267F    EB    HL:=:DE;
     2680    4D    C:=L;
     2681    21    HL:=0000;
     2684    3E    A:=20;
     2686    06    B:=17;
     2688    F5    ST:=AF;
     2689    E5    ST:=HL;
     268A    7C    A:=H;
     268B    29    HL:+HL;
     268C    8F    A:++A;
     268D    FA    JN00E4;
     2690    E3    HL:=:ST;
     2691    F5    ST:=AF;
     2692    33    SP:+1;
     2693    33    SP:+1;
     2694    33    SP:+1;
     2695    33    SP:+1;
     2696    F1    AF:=ST;
     2697    3B    SP:-1;
     2698    3B    SP:-1;
     2699    3B    SP:-1;
     269A    3B    SP:-1;
     269B    3B    SP:-1;
     269C    3B    SP:-1;
     269D    CD    JS25D8;                          AHL:-CDE
     26A0    F2    JNN26B7;
     26A3    19    HL:+DE;
     26A4    89    A:++C;
     26A5    29    HL:+HL;
     26A6    8F    A:++A;
     26A7    33    SP:+1;
     26A8    33    SP:+1;
     26A9    33    SP:+1;
     26AA    33    SP:+1;
     26AB    33    SP:+1;
     26AC    33    SP:+1;
     26AD    F5    ST:=AF;
     26AE    3B    SP:-1;
     26AF    3B    SP:-1;
     26B0    3B    SP:-1;
     26B1    3B    SP:-1;
     26B2    F1    AF:=ST;
     26B3    E3    HL:=:ST;
     26B4    C3    J26CE;

     MONITOR
     >
```

M.S.E.—L

```
G2800
26B7   29   HL:+HL;              (continuation of DEHL:= 1/DEHL)
26B8   8F   A:++A;
26B9   33   SP:+1;
26BA   33   SP:+1;
26BB   33   SP:+1;
26BC   33   SP:+1;
26BD   33   SP:+1;
26BE   33   SP:+1;
26BF   F5   ST:=AF;
26C0   3B   SP:-1;
26C1   3B   SP:-1;
26C2   3B   SP:-1;
26C3   3B   SP:-1;
26C4   F1   AF:=ST;
26C5   E3   HL:=:ST;
26C6   D5   ST:=DE;
26C7   11   DE:=0001;
26CA   19   HL:+DE;
26CB   CE   A:++00;
26CD   D1   DE:=ST;
26CE   05   B:-1;                Step counter
26CF   C2   JNZ268B;             Repeat shift and subtract until 23 done
26D2   D1   DE:=ST;
26D3   D1   DE:=ST;
26D4   C1   BC:=ST;
26D5   C3   J2664;               Jump to 2664 to normalize down
26D8   00   NULL;
26D9   7B   A:=E;          Entry 'DEHL:= 1/DEHL (signed)' (f.p. reciprocal)
26DA   A7   A:&A;
26DB   FA   JN26E2;              Jump on sign of mantissa (Section 4.7.7)
26DE   CD   JS267A;              Unsigned reciprocal
26E1   C9   RET;                 Return with positive result
26E2   CD   JS265B;              F.p. negate
26E5   CD   JS267A;              Unsigned reciprocal
26E8   CD   JS265B;              F.p. negate
26EB   C9   RET;                 Return with negative result
26EC   D5   ST:=DE;        Entry 'DEHL:/M4[BC]' (f.p. divide)
26ED   E5   ST:=HL;
26EE   CD   JS2619;              F.p. fetch
26F1   CD   JS26D9;              F.p. reciprocal
26F4   C3   J2650;               Jump to 2650 to multiply

MONITOR
>
```

```
G2800
26F7  E5    ST:=HL;        Entry 'DEHL:=M4[HL]+M4[DE]' (f.p. add)
26F8  D5    ST:=DE;
26F9  23    HL:+1;
26FA  23    HL:+1;
26FB  C3    J24A7;         Jump to 24A7 to continue
26FE  13    DE:+1;         (continuation of f.p. add)
26FF  1A    A:=M[DE];
2700  96    A:-M;          Difference of exponents
2701  FA    JN270C;
2704  47    B:=A;          If positive, interchange mantissae
2705  D1    DE:=ST;
2706  E1    HL:=ST;
2707  D5    ST:=DE;
2708  EB    HL:=:DE;
2709  C3    J2710;
270C  2F    A:#;           If negative, change sign
270D  3C    A:+1;
270E  47    B:=A;
270F  D1    DE:=ST;
2710  1A    A:=M[DE];      Fetch mantissa to be shifted
2711  6F    L:=A;
2712  13    DE:+1;
2713  1A    A:=M[DE];
2714  67    H:=A;
2715  13    DE:+1;
2716  1A    A:=M[DE];
2717  C4    JSNZ258B;      If B>0 then AHL:/2^B (rounded)
271A  E3    HL:=:ST;
271B  5E    E:=M;          Fetch other mantissa
271C  23    HL:+1;
271D  56    D:=M;
271E  23    HL:+1;
271F  4E    C:=M;
2720  23    HL:+1;
2721  E3    HL:=:ST;
2722  19    HL:+DE;        Add mantissae (now same b.p.)
2723  89    A:++C;
2724  D1    DE:=ST;
2725  EB    HL:=:DE;
2726  46    B:=M;          Unnormalized exponent
2727  EB    HL:=:DE;
2728  CD    JS25CB;        Normalize down
272B  CD    JS25A3;        Normalize up
272E  5F    E:=A;
272F  50    D:=B;
2730  C9    RET;
2731  D5    ST:=DE;        Entry 'DEHL:=M4[HL]−M4[DE]' (f.p. subtract)
2732  E5    ST:=HL;
2733  CD    JS266A;          M4[DE]:−
2736  E1    HL:=ST;
2737  CD    JS26F7;          F.p. add
273A  C1    BC:=ST;
273B  E5    ST:=HL;
273C  D5    ST:=DE;
273D  50    D:=B;
273E  59    E:=C;
273F  CD    JS266A;          M4[DE]:−
2742  D1    DE:=ST;
2743  F1    HL:=ST;
2744  C9    RET;

MONITOR
>
```

```
    G2800
    24A7   7E    A:=M;                  (continuation of f.p. add)
    24A8   A7    A:&A;
    24A9   CA    JZ24BA;                Jump to 24BA if M4[HL]=0E0
    24AC   23    HL:+1;
    24AD   13    DE:+1;
    24AE   13    DE:+1;
    24AF   1A    A:=M[DE];
    24B0   A7    A:&A;
    24B1   C2    JNZ26FE;               Continue at 26FE unless M4[DE]=0E0
    24B4   F1    AF:=ST;                (M4[DE]=0E0)
    24B5   C1    BC:=ST;
    24B6   CD    JS2619;                F.p. fetch
    24B9   C9    RET;                   Result is M4[HL]
    24BA   C1    BC:=ST;                (M4[HL]=0E0)
    24BB   F1    AF:=ST;
    24BC   CD    JS2619;                F.p. fetch
    24BF   C9    RET;                   Result is M4[DE]
    24C0   00    NULL;
```

MONITOR
>

```
     G2800
     2745   E7    JSS4;                Entry 'DEHL:= in f.p. number' (f.p. read)
     2746   01    BC:=0000;
     2749   FE    A-2B;
     274B   CA    JZ2758;
     274E   FE    A-2D;
     2750   CA    JZ2757;
     2753   4F    C:=A;
     2754   C3    J2758;
     2757   05    B:-1;
     2758   C5    ST:=BC;              Stack sign marker
     2759   97    A:-A;                Clear AHL and
     275A   67    H:=A;
     275B   6C    L:=H;
     275C   E5    ST:=HL;              stack as starting value for mantissa
     275D   F5    ST:=AF;
     275E   79    A:=C;
     275F   A7    A:&A;
     2760   C2    JNZ2764;
     2763   E7    JSS4;                Read next character
     2764   D6    A:-30;
     2766   FA    JN278C;
     2769   FE    A-0A;                Jump to 278C when mantissa terminated
     276B   F2    JNN278C;
     276E   4F    C:=A;                (decimal digit read)
     276F   F1    AF:=ST;
     2770   E3    HL:=:ST;             Previous value of mantissa in AHL
     2771   29    HL:+HL;
     2772   8F    A:++A;
     2773   47    B:=A;
     2774   54    D:=H;
     2775   5D    E:=L;
     2776   29    HL:+HL;
     2777   8F    A:++A;
     2778   29    HL:+HL;
     2779   8F    A:++A;
     277A   19    HL:+DE;
     277B   88    A:++B;               Previous value multiplied by ten
     277C   16    D:=00;
     277E   59    E:=C;
     277F   19    HL:+DE;
     2780   8A    A:++D;               New digit added in
     2781   E3    HL:=:ST;
     2782   F5    ST:=AF;              New value of mantissa on stack
     2783   7C    A:=H;
     2784   A7    A:&A;                Decimal point marker
     2785   CA    JZ2763;              If no marker loop back for next character
     2788   2D    L:-1;                If marker take one from decimal exponent
     2789   C3    J2763;               Loop back for next character
```

```
     G2800
     278C   FE    A-FE;                    (continuation of f.p. read)
     278E   C2    JNZ2795;                 Jump to 2795 if terminator not decimal point
     2791   24    H:+1;            ⎫       Set decimal point marker, and continue reading of mantissa
     2792   C3    J2763;           ⎭
     2795   45    B::=L;                   Negative count of d.p. in mantissa
     2796   F1    AF:=ST;
     2797   E1    HL::=ST;
     2798   C5    ST::=BC;
     2799   06    B::=16;
     279B   CD    JS25A3;                  Normalize
     279E   50    D::=B;
     279F   5F    E::=A;
     27A0   D5    ST::=DE;
     27A1   E5    ST::=HL;                 Mantissa stacked as f.p. integer
     27A2   CD    JSOE74;                  A:=in decimal integer    (exponent)
     27A5   E1    HL::=ST;
     27A6   D1    DE::=ST;
     27A7   C1    BC::=ST;
     27A8   80    A:+B;                    Exponent less number of d.p. in mantissa
     27A9   01    BC::=27DF;               Location of values of powers of ten
     27AC   E5    ST::=HL;
     27AD   26    H::=00;
     27AF   A7    A:&A;
     27B0   F2    JNN27B6;
     27B3   2F    A:#;
     27B4   3C    A:+1;
     27B5   25    H:-1;                    Sign and modulus of exponent separated
     27B6   0F    A:@R;                    Next bit of modulus to K
     27B7   D2    JNK27D0;                 Skip to 27D0 if zero bit
     27BA   6F    L::=A;
     27BB   7C    A::=H;
     27BC   E3    HL::=:ST;
     27BD   A7    A:&A;
     27BE   C5    ST::=BC;
     27BF   F4    JSNN264B;                If positive exponent, multiply
     27C2   C1    BC::=ST;
     27C3   E3    HL::=:ST;
     27C4   7C    A::=H;
     27C5   E3    HL::=:ST;
     27C6   A7    A:&A;
     27C7   C5    ST::=BC;
     27C8   FC    JSN26EC;                 If negative exponent, divide
     27CB   C1    BC::=ST;
     27CC   E3    HL::=:ST;
     27CD   7D    A::=L;
     27CE   E6    A:&7F;
     27D0   03    BC:+1;                   BC:+4 for next higher power of 10
     27D1   03    BC:+1;
     27D2   03    BC:+1;
     27D3   03    BC:+1;
     27D4   A7    A:&A;
     27D5   C2    JNZ27B6;                 Loop back if bits remain in exponent
     27D8   E1    HL::=ST;
     27D9   F1    AF::=ST;
     27DA   A7    A:&A;                    Sign for mantissa
     27DB   FC    JSN265B;                 If negative, f.p. negate
     27DE   C9    RET;
```

MONITOR

```
27DF   #00 00 28 04#        F.p. value of 10¹
27E3   #00 00 32 07#                     10²
27E7   #00 10 27 0E#                     10⁴
27EB   #08 AF 2F 1B#                     10⁸
27EF   #F2 86 23 36#                     10¹⁶
27F3   #6B 71 27 6B#                     10³²
```

```
G2800
27F7   FE   A-30;            (continuation of f.p. print)
27F9   CA   JZ27FD;
27FC   DF   JSS3;            Print non-zero tens digit of exponent
27FD   48   C:=B;
27FE   DF   JSS3;            Print units digit of exponent
27FF   C9   RET;
```

```
MONITOR
>
```

```
      G2800
      2800   D5    ST:=DE;          Program entry        'Disassembler'
      2801   E5    ST:=HL;                               Stack limiting addresses
      2802   7C    A:=H;
      2803   CD    JS0204;                               Print current address
      2806   7D    A:=L;
      2807   CD    JS0204;
      280A   0E    C:=20;
      280C   DF    JSS3;                                 Two spaces
      280D   DF    JSS3;
      280E   7E    A:=M;
      280F   CD    JS0204;                               Print I-byte
      2812   0E    C:=20;
      2814   DF    JSS3;                                 Two spaces
      2815   DF    JSS3;
      2816   7E    A:=M;                                 Recall I
      2817   87    A:+A;
      2818   DA    JK2821;
      281B   FA    JN2880;                               Jump to 2880 if I=01 . . . . . .
      281E   C3    J2960;                                Jump to 2960 if I=00 . . . . . .
      2821   FA    JN2A70;                               Jump to 2A70 if I=11 . . . . . .
      2824   C3    J28A3;                                Jump to 28A3 if I=10 . . . . . .
      2827   00    NULL;
      2828   06    B:=06;
      282A   11    DE:=0406;        282B   06   B:=04
      282D   CD    JS005F;                               Print head string
      2830   E1    HL:=ST;
      2831   CD    JS286F;                               Print value of KJ
      2834   E5    ST:=HL;
      2835   C3    J284F;                                Skip to 284F
      2838   06    B:=02;
      283A   11    DE:=0306;        283B   06   B:=03
      283D   11    DE:=0406;        283E   06   B:=04
      2840   11    DE:=0506;        2841   06   B:=05
      2843   11    DE:=0606;        2844   06   B:=06
      2846   11    DE:=0706;        2847   06   B:=07
      2849   11    DE:=0806;        284A   06   B:=08
      284C   CD    JS005F;                               Print tail string
      284F   0E    C:=3B;                                Print semicolon
      2851   DF    JSS3;
      2852   CD    JS0200;                               New line
      2855   E1    HL:=ST;
      2856   23    HL:+1;                                Increment addressing register
      2857   D1    DE:=ST;
      2858   D5    ST:=DE;
      2859   CD    JS0231;                           } Compare addresses and loop back until finished
      285C   FA    JN2801;                           }
      285F   CF    JSS1;                                 Call monitor

      MONITOR
      >
```

```
    G2800
    2860   11    DE:=2867;        Entry 'Find name of register'
    2863   83    A:+E;
    2864   5F    E:=A;
    2865   1A    A:=M[DE];
    2866   C9    RET;

    MONITOR
    >

    2867   "BCDEHLMA"

    G2800
    286F   23    HL:+1;           Entry 'Print value of KJ'
    2870   5E    E:=M;
    2871   23    HL:+1;
    2872   7E    A:=M;
    2873   CD    JS0204;
    2876   7B    A:=E;
    2877   CD    JS0204;
    287A   C9    RET;
    287B   00    NULL;

    MONITOR
    >

    287C   "HALT"

    G2800
    2880   47    B:=A;            (I=01 . . . . . .)
    2881   FE    A-EC;            (EC=2×76)
    2883   CA    JZ28FA;          Jump to 28FA for 'HALT'
    2886   E6    A:&70;           Otherwise instruction is 'r₁:=r₂'
    2888   0F    A:@R;
    2889   0F    A:@R;
    288A   0F    A:@R;
    288B   0F    A:@R;
    288C   CD    JS2860;          Find name of r₁
    288F   4F    C:=A;
    2890   DF    JSS3;            Print name of r₁
    2891   0E    C:=3A;
    2893   DF    JSS3;            Print ':='
    2894   0E    C:=3D;
    2896   DF    JSS3;
    2897   78    A:=B;
    2898   E6    A:&0E;
    289A   0F    A:@R;
    289B   CD    JS2860;          Find name of r₂
    289E   4F    C:=A;
    289F   DF    JSS3;            Print name of r₂
    28A0   C3    J284F;           Jump back to main loop
    28A3   47    B:=A;            (I=10 . . . . . .) Instruction is 'Aopr'
    28A4   0E    C:=41;
    28A6   DF    JSS3;            Print 'A'
    28A7   CD    JS2900;          Find and print symbols for op
    28AA   78    A:=B;
    28AB   C3    J2898;           Jump to 2898 to deal with r as for r₂
    28AE   00    NULL;
    28AF   00    NULL;

    MONITOR
    >
```

```
28B0    "NULLA:=M[BC]:=A:"
28C0    "=M[DE]:=A:$DECA:"
28D0    "@LA:@RAK:@LAK:@R"
28E0    "K:#]:=HL:=MM[:+1"
28F0    ":-1HL:+"


G2800
28F7    00    NULL;
28F8    00    NULL;
28F9    00    NULL;
28FA    21    HL:=287C;  ⎫  Location of 'HALT', to be printed as tail string
28FD    C3    J283E;     ⎭
2900    CD    JS2905;       Entry 'Find and print symbols for op'
2903    DF    JSS3;
2904    C9    RET;
2905    78    A:=E;         Entry of main part of 'find . . . op'
2906    E6    A:&70;
2908    FE    A-70;
290A    0E    C:=2D;
290C    C8    RZ;           Return with '−'
290D    0E    C:=3A;
290F    DF    JSS3;         Print ':'
2910    78    A:=B;
2911    F6    A:&70;
2913    0F    A:@R;         Mask out and shift down 'op'
2914    0F    A:@R;
2915    0F    A:@R;
2916    0F    A:@R;
2917    0E    C:=2B;
2919    C8    RZ;           Return with '+'
291A    3D    A:-1;
291B    C2    JNZ2920;      Skip to 2920 if not '++'
291E    DF    JSS3;      ⎫  If '++' print '+' and return with '+'
291F    C9    RET;       ⎭
2920    0E    C:=2D;
2922    3D    A:-1;
2923    C8    RZ;           Return with '−'
2924    3D    A:-1;
2925    C2    JNZ292A;      Skip to 292A if not '− −'
2928    DF    JSS3;      ⎫  If '− −' print '−' and return with '−'
2929    C9    RET;       ⎭
292A    0E    C:=26;
292C    3D    A:-1;
292D    C8    RZ;           Return with '&'
292F    0E    C:=23;
2930    3D    A:-1;
2931    C8    RZ;           Return with '#'
2932    0E    C:=55;
2934    C9    RET;          Return with 'U'
2935    00    NULL;


MONITOR
 >
```

```
       G2800
       2936   11   DE:=5053;        Entry 'ordinary register pair'
       2939   CD   JS2940;          Find name of register pair
       293C   DF   JSS3;
       293D   48   C:=B;            Print name of register pair
       293E   DF   JSS3;
       293F   C9   RET;
       2940   01   BC:=4342;        Entry 'Find name of register pair'
       2943   E6   A:&30;
       2945   C8   RZ;                    Return with 'BC'
       2946   01   BC:=4544;
       2949   FE   A-10;
       294B   C8   RZ;                    Return with 'DE'
       294C   01   BC:=4C48;
       294F   FE   A-20;
       2951   C8   RZ;                    Return with 'HL'
       2952   42   B:=D;
       2953   4B   C:=E;
       2954   C9   RET;                   Return with 'SP' or 'AF'
       2955   78   A:=B;            Entry 'Stacking register pair'
       2956   11   DE:=4641;        'AF' instead of 'SP'
       2959   C3   J2939;
```

```
MONITOR
>
```

```
       295C   "ZKPN"
```

```
  G2800
  2960   0F    A:@R;                    (I=00 . . . . . .)
  2961   47    B:=A;
  2962   5F    E:=A;
  2963   21    HL:=28B0;
  2966   A7    A:&A;
  2967   CA    JZ283E;          For hex. 00 print 'NULL'
  296A   2E    L:=B7;
  296C   FE    A-02;
  296E   CA    JZ284A;          For 02 print 'A:=M[BC]'
  2971   2E    L:=B4;
  2973   FE    A-0A;
  2975   CA    JZ284A;          For 0A print 'M[BC]:=A'
  2978   2E    L:=C1;
  297A   FE    A-12;            For 12 print 'A:=M[DE]'
  297C   CA    JZ284A;
  297F   2E    L:=BE;
  2981   FE    A-1A;
  2983   CA    JZ284A;          For 1A print 'M[DE]:=A'
  2986   2E    L:=C8;
  2988   FE    A-2F;
  298A   CA    JZ283B;          For 2F print 'A:≠'
  298D   2E    L:=CB;
  298F   FE    A-27;
  2991   CA    JZ283B;          For 27 print 'DEC'
  2994   2E    L:=CE;
  2996   FE    A-07;
  2998   CA    JZ283E;          For 07 print 'A:@L'
  299B   2E    L:=D2;
  299D   FE    A-0F;
  299F   CA    JZ283E;          For 0F print 'A:@R'
  29A2   2E    L:=D6;
  29A4   FE    A-17;
  29A6   CA    JZ2841;          For 17 print 'AK:@L'
  29A9   2E    L:=DB;
  29AB   FE    A-1F;
  29AD   CA    JZ2841;          For 1F print 'AK:@R'
  29B0   2E    L:=E0;
  29B2   FE    A-3F;
  29B4   CA    JZ283B;          For 3F print 'K:≠'
  29B7   FE    A-32;
  29B9   C2    JNZ29CA;         For other than 32 skip to 29CA
  29BC   0F    C:=4D;           (I=32 hex.) Print 'M'
  29BF   DF    JSS3;
  29BF   E1    HL:=ST;
  29C0   CD    JS286F;          Print value of KJ
  29C3   E5    ST:=HL;
  29C4   21    HL:=28BC; ⎫
  29C7   C3    J283B;    ⎭      Location of ':=A' to be printed as tail string
```

  MONITOR
  >

```
        G2800
        29CA   2E   L:=B4;                (continuation for I=00 . . . . . .)
        29CC   FE   A-3A;
        29CE   CA   JZ282B;               For 3A head string is 'A:=M'
        29D1   FE   A-22;
        29D3   C2   JNZ29E8;              For other than 22 skip to 29E8
        29D6   2E   L:=EA;                (I=22 hex.)
        29D8   06   B:=02;
        29DA   CD   JS005F;               Print 'MM'
        29DD   E1   HL:=ST;
        29DE   CD   JS286F;               Print value of KJ
        29E1   E5   ST:=HL;
        29E2   21   HL:=28E4; ⎫
        29E5   C3   J283E;    ⎬           Location of ':=HL' to be printed as tail string
                             ⎭
        29E8   FE   A-2A;
        29EA   C2   JNZ2B72;              For other than 2A jump to 2B72
        29ED   2E   L:=E6;
        29EF   06   B:=06;
        29F1   C3   J282D;                For 2A head string is 'HL:=MM'
        29F4   E6   A:&04;
        29F6   CA   JZ2A21;               If a register-pair instruction, jump to 2A21
        29F9   78   A:=B;                 (I=00 . . . 1 . . .)
        29FA   E6   A:&38;
        29FC   0F   A:@R;                 Mask out and shift down 'r'
        29FD   0F   A:@R;
        29FE   0F   A:@R;
        29FF   CD   JS2860;               Find name of register
        2A02   4F   C:=A;
        2A03   DF   JSS3;                 Print name of register
        2A04   78   A:=B;
        2A05   0F   A:@R;
        2A06   2E   L:=F0;  ⎫             For I=00 . . . 101 tail string is ':−1'
        2A08   DA   JK283B; ⎭
        2A0B   0F   A:@R;
        2A0C   2E   L:=ED;  ⎫             For I=00 . . . 100 tail string is ':+1'
        2A0E   D2   JNK283B;⎭
        2A11   0E   C:=3A;                (I=00 . . . 110)
        2A13   DF   JSS3;                 Print ':='
        2A14   0E   C:=3D;
        2A16   DF   JSS3;
        2A17   E1   HL:=ST;               Fetch and print J-byte
        2A18   23   HL:+1;
        2A19   7E   A:=M;
        2A1A   E5   ST:=HL;
        2A1B   CD   JS0204;
        2A1E   C3   J284F;                Jump back to main loop
        MONITOR
        >
```

```
      G2800
      2A21   68    L:=B;                    (I=00 ... 0.1)
      2A22   78    A:=B;
      2A23   E6    A:&0F;
      2A25   FE    A-09;
      2A27   C2    JNZ2A38;                 If not double-length add, skip to 2A38
      2A2A   2E    L:=F3;                   (I=00 ... 1001)
      2A2C   06    B:=04;
      2A2E   CD    JS005F;                  Print 'HL:+'
      2A31   7B    A:=E;
      2A32   CD    JS2936;                  Ordinary register pair
      2A35   C3    J284F;                   Jump back to main loop
      2A38   7D    A:=L;
      2A39   CD    JS2936;                  Ordinary register pair
      2A3C   7D    A:=L;
      2A3D   E6    A:&0F;
      2A3F   2E    L:=ED;
      2A41   FE    A-03;            ⎫
      2A43   CA    JZ283B;          ⎬       For I=00 ... 0011 tail string is ':+1'
      2A46   2E    L:=F0;           ⎭
      2A48   FE    A-0B;            ⎫
      2A4A   CA    JZ283B;          ⎬       For I=00 ... 1011 tail string is ':−1'
      2A4D   0E    C:=3A;           ⎭
      2A4F   DF    JSS3;
      2A50   0E    C:=3D;                   Print ':='
      2A52   DF    JSS3;
      2A53   C3    J2830;                   Jump back to print value of KJ
      2A56   78    A:=B;                    Entry 'Print name of condition'
      2A57   E6    A:&08;
      2A59   C2    JNZ2A5F;
      2A5C   0E    C:=4E;
      2A5F   DF    JSS3;                    Print 'N' for inverse condition
      2A5F   78    A:=B;
      2A60   E6    A:&30;
      2A62   0F    A:@R;
      2A63   0F    A:@R;
      2A64   0F    A:@R;
      2A65   0F    A:@R;
      2A66   11    DE:=295C;                Location of 'ZKPN'
      2A69   83    A:+E;
      2A6A   5F    E:=A;
      2A6B   1A    A:=M[DE];
      2A6C   4F    C:=A;
      2A6D   DF    JSS3;                    Print 'Z', 'K', 'P' or 'N'
      2A6E   C9    RET;
      2A6F   00    NULL;

      MONITOR
      >
```

```
        G2800
        2A70   1F   AK:@R;              (I=11 . . . . . .)
        2A71   47   B:=A;
        2A72   21   HL:=2B40;
        2A75   FE   A-F9;
        2A77   CA   JZ2844;             For hex. F9 print 'SP:=HL'
        2A7A   2E   L:=44;
        2A7C   FE   A-EB;
        2A7E   CA   JZ2847;             For EB print 'HL:=:DE'
        2A81   2E   L:=4B;
        2A83   FE   A-E3;
        2A85   CA   JZ2847;             For E3 print 'HL:=:ST'
        2A88   2E   L:=56;
        2A8A   FE   A-FB;
        2A8C   CA   JZ283E;             For FB print 'I:=1'
        2A8F   2E   L:=5A;
        2A91   FE   A-F3;
        2A93   CA   JZ283E;             For F3 print 'I:=0'
        2A96   2E   L:=5E;
        2A98   FE   A-E9;
        2A9A   CA   JZ2841;             For E9 print 'J[HL]'
        2A9D   2E   L:=63;
        2A9F   FE   A-C9;
        2AA1   CA   JZ283B;             For C9 print 'RET'
        2AA4   2E   L:=68;
        2AA6   FE   A-DB;
        2AA8   C2   JNZ2AB3;            For other than DB skip to 2AB3
        2AAB   06   B:=04;              (I=DB hex.)
        2AAD   CD   JS005F;             Print 'A:=G'
        2AB0   C3   J2A17;              Jump to 2A17 for J-byte
        2AB3   FE   A-D3;
        2AB5   C2   JNZ2AC8;            For other than D3 skip to 2AC8
        2AB8   0E   C:=47;              (I=D3 hex.)
        2ABA   DF   JSS3;               Print 'G'
        2ABB   E1   HL:=ST;
        2ABC   23   HL:+1;              Increment addressing register
        2ABD   7E   A:=M;               Fetch J-byte
        2ABE   F5   ST:=HL;
        2ABF   CD   JS0204;             Print value of J
        2AC2   21   HL:=2B66; ⎫
        2AC5   C3   J283B;    ⎬        Location of ':=A' to be printed as tail string
                              ⎭
        2AC8   0E   C:=4A;
        2ACA   FE   A-C3;
        2ACC   CA   JZ2AD7;             For C3 print 'J', and
        2ACF   FE   A-CD;
        2AD1   C2   JNZ2ADB;
        2AD4   DF   JSS3;                   for CD print 'JS', then
        2AD5   0E   C:=53;
        2AD7   DF   JSS3;
        2AD8   C3   J2830;                  jump to 2830 to print value of KJ
```

MONITOR
>

```
G2800
2ADB   E6   A:&07;
2ADD   C2   JNZ2AE9;
2AE0   0F   C:=52;              (conditional return)
2AE2   DF   JSS3;               Print 'R'
2AE3   CD   JS2A56;             Print name of condition
2AE6   C3   J284F;              Jump back to main loop
2AE9   3D   A:-1;
2AEA   C2   JNZ2AF6;
2AED   CD   JS2955;             Stacking register pair ('unstack' operation)
2AF0   21   HL:=2B52;    ⎫
                          ⎬     Location of ':=ST' to be printed as tail string
2AF3   C3   J283E;       ⎭
2AF6   3D   A:-1;
2AF7   C2   JNZ2B03;
2AFA   0E   C:=4A;              (conditional jump)
2AFC   DF   JSS3;               Print 'J'
2AFD   CD   JS2A56;             Print name of condition
2B00   C3   J2830;              Jump to 2830 to print value of KJ
2B03   3D   A:-1;
2B04   3D   A:-1;
2B05   C2   JNZ2B10;
2B08   0E   C:=4A;              (conditional subroutine call)
2B0A   DF   JSS3;
2B0B   0E   C:=53;              Print 'JS'
2B0D   C3   J2AFC;                  then proceed as for conditional jump
2B10   3D   A:-1;
2B11   C2   JNZ2B23;
2B14   2E   L:=50;              ('stack' operation)
2B16   C5   ST:=BC;
2B17   06   B:=04;
2B19   CD   JS005F;             Print 'ST:='
2B1C   C1   BC:=ST;
2B1D   CD   JS2955;             Stacking register pair
2B20   C3   J284F;              Jump back to main loop
2B23   3D   A:-1;
2B24   C2   JNZ2B33;
2B27   0E   C:=41;              (instruction of type AopJ)
2B29   DF   JSS3;               Print 'A'
2B2A   78   A:=B;
2B2B   87   A:+A;
2B2C   47   B:=A;
2B2D   CD   JS2900;             Find and print symbols for op
2B30   C3   J2A17;              Jump to 2A17 for J-byte
2B33   0E   C:=4A;              (special subroutine call)
2B35   DF   JSS3;               Print 'J'
2B36   0E   C:=53;
2B38   DF   JSS3;               Print 'SS'
2B39   DF   JSS3;
2B3A   78   A:=B;
2B3B   0F   A:@R;
2B3C   0F   A:@R;               Extract special subroutine number
2B3D   C3   J2B6C;
```

MONITOR
>

```
2B40    "SP:=HL:=:DEHL:=:"
2B50    "ST:=STI:=1I:=0JC"
2B60    "HLJRET:=A:=G"

  G2800
2B6C    0F    A:@R;                    (continued from 2B3D)
2B6D    E6    A:&37;                   Extracted in ASCII form (!)
2B6F    C3    J289E;                   Jump to 289E to print and rejoin main loop
2B72    FE    A-37;                    (continued from 29EA)
2B74    C2    JNZ29F4;                 For other than 37 jump to 29F4
2B77    0E    C:=4B;                   (I=37 hex.)
2B79    DF    JSS3;                    Print 'K'
2B7A    21    HL:=2B57;
2B7D    C3    J283B;                   Tail string is ':=1'
```

MONITOR
>


```
  G2800
2B80    7B    A:=E;           Entry 'F.p. print (DEHL)' (F.p. print)
2B81    0F    C:=2B;
2B83    A7    A:&A;                    Sign of mantissa
2B84    F2    JNN2B8C;
2B87    CD    JS265B;                  F.p. negate
2B8A    0F.   C:=2D;
2B8C    DF    JSS3;                    Print sign
2B8D    97    A:-A;                    Set zero for decimal exponent
2B8E    F5    ST:=AF;
2B8F    7B    A:=E;
2B90    A7    A:&A;
2B91    CA    JZ2BDE;                  Skip to 2BDE if mantissa zero
2B94    7B    A:=E;
2B95    D6    A:-28;
2B97    7A    A:=D;
2B98    DE    A:--04;
2B9A    FA    JN2BA9;                  Jump to 2BA9 if value less than ten
2B9D    01    BC:=27DF;                Location of value of ten
2BA0    CD    JS26EC;                  F.p. divide
2BA3    F1    AF:=ST;
2BA4    3C    A:+1;                    Add one to decimal exponent
2BA5    F5    ST:=AF;
2BA6    C3    J2B94;                   Loop back to 2B94
2BA9    7B    A:=E;
2BAA    D6    A:-20;
2BAC    7A    A:=D;
2BAD    DE    A:--01;
2BAF    F2    JNN2BBE;                 Jump to 2BBE if value not less than one
2BB2    01    BC:=27DF;                Location of value of ten
2BB5    CD    JS264B;                  F.p. multiply
2BB8    F1    AF:=ST;
2BB9    3D    A:-1;                    Subtract one from decimal exponent
2BBA    F5    ST:=AF;
2BBB    C3    J2BA9;                   Loop back to 2BA9
```

MONITOR
>

```
      G2800
      2BBE   7A    A:=D;                    (continuation of f.p. print)
      2BBF   3C    A:+1;
      2BC0   16    D:=00;
      2BC2   EB    HL:=:DE;                 Shift up DEHL
      2BC3   29    HL:+HL;
      2BC4   EB    HL:=:DE;
      2BC5   29    HL:+HL;
      2BC6   D2    JNK2BCA;
      2BC9   13    DE:+1;
      2BCA   3D    A:-1;                    Count down A
      2BCB   F2    JNN2BC2;                 Loop back to 2BC2
      2BCF   01    BC:=0054;                Decimal round-off (hex. 00.000054=½×10⁻⁵)
      2BD1   09    HL:+BC;
      2BD2   D2    JNK2BD6;
      2BD5   13    DE:+1;
      2BD6   4D    C:=L;
      2BD7   09    HL:+BC;
      2BD8   D2    JNK2BDC;
      2BDB   13    DE:+1;
      2BDC   6C    L:=H;
      2BDD   63    H:=E;                    HL is fractional part of mantissa
      2BDE   7A    A:=D;                    A is integral part of mantissa
      2BDF   FE    A-0A;
      2BE1   CA    JZ2BE9;
      2BE4   F7    JSS6;                    Hex.–ASCII
      2BE5   4F    C:=A;
      2BE6   C3    J2BED;
      2BE9   0E    C:=31;
      2BEB   DF    JSS3;
      2BEC   0D    C:-1;
      2BED   DF    JSS3;                    Integral part of mantissa printed
      2BEF   CD    JS07E6;                  Print fractional part of mantissa
      2BF1   0E    C:=45;
      2BF3   DF    JSS3;                    Print 'E'
      2BF4   F1    AF:=ST;
      2BF5   F2    JNN262C;                 Skip to 262C if exponent is positive
      2BF8   F5    ST:=AF;
      2BF9   0E    C:=2D;
      2BFB   DF    JSS3;                    Print '–'
      2BFC   F1    AF:=ST;
      2BFD   C3    J262A;                   Jump to 262A to continue
```

(Integral part of mantissa may be 10 as a result of rounding)

MONITOR
>

8.9   HEXADECIMAL TEXT OF SOFTWARE

```
D0000,01FF
0000 3E CF D3 FB 3E 27 D3 FB 22 FA 17 F5 E1 C3 67 00
0010 41 3E 1B B8 C3 50 00 00 C3 45 00 0E 0A DF 48 C9
0020 FF 4F D7 79 C9 00 00 00 D6 30 FE 0A F8 D6 07 C9
0030 C6 30 FE 3A F8 C6 07 C9 DB FB E6 02 CA 38 00 DB
0040 FA E6 7F 4F C9 DB FB E6 01 CA 45 00 79 D3 FA C9
0050 C2 55 00 0E 24 DF 3F 0D B8 CA 1B 00 48 C9 00 4E
0060 DF 23 05 C2 5F 00 C9 22 F8 17 E1 22 FC 17 21 00
0070 00 39 22 FE 17 60 69 22 F6 17 EB 22 F4 17 21 BA
0080 00 31 F4 17 CD F6 03 31 F4 17 CD 00 02 0E 3E DF
0090 E7 FF 44 CA 33 01 FE 47 CA C4 00 FE 49 CA E3 00
00A0 FE 4D CA 80 01 FF 52 CA CA 00 FE 53 CA 06 01 FE
00B0 58 CA 15 02 0E 3F DF C3 87 00 0D 0A 4D 4F 4E 49
00C0 54 4F 52 1B CD F7 01 22 FC 17 F3 CD 00 02 31 F4
00D0 17 D1 C1 F1 2A FE 17 F9 2A FC 17 E5 2A FA 17 FB
00E0 C9 00 00 CD F7 01 CD 00 02 E7 FE 20 CA E9 00 FE
00F0 2C CA E9 00 FE 0D CA E9 00 FE 1B CA 87 00 CD 21
0100 02 77 23 C3 E9 00 CD F7 01 E7 FE 20 CA 14 01 FE
0110 2C C2 87 00 7E CD 04 02 0E 2D DF E7 47 EF FE 00
0120 FA 2E 01 FE 10 F2 2E 01 CD 25 02 77 E7 47 78 23
0130 C3 0A 01 CD F7 01 E5 E7 FE 20 CA 42 01 FE 2C C2
0140 B4 00 CD F7 01 D1 CD 31 02 FA B4 00 EB CD 00 02
0150 7C CD 04 02 7D CD 04 02 0E 20 DF 7E CD 04 02 DB
0160 FB E6 02 CA 6F 01 DB FA E6 7F FE 1B CA 87 00 CD
0170 31 02 CA 87 00 23 7D E6 0F C2 58 01 C3 4D 01 00
0180 CD F7 01 E5 E7 FE 20 CA 8F 01 FE 2C C2 B4 00 CD
0190 F7 01 D1 CD 31 02 FA B4 00 E5 D5 E7 FE 20 CA A6
01A0 01 FE 2C C2 B4 00 CD F7 01 E5 D1 E1 CD 31 02 FA
01B0 C4 01 42 4B D1 7E 02 C5 CD 31 02 C1 CA 87 00 03
01C0 23 C3 B5 01 EB 44 4D 7A 2F 67 7B 2F 6F 23 09 EB
01D0 E3 EB 19 44 4D E1 EB 7E 02 C5 CD 31 02 C1 CA 87
01E0 00 0B 2B C3 D7 01 FE 00 FA F1 01 FE 10 F2 F1 01
01F0 C9 C3 B4 00 C3 10 00 CD 20 02 67 CD 20 02 6F C9
>


D0200,03FF
0200 0E 0D D7 C9 47 0F 0F 0F 0F E6 0F F7 4F DF 78 E6
0210 0F F7 4F DF C9 CD 00 02 C3 45 02 C3 38 00 00 00
0220 E7 EF CD E6 01 87 87 87 57 E7 EF CD E6 01 82
0230 C9 44 4A 78 B9 C2 3D 02 45 4B 78 B9 C8 A9 FA 5A
0240 03 78 91 C9 00 06 28 21 EA 02 CD 5F 00 3A F8 17
0250 A7 CD 13 03 CD 13 03 CD 12 03 CD 12 03 CD 12 03
0260 0E 20 DF DF 3A F9 17 CD 04 02 21 F6 17 CD 2D 03
0270 21 F4 17 CD 2D 03 21 FA 17 CD 2D 03 21 FE 17 CD
0280 2D 03 21 FC 17 CD 2D 03 CD 00 02 E7 FE 20 CA B1
0290 02 FE 0D CA 87 00 CD 24 03 CD 22 03 CD 1F 03 CD
02A0 1F 03 82 82 87 3C CD 22 03 82 82 32 F8 17 C3 B5
02B0 02 DF DF DF DF 0E 20 DF DF E7 FE 20 CA C8 02 CD
02C0 21 02 32 F9 17 C3 C9 02 DF 21 F6 17 CD 3C 03 21
02D0 F4 17 CD 3C 03 21 FA 17 CD 3C 03 21 FE 17 CD 3C
02E0 03 21 FC 17 CD 3C 03 C3 87 00 4E 5A 48 50 4B 20
02F0 20 41 20 20 20 20 42 43 20 20 20 20 44 45 20 20
0300 20 20 48 4C 20 20 20 20 53 50 20 20 20 20 50 43
0310 0D 0A 87 47 3E 30 F2 1A 03 3C 4F DF 78 87 C9 82
0320 82 87 57 E7 D6 30 C8 FE 01 C8 C3 B4 00 0E 20 DF
0330 DF 23 7E CD 04 02 2B 7E CD 04 02 C9 0E 20 DF DF
0340 E7 FE 20 CA 56 03 FE 0D CA 87 00 CD 21 02 23 77
0350 CD 20 02 2B 77 C9 DF DF DF C9 79 F6 7F C9 00 00
0360 CD D1 03 DB F4 3C C2 B6 03 CD E4 03 CA 63 03 3E
0370 88 D3 F7 3E 01 D3 F5 21 00 10 E5 06 C8 3E 04 CD
0380 DD 03 E1 E5 7E D3 F4 00 00 3E 02 D3 F6 3E 35 3D
0390 C2 8F 03 D3 F6 CD E3 03 CA 84 03 05 C2 7D 03 3E
03A0 98 D3 F7 E1 DB F4 BE C2 BB 03 CD E3 03 C2 A4 03
03B0 76 00 00 00 00 00 3E 02 D3 F5 76 3E 04 D3 F5 CF
03C0 00 CD D1 03 21 00 10 DD F4 77 CD E3 03 CA C7 03
03D0 CF 3E 98 D3 F7 3E 04 CD DD 03 C9 3E 01 D3 F6 97
03E0 D3 F6 C9 23 CD DB 03 DB F6 E6 10 C9 FF 77 FE 1B
03F0 C8 DF 23 C3 EC 03 4E 79 FE 1B C8 DF 23 C3 F6 03
>
```

```
    D0400,05FF
0400 21 80 11 22 10 10 21 00 10 16 0E CD 1B 02 FE 20
0410 CA 0B 04 FE 0A CA 0B 04 FE 7F CA 31 04 FE 3B CA
0420 3E 04 FE 0D CA 3E 04 77 23 4F CD F4 01 15 C2 0B
0430 04 0E 3F CD F4 01 0E 0D CD F4 01 C3 06 04 36 FF
0440 0E 3B CD F4 01 7A C6 05 57 0E 20 CD F4 01 15 C2
0450 49 04 21 00 10 C3 20 0C C5 C3 86 04 00 00 00 00
0460 CA 75 04 3E 00 47 5F CD 58 04 78 CD 58 04 7B C3
0470 7A 04 CD 58 04 78 C3 7A 04 81 CD 58 04 23 7E 3C
0480 C2 31 04 C3 36 04 E5 2A 10 10 77 23 22 10 10 E1
0490 CD 04 02 0E 20 C9 00 3E 3C C3 7A 04
04A0 7E FE 41 C2 80 05 23 7E FE 3A CA D1 09 C3 B8 09
04B0 79 FE FF CA 63 04 FE 08 CA F1 04 59 CD 1B 0B 47
04C0 79 FE FF CA 63 04 FE 08 CA E8 04 FE 09 CA D9 04
04D0 7B 87 87 87 C6 80 C3 79 04 7B FE 00 CA 9B 04 FE
04E0 02 06 3D C3 60 04 00 00 7B 87 87 87 C6 C6 C3 72
04F0 04 CD 1B 0B 47 FE 47 CA 28 05 79 FE 08 C2 05 05
0500 3E 3E C3 72 04 FE FF CA 0F 05 3E 78 C3 79 04 23
0510 7E FE FF C2 1A 05 2B C3 0A 05 FE 5B CA 32 05 CD
0520 80 0B 47 3E 3A C3 67 04 23 CD 60 0B 47 3E DB C3
0530 72 04 23 7E FE 42 CA 4E 05 FE 44 C2 63 04 23 7E
0540 FE 45 C2 63 04 06 1A 23 7E FE 5D C3 60 04 23 7E
0550 FE 43 C2 63 04 06 0A C3 47 05 23 7E FE 3A C2 63
0560 04 23 7E FE 3D C2 63 04 23 7E FE 53 C2 63 04 23
0570 7E FE 54 06 F1 C3 60 04 FE 43 06 27 C3 60 04 00
0580 FE 42 C2 05 06 23 7E FE 43 CA CE 05 1E 40 FE 3A
0590 C2 63 04 23 7E FE 2B CA BD 05 FE 2D CA C3 05 FE
05A0 3D C2 63 04 CD 1B 0B 47 79 FE 08 C2 B4 05 7B C6
05B0 C6 C3 72 04 E6 F8 C2 63 04 7B C3 79 04 7B C6 C4
05C0 C3 C6 05 7B C6 C5 47 23 7E FE 31 C3 60 04 23 7E
05D0 FE 3A C2 63 04 0E 00 23 7E FE 2B CA 60 09 FE 2D
05E0 CA 66 09 FE 3D C2 63 04 23 7E FE 53 CA F8 05 0C
05F0 C3 64 07 79 3C C3 67 04 23 7E FE 54 C2 63 04 79
>
```

```
    D0600,07FF
0600 C6 C1 C3 7A 04 FE 43 C2 11 06 23 7E 1E 48 C3 8E
0610 05 FE 44 C2 2E 06 23 7E FE 45 CA 22 06 1E 50 C3
0620 8E 05 23 7E FE 3A C2 78 05 0E 10 C3 D7 05 FE 47
0630 C2 4F 06 23 CD 60 0B 47 23 7E FE 3A C2 63 04 23
0640 7E FE 3D C2 63 04 23 7E FE 41 3E D3 CA 72 04 FE
0650 48 C2 20 07 23 7E FE 3A C2 60 06 1E 60 C3 93 05
0660 FE 4C C2 87 09 23 7E FE 3A C2 63 04 23 7E FE 2D
0670 CA BC 06 FE 2B C2 C5 06 23 7E FE 31 C2 84 06 3E
0680 23 C3 7A 04 FE 42 C2 92 06 23 7E FE 43 06 09 C3
0690 60 04 FE 44 C2 A0 06 23 7E FE 45 06 19 C3 60 04
06A0 FE 48 C2 AE 06 23 7E FE 4C 06 29 C3 60 04 FE 53
06B0 C2 63 04 23 7E FE 50 06 39 C3 60 04 23 7E FE 31
06C0 06 2B C3 60 04 FE 3D C2 63 04 23 7E FE 3A C2 EF
06D0 06 23 7E FE 53 C2 E1 06 23 7E FE 54 06 E3 C3 60
06E0 04 FE 44 C2 63 04 23 7E FE 45 06 EB C3 60 04 FE
06F0 53 C2 00 07 23 7E FE 54 06 E1 C3 60 04 00 00 00
0700 FE 4D C2 16 07 23 7E FE 4D C2 63 04 23 CD 80 0B
0710 47 3E 2A C3 67 04 CD 80 0B 47 3E 21 C3 67 04 00
0720 FE 49 C2 46 07 23 7E FE 3A C2 63 04 23 7E FE 3D
0730 C2 63 04 23 7E FE 30 C2 3F 07 3E F3 C3 7A 04 FE
0740 31 06 FB C3 60 04 FE 4A C2 C2 07 23 7E FE 53 C2
0750 8B 07 23 7E CD C0 0B 79 FE FF CA 6C 07 87 87 87
0760 C6 C4 4F 23 C5 CD 80 0B C1 C3 DE 07 7E FE 53 C2
0770 83 07 23 7E D6 30 FE 08 F2 63 04 87 87 87 C6 C7
0780 C3 7A 04 0E 0E C3 64 07 00 00 00 CD C0 0B 79 FE
0790 FF CA 9C 07 87 87 87 C6 C2 C3 62 07 7E FE 5B CA
07A0 AB 07 CD 80 0B 47 3E C3 C3 67 04 23 7E FE 48 C2
07B0 63 04 23 7E FE 4C C2 63 04 23 7E FE 5D 06 E9 C3
07C0 60 04 FE 4B C2 9E 0D 23 7E FE 3A C2 63 04 23 7E
07D0 FE 3D C2 80 09 23 7E FE 31 06 37 C3 60 04 47 79
07E0 C3 67 04 00 00 00 06 05 0E 2E DF 97 29 8F 4F 54
07F0 5D 29 8F 29 8F 19 89 C6 30 4F DF 05 C2 EB 07 C9
>
```

```
D0800,09FF
0800  3E 70 C3 93 05 FE 5B C2 47 08 23 7E FE 42 C2 1D
0810  08 23 7E FE 43 C2 63 04 06 02 C3 2B 08 FE 44 C2
0820  63 04 23 7E FE 45 C2 63 04 06 12 23 7E FE 5D C2
0830  63 04 23 7E FE 3A C2 63 04 23 7E FE 3D C2 63 04
0840  23 7E FE 41 C3 60 04 FE 4D C2 72 08 23 CD 80 0B
0850  47 23 7E FE 3A C2 63 04 23 7E FE 3D C2 63 04 23
0860  7E FE 48 C2 63 04 23 7E FE 4C C2 63 04 3E 22 C3
0870  67 04 CD 80 0B 47 23 7E FE 3A C2 63 04 23 7E FE
0880  3D C2 63 04 23 7E FE 41 C2 63 04 3E 32 C3 67 04
0890  FE 52 C2 C2 08 23 7E FE FF C2 A2 08 3E C9 2B C3
08A0  7A 04 CD C0 0B 79 FE FF CA B3 08 87 87 87 C6 C0
08B0  C3 7A 04 7E FE 45 C2 63 04 23 7E FE 54 06 C9 C3
08C0  60 04 FE 53 C2 71 09 23 7E FE 50 C2 0D 09 23 7E
08D0  FE 3A C2 63 04 23 7E FE 3D C2 F5 08 23 7E FE 48
08E0  C2 EC 08 23 7E FE 4C 06 F9 C3 60 04 CD 80 0B 47
08F0  3E 31 C3 67 04 FE 2B C2 FF 08 06 33 C3 06 09 FE
0900  2D C2 63 04 06 3B 23 7E FE 31 C3 60 04 FE 54 C2
0910  63 04 23 7E FE 3A C2 63 04 23 7E FE 3D C2 63 04
0920  23 7E FE 42 C2 30 09 23 7E FE 43 06 C5 C3 60 04
0930  FE 44 C2 3E 09 23 7E FE 45 06 D5 C3 60 04 FE 48
0940  C2 4C 09 23 7E FE 4C 06 E5 C3 60 04 FE 41 C2 63
0950  04 23 7E FE 46 06 F5 C3 60 04 D1 C3 BB 0A 00 00
0960  79 C6 03 C3 69 09 79 C6 0B 47 23 7E FE 31 C3 60
0970  04 FE 45 C2 9C 09 23 7E 1E 58 C3 8E 05 00 00 00
0980  FE 23 06 3F C3 60 04 FE 41 C2 63 04 23 7E FE 4C
0990  C2 63 04 23 7E FE 54 06 76 C3 60 04 FE 4E C2 F8
09A0  0C 23 7E FE 55 C2 63 04 23 7E FE 4C C2 63 04 23
09B0  7E FE 4C 06 00 C3 60 04 FE 46 CA 5A 05 FE 4B C2
09C0  E5 09 23 7E FE 3A C2 63 04 23 7E 01 1F 17 C3 EE
09D0  09 23 7E FE 23 C2 EB 09 23 7E 2B 3C C2 E4 09 3E
09E0  2F C3 7A 04 2B CD 20 0B C3 B0 04 01 0F 07 FE 40
09F0  C2 E4 09 23 7E FE 4C CA 75 04 FE 52 41 C3 60 04
>
```

```
D0A00,0BFF
0A00  CD 60 0B 5F 23 CD 60 0B C9 FE 00 FA 12 0A CD 00
0A10  0A C9 79 FE 28 C2 63 04 23 7E FE 4C C2 56 0A 23
0A20  CD 60 0B E5 26 00 6F 4F 29 EB 21 40 10 19 5E 23
0A30  56 7B FE 00 C2 3D 0A 7A FE 00 CA 40 0A C3 B3 0A
0A40  2A 10 10 23 EB 2A 12 10 71 23 73 23 72 23 22 12
0A50  10 16 FD C3 B3 0A FE 58 C2 C0 0A 23 7E 4F CD 00
0A60  0B 78 FE 00 FA 63 04 E5 CA 85 0A 21 1E 10 5F 16
0A70  00 19 19 4E 23 46 60 69 EB E1 D5 23 7E FE 29 C2
0A80  8B 0A C3 5A 09 21 00 10 C3 78 0A FE 2B C2 95 0A
0A90  0E 00 C3 9C 0A FE 2D C2 63 04 0E 01 23 CD 60 0B
0AA0  E3 5F 16 00 79 FE 00 CA B1 0A 7A 2F 57 7B 2F 5F
0AB0  13 19 EB E1 23 7E FE 29 C2 63 04 7B 5A C9 00 00
0AC0  FE 49 C2 63 04 23 7E FE 2B C2 D1 0A 0E 00 C3 D8
0AD0  0A FE 2D C2 63 04 0E 01 23 CD 60 0B E5 5F 16 00
0AE0  79 FE 00 CA ED 0A 7A 2F 57 7B 2F 5F 13 2A 3E 10
0AF0  19 EB 2A 10 10 19 23 23 23 11 80 EE 19 C3 B2 0A
0B00  D6 30 FA 14 0B FE 0A FA 19 0B D6 11 FA 14 0B FE
0B10  06 FA 17 0B 06 FF C9 C6 0A 47 C9 23 23 C3 89 0B
0B20  0E 00 7E FE 3A CA 2F 0B FF 2D CA 52 0B 0D C9 23
0B30  7E FE 2B CA 55 0B 0C 0C FE 2D CA 55 0B 0C 0C FE
0B40  26 C8 0C FE 23 C8 0C FE 55 C8 0C FE 3D C8 0E
0B50  FF C9 0E 07 C9 47 23 7E B8 C2 5E 0B 0C C9 2B C9
0B60  7E CD 00 0B 78 3C CA 7B 0B 50 23 7E CD 00 0B 78
0B70  3C CA 7B 0B 7A 87 87 87 80 C9 0E FF 7D C9 00
0B80  7E 4F CD 00 0B 78 C3 09 0A 7E FE FF 2B C2 B6 0B
0B90  7E 0E 00 D6 42 C8 0C 3D C8 0C 3D C8 0C 3D C8 0C
0BA0  D6 03 C8 0C D6 04 C8 0C 3D C8 0C C6 0C C8 0C 0C
0BB0  C6 10 C8 0E FF C9 0E 07 C9 0E 00 CD 60 0B C9 00 00 00
0BC0  FE 4E C2 85 0D 0E 07 23 7E FE 47 F2 D0 0B 2B C9
0BD0  0D FE 4E C8 0D 0D FE 50 C8 0D 0D FE 4B C3 97 0D
0BE0  26 30 EB 3E 0E C5 D5 CD 9E 0F D1 C1 19 CD F1 0F
0BF0  CD 1A 0C C8 E5 CD F1 0C 23 7C B5 E1 C2 E2 0B C9
>
```

```
DOCC0,ODFF
0C00  06 00 21 20 10 70 23 7D FE C0 C2 05 0C 78 32 14
0C10  10 21 C0 10 22 12 10 C3 00 04 C5 CD 31 02 C1 C9
0C20  3A 14 10 FE 00 C2 8A 0C 7E FE 58 C2 59 0C 23 7E
0C30  CD 00 0B 78 FE 00 FA 63 04 E5 26 00 6F 29 EB 21
0C40  20 10 19 E3 23 7E FE 3A C2 63 04 23 CD 60 0B E3
0C50  77 23 3E 00 77 E1 C3 7D 04 3E 01 32 14 10 E5 2A
0C60  20 10 EB 21 00 10 19 22 20 10 21 20 10 4E 23 46
0C70  23 5E 23 56 EB 09 EB 72 2B 73 7C FE 10 C2 6D 0C
0C80  7D FE 3E C2 6D 0C E1 C3 A0 04 7E FE 58 CA 63 04
0C90  C3 A1 04 CD 60 0B FE 40 F2 63 04 E5 2A 3E 10 EB
0CA0  2A 10 10 19 EB 21 80 EE 19 EB 06 00 4F 21 40 10
0CB0  09 09 73 23 72 E1 23 7E FE 3A C2 63 04 23 C3 A0
0CC0  04 21 C0 10 3A 12 10 BE C2 D2 0C 3A 13 10 BC CA
0CD0  FE 0C 7E E5 26 00 6F 29 EB 21 40 10 19 5E 23 56
0CE0  E1 23 4F 23 46 7B 02 03 7A 02 23 C3 C4 0C CF 00
0CF0  00 7D 93 6F 7C 9A 67 C9 FE 46 C2 00 0D C3 C1 0C
0D00  FE 56 C2 93 0C CD 00 02 CD 66 0D FE 22 C2 1E 0D
0D10  CD 66 0D FE 22 CA 36 04 CD 59 0D C3 10 0D FE 23
0D20  C2 63 04 CD 66 0D CD 00 0B 78 FE 00 FA 63 04 87
0D30  87 87 87 57 CD 66 0D CD 00 0B 78 FE 00 FA 63 04
0D40  82 CD 59 0D CD 66 0D FE 20 CA 44 0D FE 0D CA 44
0D50  0D FE 23 C2 26 0D C3 36 04 C5 E5 2A 10 10 77 23
0D60  22 10 10 E1 C1 C9 CD 1E 02 4F CD F4 01 79 C9 C5
0D70  D5 44 4D 78 E6 C0 C2 B4 00 CD E0 0B 29 D1 C1 C9
0D80  00 00 00 00 0C 0E 05 FE 50 C8 0D 0D FE 4B C8 0D
0D90  0D FE 5A C8 0D 0D C9 C8 0D 0D C3 C5 0D 00 FE 4C
0DA0  C2 AA 0D 23 7E 1E 68 C3 8E 05 FE 4D C2 90 0D 23
0DB0  7E FE 3A C2 05 08 23 23 7E FE 4D CA 63 04 2B 2B
0DC0  1E 70 C3 93 05 FE 5A C8 0D C9 16 2B 7C FE 80 C2
0DD0  D9 0D 7D FE 00 CA 4E 0E 7C FE 00 F2 E6 0D 14 14
0DE0  2F 67 7D 2F 6F 23 01 F0 D8 CD 5D 0E 01 10 27 09
0DF0  7B FE 30 C2 F9 0D 5A 16 20 D5 01 18 FC CD 5D 0E
>

DOE00,OFFF
0E00  01 E8 03 09 53 01 9C FF CD 5D 0E 01 64 00 09 26
0E10  30 7D FE 0A FA 1D 0E D6 0A 24 C3 12 0E C6 30 6F
0E20  C1 78 FE 20 C2 3F 0E 7A FE 30 C2 3F 0E 51 48 7B
0E30  FE 30 C2 3F 0E 5A 51 7C FE 30 C2 3F 0E 63 5A 79
0E40  48 47 DF 48 DF 4A DF 4B DF 4C DF 4D DF C9 21 57
0E50  0E 06 06 CD 5F 00 C9 2D 33 32 37 36 38 1E 30 09
0E60  7C FE 00 F8 1C C3 5F 0E 26 00 6F FE 00 F2 CA 0D
0E70  25 C3 CA 0D 11 00 00 E7 FE 2B CA 83 0E FE 2D C2
0E80  84 0E 14 E7 EF CD E6 01 5F E7 FE 30 FA B4 0E FE
0E90  3A F2 B4 0E D6 30 47 7B FE 0D F2 B4 00 87 4F 87
0EA0  87 81 80 5F FE 00 F2 89 0E 87 C2 B4 00 15 C2 B4
0EB0  00 E7 7B C9 7B 15 F8 2F 3C C9 21 00 00 54 E7 FE
0EC0  2B CA CA 0E FE 2D C2 CB 0E 14 E7 EF CD E6 01 6F
0ED0  E7 FE 30 FA 0D 0F FE 3A F2 0D 0F D6 30 5F 01 33
0EE0  F3 09 7C FE 00 F2 B4 00 01 CD 0C 09 29 44 4D 29
0EF0  29 09 06 00 4B 09 7C FE 00 F2 D0 0E FE 80 C2 B4
0F00  00 7D FE 00 C2 B4 00 15 C2 B4 00 E7 C9 15 F8 7C
0F10  2F 67 7D 2F 6F 23 C9 00 79 FE 00 F0 7C 93 67 C9
0F20  21 00 00 79 54 06 08 29 07 D2 2D 0F 19 05 C2 27
0F30  0F C9 7B FE 00 F0 7C 91 67 C9 CD 20 0F CD 18 0F
0F40  CD 32 0F C9 F5 C5 E5 4A CD 20 0F EB E1 C1 F1 C9
0F50  0C 7A B8 F2 5D 0F 0C 87 F2 52 0F 1F 0D 57 21 00
0F60  00 29 7C FE 00 FA B4 00 78 BA FA 6F 0F 92 23 87
0F70  47 0D C2 61 0F C9 1E 00 78 FE 00 F2 82 0F 2F 3C
0F80  47 1C 7A FE 00 F2 8C 0F 2F 3C 57 1D CD 50 0F 7B
0F90  FE 00 C8 7C 2F 67 7D 2F 6F 23 C9 EB C5 D1 47 04
0FA0  CD 1A 0C F2 AF 0F 04 29 D2 A0 0F CD F2 0F 05 EB
0FB0  E5 21 00 00 29 DA B4 00 E3 CD 1A 0C FA C5 0F CD
0FC0  F1 0C E3 23 E3 29 E3 05 C2 B4 0F C1 C9 F5 26 00
0FD0  78 A7 F2 DC 0F 2F 47 79 2F 4F 03 24 7A A7 F2 E8
0FE0  0F 2F 57 7B 2F 5F 13 25 F1 E5 CD 9B 0F F1 C3 90
0FF0  0F 23 7D E6 FE 0F 6F 7C 1F 67 D0 7D EE 80 6F C9
>
```

```
D2400,25FF
2400 3E 10 F5 97 67 6F EB 29 EB 1F A7 29 D2 10 24 13
2410 F2 18 24 09 D2 18 24 13 E3 25 E3 C2 06 24 F1 C9
2420 21 00 00 78 A7 F2 29 24 19 7A A7 F2 2F 24 09 7C
2430 2F 67 7D 2F 6F 23 E5 CD 00 24 EB C1 09 EB C9 00
2440 CD 20 24 EB 29 EB 29 D2 4B 24 13 29 D2 50 24 13
2450 EB C9 11 00 00 D5 5E 23 56 23 E3 19 A7 CA 6D 24
2460 3D EB F5 C5 CD 40 24 C1 F1 E3 C3 56 24 D1 C9 00
2470 E5 EB 42 4B CD 40 24 44 4D 3E 03 21 88 24 CD 52
2480 24 EB C1 CD 40 24 29 C9 FD FF 89 00 55 F5 00 40
2490 CD 70 24 EB 42 4B CD 40 24 CD CF 24 EB 21 00 40
24A0 CD F1 0C CD 6F 0D C9 7E A7 CA BA 24 23 13 13 1A
24B0 A7 C2 FE 26 F1 C1 CD 19 26 C9 C1 F1 CD 19 26 C9
24C0 00 67 2E 00 29 44 4D 11 7D 47 CD 40 24 29 C9 CD
24D0 F1 0F 7C E6 40 87 84 67 C9 CD 70 24 E5 CD 93 24
24E0 C1 EB 3E 0F CD CD 0F C9 0E 20 DF 0E 2B 29 D2 F6
24F0 24 CD 93 0F 0E 2D DF 0E 30 DF 06 04 CD E8 07 C9
2500 44 4D 11 97 72 CD 20 24 EB C9 E5 D5 C5 44 4D CD
2510 00 24 C1 E3 D5 C5 EB 48 79 17 9F 47 CD 56 25 E3
2520 D5 EB 4A CD 3A 0F E5 7B 17 9F 57 21 0A 00 39 F9
2530 C1 21 F4 FF 39 F9 CD 62 25 C1 EB 09 44 4D E1 09
2540 44 4D E1 19 D2 48 25 03 54 5D E1 19 D2 50 25 03
2550 54 5D E1 33 33 C9 21 00 00 78 A7 F2 2F 24 19 C3
2560 2F 24 21 00 00 C3 29 24 F5 CD F2 0F F1 07 1F 1F
2570 F5 7C 17 0F 67 F1 C9 D5 11 01 00 19 CE 00 CD 68
2580 25 D1 C9 CD 68 25 05 C2 83 25 C9 05 CA 95 25 CD
2590 68 25 C3 8B 25 D5 11 01 00 19 CE 00 CD 68 25 D1
25A0 C9 06 00 F5 A7 C2 B2 25 7C A7 C2 B2 25 7D A7 CA
25B0 C7 25 F1 F5 E6 E0 FE 20 CA C9 25 FE C0 CA C9 25
25C0 F1 29 8F 05 C3 A3 25 06 00 F1 C9 4F 07 17 CE 00
25D0 1F 79 D0 04 CD 77 25 C9 C5 47 7D 93 6F 7C 9A 67
25E0 78 99 C1 C9 EB 50 59 01 20 00 09 D2 EF 25 13 EB
25F0 29 EB 29 D2 F7 25 13 EB 29 EB 29 D2 FF 25 13 6C
>
```

```
D2600,27FF
2600 63 7A C9 00 00 00 00 00 F5 7D 02 03 7C 02 03 7B
2610 02 03 7A 02 0B 0B 0B F1 C9 F5 0A 6F 03 0A 67 03
2620 0A 5F 03 0A 57 0B 0B 0E F1 C9 2F 3C 0E 30 D6 0A
2630 FA 37 26 0C C3 2E 26 C6 3A 47 79 C3 F7 27 CD 0A
2640 25 CD E4 25 C1 CD A3 25 50 5F C9 D5 E5 CD 19 26
2650 7A 43 D1 E3 84 4D E1 F5 C3 3E 26 EB 44 4D 97 67
2660 6F CD D8 25 CD CB 25 5F 50 C9 D5 42 4B CD 19 26
2670 CD 5B 26 C1 C5 CD 08 26 D1 C9 7A 2F 3C 3C F5 EB
2680 4D 21 00 00 3E 20 06 17 F5 E5 7C 29 8F FA B4 00
2690 E3 F5 33 33 33 33 F1 3B 3B 3B 3B 3B 3B CD D8 25
26A0 F2 B7 26 19 89 29 8F 33 33 33 33 33 33 F5 3B 3B
26B0 3B 3B F1 E3 C3 CE 26 29 8F 33 33 33 33 33 33 F5
26C0 3B 3B 3B 3B F1 E3 D5 11 01 00 19 CE 00 D1 05 C2
26D0 8B 26 D1 D1 C1 C3 64 26 00 7B A7 FA E2 26 CD 7A
26E0 26 C9 CD 5B 26 CD 7A 26 CD 5B 26 C9 D5 E5 CD 19
26F0 26 CD D9 26 C3 50 26 E5 D5 23 23 C3 A7 24 13 1A
2700 96 FA 0C 27 47 D1 E1 D5 EB C3 10 27 2F 3C 47 D1
2710 1A 6F 13 1A 67 13 1A C4 8B 25 E3 5E 23 56 23 4E
2720 23 E3 19 89 D1 EB 46 EB CD CB 25 CD A3 25 5F 50
2730 C9 D5 E5 CD 6A 26 E1 CD F7 26 C1 E5 D5 50 59 CD
2740 6A 26 D1 E1 C9 E7 01 00 00 FE 2B CA 58 27 FE 2D
2750 CA 57 27 4F C3 58 27 05 C5 97 67 6C E5 F5 79 A7
2760 C2 64 27 E7 D6 30 FA 8C 27 FE 0A F2 8C 27 4F F1
2770 E3 29 8F 47 54 5D 29 8F 29 8F 19 88 16 00 59 19
2780 8A E3 F5 7C A7 CA 63 27 2D C3 63 27 FE FE C2 95
2790 27 24 C3 63 27 45 F1 E1 C5 06 16 CD A3 25 50 5F
27A0 D5 E5 CD 74 0F E1 D1 C1 80 01 DF 27 E5 26 00 A7
27B0 F2 B6 27 2F 3C 23 0F DD DD 27 6F 7C E3 A7 C5 F4
27C0 4B 26 C1 E3 7C E3 A7 C5 FC EC 26 C1 E3 7D E6 7F
27D0 03 03 03 A7 C2 B6 27 E1 F1 A7 FC 5B 26 C9 00
27E0 00 28 04 00 00 32 07 00 10 27 0E 08 AF 2F 1B F2
27F0 86 23 36 6B 71 27 6B FE 30 CA FD 27 DF 48 DF C9
>
```

```
D2800,29FF
2800 D5 E5 7C CD 04 02 7D CD 04 02 0E 20 DF DF 7E CD
2810 04 02 0E 20 DF DF 7E 87 DA 21 28 FA 80 28 C3 60
2820 29 FA 70 2A C3 A3 28 00 06 06 11 06 04 CD 5F 00
2830 E1 CD 6F 28 E5 C3 4F 28 06 02 11 06 03 11 06 04
2840 11 06 05 11 06 06 11 06 07 11 06 08 CD 5F 00 0E
2850 3B DF CD 00 02 E1 23 D1 D5 CD 31 02 FA 01 28 CF
2860 11 67 28 83 5F 1A C9 42 43 44 45 48 4C 4D 41 23
2870 5E 23 7E CD 04 02 7B CD 04 02 C9 00 48 41 4C 54
2880 47 FE EC CA FA 28 E6 70 0F 0F 0F 0F CD 60 28 4F
2890 DF 0E 3A DF 0E 3D DF 78 E6 0E 0F CD 60 28 4F DF
28A0 C3 4F 28 47 0E 41 DF CD 00 29 78 C3 98 28 00 00
28B0 4E 55 4C 4C 41 3A 3D 4D 5B 42 43 5D 3A 3D 41 3A
28C0 3D 4D 5B 44 45 5D 3A 3D 41 3A 23 44 45 43 41 3A
28D0 40 4C 41 3A 40 52 41 4B 3A 40 4C 41 4B 3A 40 52
28E0 4B 3A 23 5D 3A 3D 48 4C 3A 3D 4D 5B 3A 2B 31
28F0 3A 2D 31 48 4C 3A 2B 00 00 00 21 7C 28 C3 3E 28
2900 CD 05 29 DF C9 78 E6 70 FE 70 0E 2D C8 0E 3A DF
2910 78 E6 70 0F 0F 0F 0E 2B C8 3D C2 20 29 DF C9
2920 0E 2D 3D C8 3D C2 2A 29 DF C9 0E 26 3D C8 0E 23
2930 3D C8 0E 55 C9 00 11 53 50 CD 40 29 DF 48 DF C9
2940 01 42 43 E6 30 C8 01 44 45 FE 10 C8 01 48 4C FE
2950 20 C8 42 4B 78 11 41 46 C3 39 29 5A 4B 50 4E
2960 0F 47 5F 21 B0 28 A7 CA 3E 28 2E B7 FE 02 CA 4A
2970 28 2E B4 FE 0A CA 4A 28 2E C1 FE 12 CA 4A 28 2E
2980 BE FE 1A CA 4A 28 2E C8 FE 2F CA 3B 28 2E CB FE
2990 27 CA 3B 28 2E CE FE 07 CA 3E 28 2E D2 FE 0F CA
29A0 3E 28 2E D6 FE 17 CA 41 28 2E DB FE 1F CA 41 28
29B0 2E E0 FE 3F CA 3B 28 FE 32 C2 CA 29 0E 4D DF E1
29C0 CD 6F 28 E5 21 BC 28 C3 3B 28 2E B4 FE 3A CA 2B
29D0 28 FE 22 C2 E8 29 2E EA 06 02 CD 5F 00 E1 CD 6F
29E0 28 E5 21 E4 28 C3 3E 28 FE 2A C2 72 2B 2E E6 06
29F0 06 C3 2D 28 E6 04 CA 21 2A 78 E6 38 0F 0F 0F CD
>
```

```
D2A00,2BFF
2A00 60 28 4F DF 78 0F 2E F0 DA 3B 28 0F 2E ED D2 3B
2A10 28 0E 3A DF 0E 3D DF E1 23 7E E5 CD 04 02 C3 4F
2A20 28 68 78 E6 0F FE 09 C2 38 2A 2E F3 06 04 CD 5F
2A30 00 7B CD 36 29 C3 4F 28 7D CD 36 29 7D E6 0F 2E
2A40 ED FE 03 CA 3B 28 2E F0 FE 0B CA 3B 28 0E 3A DF
2A50 0E 3D DF C3 30 28 78 E6 08 C2 5F 2A 0E 4F DF 78
2A60 E6 30 0F 0F 0F 0F 11 5C 29 83 5F 1A 4F DF C9 00
2A70 1F 47 21 40 2B FF F9 CA 44 28 2E 44 FE EB CA 47
2A80 28 2E 4B FE E3 CA 47 28 2E 56 FE FB CA 3E 28 2E
2A90 5A FE F3 CA 3E 28 2E 5E FE E9 CA 41 28 2E 63 FE
2AA0 C9 CA 3B 28 2E 68 FE DB C2 B3 2A 06 04 CD 5F 00
2AB0 C3 17 2A FE D3 C2 C8 2A 0E 47 DF E1 23 7E E5 CD
2AC0 04 02 21 66 2B C3 3B 28 0E 4A FE C3 CA D7 2A FE
2AD0 CD C2 DB 2A DF 0E 53 DF C3 30 28 E6 07 C2 E9 2A
2AE0 0E 52 DF CD 56 2A C3 4F 28 3D C2 F6 2A CD 55 29
2AF0 21 52 2B C3 3E 28 3D C2 03 2B 0E 4A DF CD 56 2A
2B00 C3 30 28 3D 3D C2 10 2B 0E 4A DF 0E 53 C3 FC 2A
2B10 3D C2 23 2B 2F 50 C5 06 04 CD 5F 00 C1 CD 55 29
2B20 C3 4F 28 3D C2 33 2B 0E 41 DF 78 87 47 CD 00 29
2B30 C3 17 2A 0E 4A DF 0E 53 DF DF 78 0F 0F C3 6C 2B
2B40 53 50 3A 3D 48 4C 3A 3D 3A 44 45 48 4C 3A 3D 3A
2B50 53 54 3A 3D 53 54 49 3A 3D 31 49 3A 3D 30 4A 5B
2B60 48 4C 5D 52 45 54 3A 3D 41 3A 3D 47 0F E6 37 C3
2B70 9E 28 FE 37 C2 F4 29 0E 4B DF 21 57 2B C3 3E 28
2B80 7B 0E 2B A7 F2 8C 2B CD 5B 26 0F 2D DF 97 F5 7B
2B90 A7 CA DE 2B 7B D6 28 7A DE 04 FA A9 2B 01 DF 27
2BA0 CD EC 26 F1 3C F5 C3 94 2B 7B D6 20 7A DE 01 F2
2BB0 BE 2B 01 DF 27 CD 4B 26 F1 3D F5 C3 A9 2B 7A 3C
2BC0 16 00 EB 29 EB 29 D2 CA 2B 13 3D F2 C2 2B 01 54
2BD0 00 09 D2 D6 2B 13 4D 09 D2 DC 2B 13 6C 63 7A FE
2BE0 0A CA E9 2B F7 4F C3 ED 2B 0E 31 DF 0D DF CD E6
2BF0 07 0E 45 DF F1 F2 2C 26 F5 0E 2D DF F1 C3 2A 26
>
```

Index

References are to pages; exceptionally, a reference in parentheses is to the entry point of a program or subroutine of the software package, see pp 225–306 and 307–312.

absolute addresses, 115, 147, 176, 193
access time, 13
accumulator, 11, 12, 30, 64, 71, 80, 122
  floating-point, 142, 189
addition, 30–34
  BCD, 45–6, 150–1, 152
  fixed-point,135–6
  floating-point,143–4, 189, (26F7)
  triple-length, 141
address, 3, 25, 111, 159, 177
  buffering and decoding, 16
  bus, 3, 16, 172
  next instruction, 1
  notation for, 25–8, 177
  return, 47, 48–50, 122
addresses, absolute, 115, 147, 176, 193
  privileged, 27, 50, 211–12
  reserved (6800), 64
  treatment by assembler, 179, 221
addressing, 26–8, 150–1
  elements of an array, 150, 162, 169, 191
register, 11, 13, 117, 150
ALGOL
  60, 39, 163, 194–6, 208
  68, 196
  Group (IFIP), 22
algorithm, for division, 131–2
  for evaluation of polynomial, 191
  for evaluation of square root, 190
  for sorting, 163–4, 209
AND (conjunction), 37
annotated text of software, 224–306

APL, 208
applications programmers, 206
approximation of trigonometric functions, 187–8, 192, 223
arithmetic, and logical operations, 28–46
  binary-coded-decimal, 45–6, 149–55
  expression, 194, 206
  fixed-point, 134–7, 184–8, 222–3
  floating-point, 137–49, 188–9, 207, 223
  -logic unit, 11
  of binary integers, 30–7, 124–33, 184–7, 222
  shift, 41, 141, 185, 222–3
  subroutines, 184–9, 222–3
array elements, addressing, 150, 162, 169, 191
ASCII, 112–13, 156, 161, 180
  coded keyboard, 22, 111
  conversion subroutines, 114–24, 184–5, 213, (0028, 0030, 0B00)
assembled object program, 180, 218
assembler, 22, 115, 146–8, 156, 176, 179–80, 189, 205, 211, (0C00)
  description of, 171, 179–80, 217–21
  directive, 180
assembly, of program, 176, 179–80
  language, 176, 195, 205
assignment, 23, 25
  operations, 29, 65, 72, 78
auxiliary registers (Z80), 57
  routines for floating-point arithmetic, 141–2, 223

back-assembler, 22 (*see also* disassembler)
backing store, 13
base, of stack, 46
BASIC, 194, 196, 202, 208
baud rate, 51
beginner's system, 111–12
binary
    arithmetic, floating-point, 137–49, 188–9, 223
        on integers, 30–7, 124–33, 184–7, 222
        on non-integral quantities, 134–7, 184–9, 222–3
    coded decimal (BCD), 45, 169
        arithmetic, 45–6, 149–55
    integer, 29, 124–33
    places, 134–7
    point, 134, 137
bits, 24
    filler, 34
    least and most significant, 30
    notation for, 25
    operations on, 57
    parity, 112
    sign, 30, 124–5, 136
    significant, 134
    start and stop, 51
block instructions (*Z80*), 58–60, 156–62, 201
    structure, 208
Boolean operations, 28, 37–8, 185
Booth's algorithm (multiplication), 130
borrow, 35–7
    bit, 151–3
branch instruction, 12
branches, of assembler, 219
    of disassembler, 221–2
    of monitor, 177–8, 212, 213–16
breakpoints, 178
buffering, address, 6, 16, 18
bus, address, 3, 16, 172
    control, 11
    data, 3, 11, 53, 172
byte, 19, 24, 177
    input subroutine, 182, (0220)
    meanings of, 28
    output subroutine, 184, (0204)
bytes of an instruction, 23, 179
    upper and lower, 26

calculators and BCD arithmetic, 149
call, of a subroutine, 48, 117, 192
carry flag, 30, 150, 162, 167
change of length of number, 34, 124–5, 142
clock, 9, 13, 53, 59
    period, 96–110, 173

code, ASCII, 112–13
    operation, 19, 170
'compare' operations, 38–40
comparison of binary numbers, 125–6, 159, 162
    subroutines for, 125–6, 185, (0231, 0C1A)
compiler, 194–8, 204, 206
complement, twos, 30
computer, computation, 20
computer science, 199–200
condition flag, 12, 28, 39, 64, 71, 77, 80, 148, 169, 178, 202 (*see also* flag)
conditional, jump, 12, 27, 48, 117
    return, 50, 117
conjunction (AND), 37
console device, 111–12, 144–5, 177–8, 212–13
constants, 146, 176, 194, 206
control, bus, 11
    lines, signals, 3, 8
'copy' instructions, 23, 25, 58
copying blocks of information, 156–9, 177–8, 214–15
core store, 13, 112
cosine subroutine, 188, 189, 223, (2490)
counter, program, 11, 12, 27, 211, 215
counting jump (*Z80*), 57
cross-assembler, 22
    -compiler, 198
cue-mark, 177, 212
cycle, instruction, 1, 19, 53
cyclic shift (rotation), 42–3

data, 1, 19
    bus, 3, 11, 53, 172
    processing, 19
    register, 11
'debugging', 111, 178
    aids, 175–6
decimal, adjustment, 45–6, 149
    digits, reading of, 114–17
    integers, input and output of, 118–24, 182–4
    places, 134, 155
    round-off, 145, 155
    values, 20, 21
declarations, of constants and X-blocks, 179–80
    of peripherals, 204
    of variables, 208
decoder, address, 16
    instruction, 11, 19
'decrement' operation, 44, 158
degrees to radians, subroutine, 188, (24C1, 24C4)

delay loop, 51, 173
development, of programs, 198, 200, 206, 210–11
  system, 200–201, 210–11
device, number, 3, 53, 59, 211
  peripheral, 3, 18, 50–3, 59, 172–4, 204
diagnostics (error messages), 122–3
dictionary of instructions, 95–110
direct addressing, 26, 27
directive, assembler, 180
disassembler, 22, 156, 176, 180, 189, 211, (2800)
  description, 170–1, 221–2
  use, 146–8
disjunction (OR), 37
division, 119, 124, 130–3, 145
  fixed-point, 136–7, 186–7
  floating-point, 143, 189, (26EC)
  multiple-length, 132–3
    subroutines, 187
  single-length, 130–3, 186
  triple-length, 142
double-length
  addition, 32
    BCD, 150
  subtraction, 36
    subroutine, 185, (0CF1)
  value, 25, 30, 117
dynamic order, 19
  RAM, 15

'echo' subroutine, 183, 213, (0010)
editing of PROM, 181
error message, 122–3
errors in software package, 210, 223–4
exclusive OR (XOR), 37
execution, of instruction, 1, 11, 19, 53
  of program, 111
  times of instructions, 95–110
exponent, 137–41, 142–5, 183, 184, 190
expression, higher-level, 189, 192, 194, 202, 206
  levels of, 195
  power of, 189, 195
extended addressing, 27
external hardware for arithmetic, 126

Fahrenheit-Centigrade conversion, 146–8, 189, 192–5, 203
failure routine, 114, 122–3
fetch and store subroutines, 142–3, 189, 191, (2608, 2619)
fields, records, files, 171
fixed-point, representation, 134
  addition and subtraction, 135–6
  division, 136–7

multiplication, 134, 222–3
  subroutines, 184–8, 222–3
flag, carry, 30, 150, 162, 167
  half-carry, 45
  interrupt, 54
  negative, 31, 148, 167, 185
  overflow, 31, 40
  parity, 64, 73, 80, 82
  software, 123
  subtraction, 45
  zero, 28, 148, 185
flags, condition, 12, 28, 39, 64, 71, 77, 80, 148, 169, 178, 202
  and floating-point numbers, 148–9
  in *6800*, 64–7
  in *8080/8085*, 71–3, 77
  in *Z80*, 78, 80, 82–3
flip-flop, interface to, 172–3
  interrupt, 54
  JK, 1
floating-point, accumulator, 142, 189
  arithmetic, 137–49, 188–9, 207, 223
  auxiliary routines, 141–2, 223
  binary numbers, 137–49
  input, 144–5, 189, (2745)
  normalization, 138–41, 188
  output, 144–5, 189, (2B80)
  representation and conventions, 138–9
  subroutines, 142–8, 188–9, 211, 223
  table of values, 140
FORTRAN, 194, 196, 197, 202
fractional, part of number, 134
  part of quotient, 133
fractions, BCD, 155
  decimal output subroutines, 184, 222, (07E6, 07E8)
functions, standard, 187–9

gateway (input-output port), 53, 71, 80
graphical display, 192, 202
graphics monitor, 211

half-carry flag, 45
HALT instruction, 72–3, 79, 82, 117
hardware, external, for arithmetic, 126
head string, 221
hexadecimal, convention, 20
  digits, 24, 111, 177, 179
  text of software, 307–20
  values, 21, 177
high-level, programming languages, 39, 194–6, 202, 205–207
  text, 193
higher-level expression, 189, 192, 194, 202, 206

history of software package, 210–11

identifier, 23, 204, 206, 208
IFIP ALGOL Group, 22
IFIP Congress 1977, 197
immediate operand, 19, 32, 194
improvements possible in software package, 223–4
'increment' operation, 44, 115, 158
incremental sign corrections, 129–30
index register, 11, 13, 27
   'compare' (*6800*), 40
indexed addressing, 27, 114
   addition in, 34
indirect addressing, 26, 114
inertia, language, 199
information processing, 19, 198
initialization of, assembler, 180, 218
   interface, 203, 205, 212
input device, 3, 18, 173–4
input-output, 18, 50–3, 59, 172–4
   of decimal integers, 118–24, 182, 184
   of floating-point numbers, 144–5, 183, 184, (2745, 2B80)
   subroutines, 182–4, 189
instruction, 1, 179
   cycle, 1, 19, 53
   decoder, 11, 19
   execution, 11, 53
      times, 95–110
   read routine, in assembler, 218
   register, 1, 11
   representation, 20
   set, 19, 61, 175, 189, 201–202
      of *6800*, 64–70
      of *8080*, 71–6, 179
      of *8085*, 71–7
      of *Z80*, 78–95
integer, binary, 29, 124–33
   decimal, input subroutines, 118–24, 182, (0E74, 0EBA)
      output subroutines, 118–24, 184, (0DCA, 0E68)
integral part, 134, 136
integrated circuits, 6, 9, 18, 126, 198
Intel, 7, 18, 52, 71, 173, 210
   MCS-80 monitor, 210–11, 217
   SDK kit, 210
interactive working, 208
interchange operation, 24, 57, 169
interface, 18, 50–3, 59, 172–4, 203–204, 211
   components, 18, 173–4, 198, 205, 210
   on-off switch, 172
interlocking loops, 209
internal organization of microprocessors,

   9–13, 122
interpreter, reverse Polish, 211
interrupt, interruption, 53–7
   6800, 64, 117
   8080, 71
   8085, 77
   Z80, 80
inversion (NOT), 34, 37

JK flip-flop, 1
jump instructions, 3, 48, 115
   address in, 27, 48, 179
   conditional, 12, 27, 48, 117
   counting, 57
   relative, 12, 48, 115, 117, 122, 176
   to subroutine, 49
   unconditional, 12, 27, 48
jump list, in assembler, 218

Karnaugh map, 62–3, 221
   6800, 68–9
   8080/8085, 74–5, 77, 170
   Z80, 84–93
keyboard, 22, 51, 111, 114, 118, 144–5, 177–8, 213

label, 115, 176, 179, 207
   table, in assembler, 180, 218
language, 156, 196–209
   assembly, 176, 195, 205
   high-level, 39, 194–6, 202, 205–207
   inertia, 199
   multi-level, 195, 206
   programming, 22, 194–6, 202, 205
length of number, change of, 34, 124–5, 142
level, higher, 189
   machine-code, 175, 189, 192, 195
library, software, 175
   subroutine, 175, 181–9
list, searching, 159–62
location, storage, 25, 111–12
logical, operations, 28, 37–8, 185
   shift, 42
long division, 131–2
long multiplication, 126–7
loops, nested and interlocking, 196, 209
   time-delay, 51, 173
low-level language, 195, 205, 206

machine-code level, 175, 189, 192, 195
machine-independent, 193, 202, 206
machine word, 19, 24
macros, 207, 208
main store, 13
mantissa, 137–41, 142–5, 183–4, 190

memory, 1 (*see also* store)
  programmable read-only (PROM), 14
  random access (RAM), 15
  read-only (ROM), 14
microprocessor, 1, 20, 196–9, 200
minicomputers, 198
mnemonics, 22
mode, interrupt, 56
money calculations, 155
monitor, 111–12, 117, 123, 146–8, 170, 175–8, 189, 191, 211–16, (0000)
  graphics, 211
  main part, 212–13
  PROM, 111–12, 211–17
monostable, 173
Motorola, 7, 18, 52, 64
multi-level language, 195, 206.
multi-processor systems, 202
multiple-length
  addition, 33
    BCD, 150–1
  numbers, 30
  quotient, 132–3
  subtraction, 37, 185
multiplication, 118, 126–30, 134, 145
  BCD, 153–5
  by external hardware, 48, 126
  floating-point, 143, 189, (264B)
  nested, 191
  of fixed-point numbers, 134, 185–6, 222–3
  of multiple-length numbers, 128–30, 186, 222–3
  single-length, 126–8, 185–6
  subroutines, 48, 143, 185–6, 222–3
  triple-length, 128–30, 141–2, 186, (250A)

negation, 34
  BCD, 152
  floating-point, 143, (265B, 266A)
negative flag, 31, 148, 167, 185
nested loops, 196, 209
nested multiplication, 191
Newton's iterative method, 190
next instruction address, 1
nibble, 24, 45, 149
  shift (*Z80*), 43
non-equivalence (XOR), 37
non-integral numbers, 133
  fixed-point representation, 134
non-numerical quantities, 156
non-terminating program, 123, 194
normalization, 138–41, 144, 188
NOT (inversion), 34, 37
notation, 'scientific', 137
notational system, 22, 175, 207–209

informally extended, 142, 193, 201, 208
  questions raised, 201–202
notations, for floating-point operations, 142–3, 189
  general, 23
  language and, 156, 201–207
  'step' and 'block' instructions, 60
numbers, fixed-point, 134
  floating-point, 138–40
  multiple-length, 30

object program, 179, 200, 218
  assembled, 180
object system, 200
octal, 20, 21
operand, immediate, 19, 32, 194
operation code, 19
operations, arithmetic and logical, 28–46
  assignment, 23, 25, 29, 65, 72, 78
  decrement and increment, 44
  logical (Boolean), 37–8
  shift and rotate, 41–4, 135–6, 185
  stack, 46–7
  test and compare, 38–40
operator subroutine in assembler, 220
OR (disjunction), 37
output, 18, 50–3, 172–4
  device, 3, 18, 172
  instruction, 59
  of decimal integers, 118–24, 184, (0DCA, 0E68)
  of floating-point numbers, 144–5, 184, (2B80)
  routine, of assembler, 218–19
  subroutines, 183–4
overflow in, addition, 31
    BCD, 152–3
  'compare' operations, 40
  negation and subtraction, 35

'packed decimal' arithmetic, 45
'packed' information, 169–71
parallel interface adapters, 18, 173–4, 202, 205
parameter, of subroutine, 117, 145, 189, 193
parity bit, 112
PASCAL, 196
peripheral device, 3, 18, 50–3, 59, 172–4, 202
PL/I, 194, 196
pointer, stack, 11, 12, 46, 122, 215
polynomial evaluation, algorithm, 191
  subroutine, 187, 190–1, 192, (2452)
'pop', 'pull', 'push' operations, 46
port, 53, 59, 71, 80

power of expression, 189, 195
power supplies, 9
precision, 136, 137
priority, of interruptions, 54
privileged addresses, 27, 50, 211–12
process, procedure, processor, 19, 20
processing an instruction, in assembler, 180, 219
processing of a file, 171
production work, 200
program, 3, 19
  counter, 11, 12, 27, 211, 215
  development, 197, 200–201
  high-level, 194, 202–205
  non-terminating, 123, 194
  object, 179, 180, 218
  testing, 111, 117, 175
programmer, 111–12, 115, 199, 206
  PROM, 174, 181, 202–207, 210–11, 217
  task of, 111, 208
programming, 111 *et seq.*
  aids, 175–6
  at higher levels, 175–96
  languages, 22, 194–6, 202–205
  non-numerical operations, 156–74
  PROM, 14, 181, 210, 217, (0360)
  with floating-point subroutines, 146–8
programs for PROM programmer, 181, 202–207, 210, 217, (0360, 03C0)
PROM, 14, 111–12, 175, 181, 210–11, 217
  programmer, 174, 181, 210–11, 217
    programs, 181, 202–207, 210–11, 217, (0360, 03C0)
  reading, 181, 202–207, 217, (03C0)
pulse, programmed generation of, 172, 202
  width controlled by program, 173–4

quotient, and remainder, 119, 124, 130, 136
  fractional part of, 133
  multiple-length, 132–3

radians to degrees, subroutine, 188, (2500)
RAM, 15, 111, 163, 177, 179, 181, 210–11
  use by resident subroutines, 130, 158, 192
random access processing, 171
range, double-length, 30, 119, 149
  floating-point, 138–9, 183, 184
  single-length, 29, 118–19, 149
ranges of variables, 137, 195–6
reading decimal digits, 114–17
  integers, 118–24, 182
reading floating-point numbers, 183, (2745)
  hexadecimal integers, 182, (01F7, 0220)
  PROM, 181, 202–207, (03C0)
reciprocal, 133, 142

floating-point, 142, 143, 189, (267A, 26D9)
records and files, 171
refreshing dynamic RAM, 15, 80
register, addressing, 11, 13, 117
  auxiliary (*Z80*), 57
  condition flag, 12, 28, 169–70
  data, 11
  index, 11, 13, 27, 114
  instruction, 1, 11
  notation for, 23
  subroutine in assembler, 220
registers in *6800*, 64
  8080/8085, 71, 178
  Z80, 80
relative addressing, 27, 115
  addition in, 34
relative jump, 12, 48, 115, 117, 122, 176
relay as output device, 172
remainder and quotient, 119, 124, 130, 136
representation of fixed-point numbers, 134
  floating-point numbers, 138–9, 183, 184
  instructions, 20
request for interruption, 54
reserved addresses (*6800*), 64
RESET signal, 8, 64, 71, 77, 80, 111, 123, 178, 211–12
resident subroutine library, 189
'restart' instructions, 50
result, of instruction, 1
  of subroutine, 181, 192
return address, 47, 48–50, 122
  from interruption, 55
  from subroutine, 48
    conditional, 50, 117
reverse Polish interpreter, 211
ROM, 14, 210–11
'rotate' operations, 41–4
rounding, 136–7, 139, 141, 145, 155, 185, 223

'scientific' notation, 137
'search' instructions (*Z80*), 58
searching a list, 159–62
secondary store, 13, 18, 201
semantics, 207–208
semiconductor storage, 13–18
sequential processing, 171
'Shellsort', 163–9, 195–6
'shift' operations, 41–4, 135–6, 185
shifting triple-length numbers, 141, 185
shortcomings of software package, 223–4
sign, and modulus, 30
sign bit, 30, 124–5, 136
  correction, 127–30, 154

signed and unsigned values, 29
signed BCD integers, 151–3
  multiplication, 127–30, 154
significant bits, 134
  most and least, 30
  figures, 134, 144–5, 190
sine subroutine, 187, 189, 192, 223, (2470)
software, 111, 175, 189, 197–209
  for peripherals, 172–4
  'interrupt', 56, 117
  library, 175
  package, 175–89, 210–320
  planning and design, 196–209
sorting, 162–9, 209
special peripheral devices, 18, 172–4, 202
special subroutines, 50, 212, 213
specification, of elementary monitor, 111–12
  of multi-level language, 206–209
square root, algorithm, 190
  subroutines, 187, 189–90, (0BE0, 0D6F)
stack, 12, 46–7, 54, 122, 123, 141, 143, 157,
    191, 212, 215
  necessary misuse of, 130
  operations, 46–7
  pointer, 11, 12, 46, 122, 215
standard functions, 187–8, 189
start bit, 51
statements, 208
static order, 19
static RAM, 15
'step' instruction (*Z80*), 58
stop bit, 51
storage location, 25, 111–12
store, 1, 13–18
string input subroutines, 182, (03EC)
string output subroutines, 183, (005F, 03F6)
structural elements, 206
structure, 171, 194, 196–209
  and style, 207–209
  nested loop, 196
  of disassembler, 221
  of program, 194, 204–205
style, 207–209, 210
subroutines, 48, 117, 175, 181–9, 222–3
  fixed-point arithmetic, 184–8, 222–3
  floating-point arithmetic, 142–8, 188–9,
    191, 207, 223
  for assembler, 220–1
  for disassembler, 222
  in monitor PROM, 112, 216–17
  integral and fixed-point, 184–8, 222–3
  resident, 181–9
  user's description, 181–9
subtraction, 35–7
  BCD, 45–6, 153

fixed-point, 135–6, 185
flag (*Z80*), 45
floating-point, 143, 144, 189, (2731)
triple-length, 141, 185, (25D8)
switch, interface for, 172
symbolic names, 193, 204, 206
syntax, 208
system, beginner's, 111–12
  controller (Intel 8228), 6, 71
  development, 200–201
  microprocessor, 3, 200–201
  notational, 22
systems programmers, 206

table look-up, 171
tail string, 221
tangent subroutine, 188, (24D9)
teletype, 18, 51, 52, 145, 210–13
temperature conversion program, 146–8,
  189, 192–5, 203
'test' operations, 38–40
testing programs, 111, 117, 175, 211
three-state (tri-state) buffer, 14
time-critical passages in programs, 51, 54,
  59, 173–4
time-delay loop, 51, 173
timing and control unit, 9
tools for programming, 175
transcription routines, 176
translation, 123, 156, 164–9, 195–6, 202
translator, 194, 196
transparent, 143, 157
tree structure of assembler, 219
truncation, 141, 155
twos complement, 30

unconditional jump instruction, 12, 27, 48
unsigned values, 29

values, double-length, 25, 30
  external and internal forms of, 114, 124
  multiple-length, 30
  representation of, 24, 138–9, 140, 177, 179
  signed and unsigned, 29
visual display unit (VDU), 18, 52, 111, 171,
  211–13

wait, for interruption, 56
'wait' interface, 52, 59
Wallace tree, 129
well-structured problems and programs,
  209
word, 19
  length, 24
working store, 179

storage space, 112, 176, 179

X-blocks, 179
X-table, in assembler, 180, 218

XOR (exclusive OR), 37

zero flag, 28, 148, 185
Zilog, Inc, 7, 18, 80